THE OPUS MAJUS OF
ROGER BACON

BACON'S STUDY AT OXFORD

From a Gough Print

THE
OPUS MAJUS
OF
ROGER BACON

A Translation by

ROBERT BELLE BURKE

PROFESSOR OF LATIN AND DEAN OF THE COLLEGE
UNIVERSITY OF PENNSYLVANIA

VOLUME II

PHILADELPHIA
UNIVERSITY OF PENNSYLVANIA PRESS
LONDON: HUMPHREY MILFORD
OXFORD UNIVERSITY PRESS
MCMXXVIII

COPYRIGHT 1928 BY
UNIVERSITY OF PENNSYLVANIA PRESS

Printed in the United States of America

CONTENTS

VOLUME II

ILLUSTRATIONS

VOLUME II

THE OPUS MAJUS OF
ROGER BACON

PART FIVE OF THIS PLEA

CONCERNING OPTICS, IN THREE PARTS

*The first part treats of matters common to the other two; the second
deals mainly with direct vision; the third with reflected and
refracted vision. In Part One there are twelve distinctions.*

FIRST DISTINCTION

*This distinction deals with the properties of this science, with
the parts of the mind and brain and with the
organ of vision, in five chapters.*

CHAPTER I

Concerning the properties of this science.

HAVING explained the fundamental principles of wisdom, both sacred and human, which are found in the tongues from which the sciences of the Latins have been translated, and likewise in mathematics, I now wish to discuss some principles which belong to optics. If the consideration just mentioned is noble and pleasing, the one in hand is far nobler and more pleasing, since we take especial delight in vision, and light and color have an especial beauty beyond the other things that are brought to our senses, and not only does beauty shine forth, but advantage and a greater necessity appear. For Aristotle says in the first book of the Metaphysics that vision alone reveals the differences of things; since by means of it we search out experimental knowledge of all things that are in the heavens and in the earth. For those things that are in the heavenly bodies are studied by visual instruments, as Ptolemy and the other astronomers teach. So also are those things that are generated in the air, like comets, rainbows, and the like. For their altitude above the horizon, their size, form, number, and all things that are in them, are verified by the methods of viewing them with instruments. Our experience of things here in the earth we owe to vision, because a blind man can have no experience worthy of the name concerning this world. Hearing causes us to believe because we believe our teachers, but we cannot try out what we learn except through vision. If, moreover, we should adduce taste and touch and smell, we assume a knowledge belonging to beasts. For brutes are busied with the things pertaining to taste and touch, and exercise their sense of smell because of taste and touch, but the things are of little value, few in number, and common to us and to brutes concerning which these senses give verification, and therefore they do not rise to the rank of human wisdom. But because of necessity, utility, and difficulty, sciences are formed, since art has to do with the difficult and with the good, as Aristotle says in the second book of the Ethics. For if what is sought is easy, there is no need for the formation of a science. Likewise although a matter be difficult yet not useful, no science is developed concerning it, because the labor would be foolish and vain. Also unless a subject were very useful and possessed many excellent truths, it does not require the formation of a separate science, but it suffices that this subject be treated in some particular book or chapter along with other matters in general science. But concerning vision alone is a separate science formed among philosophers, namely, optics, and not concerning any other sense. Wherefore there must be a special utility in our knowledge through vision which is not found in the other senses. What I have now touched upon in general, I wish to show in particular by disclosing the basic principles of this very beautiful science. It is possible that some other science may be more useful, but no other science has so much sweetness and beauty of utility. Therefore it is the flower of the whole of philosophy and through it, and not without it, can the other sciences be known. We must note, moreover, that Aristotle first treated this science, of which he says in the second book of the Physics that the subject is placed under another head. He also mentions it in his book on Sense and the Sensible, and has proved Democritus in error, because he did not name refractions and reflections of vision with reference to the optic and concave visual nerves. This book has been translated into Latin. After him Alhazen treats the subject more fully in a book which is extant. Alkindi also has arranged some data more fully, likewise authors of books on vision and mirrors.

Optical Science

CHAPTER II

Concerning the internal faculties of the sensitive soul, which are imagination and the common sense (sensus communis).

SINCE the optic, that is, the concave nerves causing vision have their origin in the brain, and writers on optics ascribe to a distinct function through the medium of vision the formation of judgments concerning twenty species of visible things, which will be considered later, and since it is not known whether that distinct function is among the functions of the soul, the organs of which are distinct in the brain, and since many other things to be treated of later suppose a definition of the functions of the sensitive soul, therefore we must begin with the parts of the brain and the functions of the soul, in order that we may discover those things that are necessary for vision. Writers on optics give us a means to this end by showing how the visual nerves descend from the membranes of the brain and from the lining of the cranium, but no one explains all things necessary in this matter. I say, then, as all writers on the subjects of nature, all physicians and authorities on optics agree, that the brain is enfolded by a double membrane, one of which is called the pia mater, which enfolds the brain by direct contact; and the other, the dura mater, which adheres to the concave side of the bone of the head called the cranium. For this latter membrane is harder, so that it may resist the bone, and the other is softer and tenderer owing to the softness of the brain, the substance of which is like marrow and ointment, with phlegm as the chief constituent, and with three distinctions, which are called chambers, cells, parts, and divisions. In the first cell there are two faculties: the one in the anterior part is the common sense, as Avicenna states in the first book on the Soul, which is like a fountain with respect to the particular senses, and like the center with respect to the lines extending from that same point to the circumference, according to Aristotle in the second book on the Soul. This common sense judges concerning each particular sensation. For the judgment is not completed in regard to what is seen before the form comes to the common sense, and the same is true in regard to what is heard and to the other senses, as is clear from the end of the work on Sense and the Sensible, and in the second book on the Soul. This common sense forms a judgment concerning difference of impressions on the senses, as, for example, that in milk whiteness is different from sweetness, a distinction which sight cannot make, nor taste, because they do not distinguish things in other categories, as Aristotle maintains in the second book on the Soul. It judges concerning the operations of the particular senses, for vision does not perceive that it sees, nor hearing that it hears, but another faculty does, namely, the common sense, as Aristotle maintains in the second book on Sleep and Waking. But the final action of this faculty is to receive the forms coming from the particular senses and to complete a judgment concerning them. But it does not retain these impressions, owing to the excessive slipperiness of its own organ, according to the statement of Avicenna in the first book on the Soul. Therefore there must be another faculty of the soul in the back part of the first cell, the function of which is to retain the forms coming from the particular senses, owing to its tempered moistness and dryness, which is called imagination and is the coffer and repository of the common sense. Avicenna cites as an example a seal, the image of which water readily receives, but does not retain owing to its superabundant moistness; wax, however, retains the image very well, owing to its tempered moistness with dryness. Wherefore he says that it is one thing to receive and another to retain, as is clear from these examples. Such is the case in the organ of the common sense and of imagination. The whole faculty, however, composed of these two, namely, that which occupies the whole first cell, is called phantasia or the *virtus phantastica*. For according to the second book on the Soul and that on Sleep and Waking and the book on Sense and the Sensible, it is evident that phantasia and the common sense are the same according to subject but differ according to being, as Aristotle says, and that phantasia and imagination are the same according to subject but differ according to being. Wherefore phantasia includes both faculties and does not differ from them except as the whole from the part. Therefore since the common sense receives the form, and imagination retains it, a complete judgment follows regarding the thing, a judgment formed by phantasia.

Optical Science

CHAPTER III

Concerning the attributes that are apprehended by special senses, by the common sense and by imagination.

WE must note that imagination and the common sense and any particular sense form judgments of themselves only concerning twenty-nine properties; as sight concerning light and color; touch concerning heat and cold, moistness and dryness; smell concerning odors; taste concerning savor. These are the nine special properties that belong to their own senses, as I have named them, of which no other particular sense can form a judgment. There are, moreover, twenty other properties, namely, distance, position, figure, magnitude, continuity, discreetness or separation, number, motion, rest, roughness, smoothness, transparency, thickness, shadow, darkness, beauty, ugliness, also similarity and difference in all these things and in all things composed of them. Besides these qualities there are some that are placed under one or more of these qualities, as order under position, and writing and painting under figure and order. Further examples are straightness and crookedness, and concavity and convexity, which are placed under figure; multitude and fewness, which are placed under number; equality, augmentation, and diminution, which are placed under similarity and difference; eagerness, laughter, and sadness, which are apprehended from the figure and form of the face; lamenting, which is apprehended from the form of the face together with the shedding of tears; and moistness and dryness, which are placed under motion and rest, since from the sense of vision moistness is not apprehended except from the liquidity of the moist body and from the motion of one part of it before another, and since dryness is apprehended from the retention of the parts of the dry body and from the absence of liquidity. Here, however, we must consider that Aristotle maintains in the second book on Generation that moist and dry are in one way primary attributes which naturally belong to the elements, and that through these attributes spring the non-elemental moistness and dryness, which are reduced to the primary attributes and are caused by them. Concerning, then, these primary attributes it has been stated that they are

[423]

proper objects of sense and perceptible by touch alone. We are speaking, however, concerning the others. For primary moistness is that which passes over easily into all forms, possessing no definite bounds of its own, but conforming readily to the limits of something else, as in the case of air particularly and next in order in the case of water. Dry is the opposite, particularly in the case of earth, secondarily in the case of fire. But here moistness is used in the sense of liquid and slippery, and dry in the sense of arid and coagulated. The same is true concerning many other attributes, which are reduced to the forms and principal modes enumerated above belonging to visible things. All these matters are explained in the first book of Ptolemy on Optics and in the second book of Alhazen on Aspects, and in other authors on optics. There are, moreover, common qualities, some of which Aristotle defines in the second book on the Soul and in the beginning of his work on Sense and the Sensible, as, for example, magnitude, figure, motion, rest, and number. These are not the only common qualities but also all those mentioned before, although most writers on the subjects of nature do not consider this fact, because they are not expert in the science of optics. For common properties are not so called because they are perceived by the common sense, but because they are determined by all the special senses or by several of them, and particularly by sight and touch, since Ptolemy states in his second book on Optics that touch and sight participate in all these twenty. These twenty-nine, with those that are reduced to them, are apprehended by the special senses, and by the common sense, and by imagination, and these faculties of the soul cannot judge of themselves concerning other qualities except by accident.

Chapter IV

*Concerning the investigation of the estimative,
memorative, and cogitative faculties.*

But there are other sensibles *per se,* for animals use sense alone, since they do not possess intellect. The sheep, even if it has never seen a wolf, flees from it at once; and every animal experiences fear at the roaring of a lion, although it has never heard a lion before nor seen one. The same is true in regard to many things that are hurtful and contrary to the constitution or complexion of animals. The same principle holds good as regards what is useful and in conformity with their natures. For although a lamb may never have seen another lamb before, it runs to one and willingly remains with it, and the same is true concerning other animals. Brutes, therefore, have some perception in things advantageous and in things harmful. There is then something sensibly in them besides the twenty-nine properties mentioned above and besides those that are reduced to them. For there must be something more active and productive of change in the sentient body than light and color, because it not only causes apprehension but also a state of fear or love or flight or delay. This is the property of the complexion belonging to each object by which it is assimilated to others in a nature special or general. Through this quality things agree, are strengthened and invigorated, or differ and oppose one another and are mutually harmful. Wherefore not only do light and color produce their forms and impressions, but to a far greater degree do the properties of complexions, nay, the very natures of things as regards their substance, agreeing or disagreeing with one another, produce strong impressions, which change greatly the sensitive soul, so that it is moved to states of fear, horror, flight, or the opposites. These forms or impressions coming from things, although they change and alter special senses and the common sense and imagination, just as they do the air through which they pass, yet no one of those faculties of the soul judges concerning these impressions, but of necessity a far nobler and more powerful faculty of the sensitive soul does, which is called estimation or the estimative faculty, as Avicenna states in the first book on the Soul, a faculty which he says perceives the insensible forms connected with sensible matter. Sensible matter is spoken of here as that which is apprehended by the special senses and by the common sense, as are the aforesaid twenty-nine. We call insensible form that which is not taken cognizance of by those senses of themselves, since they are commonly called senses, although other faculties of the sensitive soul may equally well be called senses, should we wish so to name them, because they are parts of the sensitive soul. For every part of the sensitive soul can be called a sense, because it is in truth a sense, and a sensitive faculty. The statement, therefore, that qualities belonging to complexions are not apprehended by a sense must be understood as applying to a special sense and the common sense and imagination; but they can readily be apprehended by estimation, which although not called a sense is, however, a part of the sensitive soul.

But estimation does not retain a form, although it receives it like the common sense, and it therefore requires another faculty in the remotest part of the posterior cell to retain forms coming to the estimative faculty and to be its storehouse and repository, just as imagination is the storehouse of the common sense. This is the memorative faculty, as Avicenna states in the first book on the Soul. Cogitation or the cogitative faculty is in the middle cell and is the mistress of the sensitive faculties. It takes the place of reason in brutes, and is therefore called the logical, that is, the rational faculty, not because it employs reason, but because it is the ultimate perfection of brutes, just as reason is in man, and because the rational soul in man is united directly with it. By this faculty the spider weaves its geometrical web, and the bee makes its hexagonal house, choosing one of the figures that fill out space, and the swallow its nest. The same is true of all the works of brutes that are similar to human art. Man by means of this faculty sees wonderful things in dreams, and all the faculties both posterior and anterior of the sensitive soul serve and obey it, because they all exist on account of it. For the forms or species that are in the imagination multiply themselves into the cogitative faculty, although they exist in the imagination according to their nature primarily because of phantasia, which uses those forms; but the cogitative faculty holds those forms in a nobler way, and the forms of the estimative and memorative faculties exist in the cogitative faculty in accordance with a nature nobler than that existing in those faculties, and therefore the cogitative faculty uses all the other faculties as its instruments. In man there is in addition from without and from creation the rational soul, which is united with the cogitative faculty primarily and immediately, and uses this faculty chiefly as its own special instrument. Species are formed in the rational soul by this faculty. Wherefore when this faculty is impaired the judgment of reason is especially perverted, and when it is in a healthy condition the intellect functions in a sound and rational way.

Chapter V

An exposition of authorities at variance regarding the faculties mentioned.

But the Latin text of Aristotle does not disclose to us this division, for there is no mention expressly made except in regard to the common sense, imagination, and memory. But since the text of Aristotle owing to faulty translation cannot be understood in this part of his work, and the same difficulty is found in other passages, and since Avicenna was the perfect imitator and expositor of Aristotle in nearly every respect, and was the greatest philosopher subsequent to him, as the Commentator states in the chapter on the Rainbow, we must for this reason hold to the opinion of Avicenna, which is clear and perfect, although the translators of the works of Avicenna, as in his book on the Soul, and in that on Animals, and in his books on Medicine, have translated differently and have changed words, so that Avicenna's meaning has not been translated to the same purport throughout, since in his book on Animals we find that the estimative faculty takes the place of reason in brutes, and so too we sometimes find elsewhere contradiction with respect to the aforesaid matters; but the fact is of little moment that different translators use different words, and sometimes in part of a subject show some diversity. But we must hold to his view as expressed in his book on the Soul, because he there discusses the faculties of the soul as his principal topic, but elsewhere his mention of this subject is rather incidental. Moreover, that work has been translated far better than his other books, a fact that is evident, since it has few or no words belonging to other tongues, while his other books have them in countless numbers. If one really considers what has been said above, he must assume that there are three faculties wholly different, according to the three cells. For a diversity of objects shows us a diversity of faculties. For there are two kinds of properties, one external, as the twenty-nine mentioned above, the other internal hidden from external sense, as the quality of a harmful or useful complexion, or rather the essential nature itself whether useful or harmful. There must then for this reason be two kinds of senses, one containing the special senses and the common sense and the imagination, which are influenced by the first class of qualities; and the other containing the estimative faculty and memory, which are referred to the second class of qualities. But the cogitative faculty, owing to the excellence of its functions as compared with other faculties, is distinguished from them. In the generally accepted translation of Aristotle the whole faculty is called memory, which has the power of retaining forms, and therefore not only the storehouse of the common sense, but also that of the estimative faculty, is called memory. Therefore what is here called imagination is comprehended under memory in the translation of Aristotle that is in common use. But without doubt memory must be a double faculty with two quite distinct parts, so that one shall be the storehouse of the common sense and the other that of the estimative faculty; and these will differ in species, subject, organ, and operation. Moreover, although these faculties have been placed in the brain, we must understand that the marrow-like substance of the brain is not itself sensitive, as Avicenna teaches in the tenth book on Animals, respectfully correcting Aristotle on this point.

For the marrow in other parts of the body is not sensitive, and therefore it is not so here. But it is the container and storehouse of the sensitive faculties, containing slender nerves in which sense and sensible forms are located. But in order that all doubt may be removed, we must consider that the sensitive soul has a twofold organ or subject; one is basic and the seat of life, namely, the heart, according to Aristotle and Avicenna in the books on Animals; the other is that which is first changed by the forms of qualities, and in which the operations of the senses are more manifest and distinguished, namely, the brain. For if the head is injured an evident injury is suffered by the sensitive faculties, and an injury to the head is more evident to us than one to the heart, and frequently occurs. For this reason in accordance with the more obvious consideration we place the sensitive faculties in the head; and this is the opinion of physicians who do not think that the origin of the faculties

is in the heart. But Avicenna in the first book on the Art of
Medicine says that, although the opinion of physicians is the
more obvious to the sense, yet the opinion of the Philosopher is
the truer one, since all the nerves and veins and all the faculties
of the soul have their origin first of all in the heart, as Aristotle
proves in the twelfth book on Animals, and Avicenna in the
third book on the same subject. .

SECOND DISTINCTION

Containing three chapters. The first deals with the nerves leading to the eye.

CHAPTER I

CLEARLY, therefore, in order that there may be no scruple of doubt in what follows, the structure of the eye must be studied, because without this nothing can be known concerning the method of vision. But some writers say less, some more, and in certain things they are at variance. For authors on perspective more commonly pass over these matters, assuming a knowledge of the natural philosophers and of the writers on medicine, as though every one who reads the science of perspective has already consulted the writers on medicine and on nature. Therefore their discussion is in itself obscure, nor can we understand it unless we have recourse to the fuller treatment of the subject by the writers on medicine and on natural philosophy. For this reason something more must be said here on this topic than is found in the writers on perspective. Although it may be too difficult to attest these matters, and to explain those that are attested, yet I hope that these facts can be made clear by certain authors. But that I may not draw upon sources of individual opinions to too great an extent, I shall confine my description of the structure of the eye mainly to three authorities—Alhazen in his first book on Perspective, Constantinus in his book on the Eye, and Avicenna in his books; for these writers are sufficient and they treat more definitely the matters in which we are interested. I cannot, however, give the exact words of each, because they are sometimes at variance owing to faulty translation, but from them all I shall form a single statement of the truth. All, then, are agreed that there are two parts in the anterior cavity of the brain, which are called ventricles, or concavities, or cells. These ventricles cannot be organs of the common sense and of the imagination, of which mention was made previously. For those faculties are arranged anteriorly and posteriorly, while these ventricles are placed on the right and on the left, as Constantinus states. For the entire brain cell can be divided into an anterior part and a posterior part, as was stated above. There is, however, a division according to right and left. The anterior part of it, namely, the place of the common sense, has a right and left, where are the two ventricles in a measure distinct. From the pia mater, which covers both ventricles, comes a double nerve, one from the right ventricle, and the other from the left, and these are the optic nerves, that is, the concave ones, according to the authors mentioned. The hollow does not begin at the middle of the anterior part of the brain, because there is located the organ of smell. This is a single nerve with two small bits of flesh on the sides like the tips of the teats, as Avicenna teaches in the tenth book on Animals. But according to Avicenna, and the author* on Perspective, and Constantinus, these visual nerves of which we are speaking come out at the bottom of the ventricles of the anterior part. This is the explanation of Constantinus, who teaches us to examine the heads of large animals, when they are killed not in the summer or in the heat, and we shall find a small opening in the skull through which the nerve passes, and then we should examine the membrane of the pia mater cautiously lest it be broken, and we shall find that a nerve comes out at the bottom of the anterior part of the brain. But the two nerves, as we have stated, from the two directions right and left, meet, according to all authorities, and after meeting again are divided. It was, moreover, better that they should meet in the opening than before it or after it. For in either of these cases they would make two openings in the bone of the head, but it is better that the nerve should pass through one opening than through two. The bone is firmer the less it is perforated. Therefore, since nature acts in the better way possible, the junction will be in the opening of the skull, at which place they are again divided. The nerve that comes from the right goes to the left eye and the one from the left to the right eye, so that there is a direct extension of the nerves from their origin to the eyes. For if the nerve coming from the right part of the anterior cell of the brain passed to the right eye, there would be an angle in the common nerve where they meet and the nerve would be bent and would not extend directly to the eye. But this would hinder vision, because vision always selects straight lines as far as

* Alhazen.

possible. Moreover, since the bone of the eye is concave with an opening toward the head, the nerve enters the opening of the eye and spreads out in the hollow of the bone like the utensil with which wine is put in jars. Let, then, *abc* be the skull, and *d* be the right part of the anterior cavity of the brain, and *e* the left, enveloped by the pia mater, from the bottom of which let two nerves come forth on the right and left, meeting in the opening in the skull, and afterwards dividing, so that the nerve coming from the right goes to the left eye, which is *f*, and the nerve from the left to the right eye, which is *g*, and let them enter the openings of the concave bones, so that they spread out in that hollow, as is shown in the figure. But we must understand that just as the two nerves are derived from the pia mater, so are they also derived from the dura mater, and similarly from the lining of the skull, in which externally it is wrapped, and these three nerves are concave and meet in the opening, and one nerve is formed with three nerve coats, and this nerve so formed goes to each eye, and each eye has naturally a position similar with respect to the meeting of these nerves in the opening and at an equal distance from it, so that vision may be completed with greater certainty.

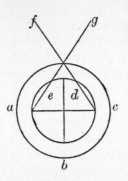

FIG. 24.

CHAPTER II

*Concerning the coats of the eye formed from
the three nerves mentioned.*

THE eye, therefore, has three coats or membranes, and three humors, and a web like that of a spider. Its first coat is formed from the interior coat of the nerve, which comes from the pia mater, according to all authorities, and spreads out from the end of the nerve where it enters the opening in the bone, and is ramified like a concave net in its first part. It is therefore called rete or retina, according to Avicenna in the third book on Medicine and according to Constantinus, and is supplied

with veins, arteries, and slender nerves. Its second part is
thicker, as Avicenna says, and spreads out spherically up to
the fore part of the eye with an opening in the middle of its
own fore part, in order that the impressions of light and color
and other visible things may be able to pass through the middle
of the eye to the nerve coming from the brain. For this opening
is placed directly opposite the extremity of the nerve at which
the retina expands, and therefore in this whole coat Alhazen
states there are two openings, one in front and the other behind, which is the extremity of the concave nerve. This second
part is called the uvea, since it is similar to a grape [*uva*],
owing to the fact that it has an opening in its anterior part
like that left in a grape when its stalk is removed, as Avicenna
says in the third book on Medicine. From the coat of the nerve
coming from the dura mater, the second coat of the eye is expanded, according to all authorities. This coat has two parts.
For the first part is composed of veins, nerves, and arteries, and
is called secundina, because it is similar to the after-birth
[*secundinae*]; and the second part spreads as far as the anterior of the eye, and there part of it is apparent, namely, the
portion of a sphere, which forms a circle above the extremity
of the uvea, and is like transparent horn and is therefore called
cornea. It is composed, as Avicenna says in the book mentioned,
of four thin rindlike coats, and they are like rinds, so that if
one of them should be stripped off, the others would not be
injured because of it. The result is that this coat is strong because of the injuries and attacks coming from the air, and yet
it is very transparent, so that the large number of its coats does
not hinder the passage of the impressions of visible things.
The third coat of the eye is formed from that third skin of
the nerve that comes from the membrane of the skull, and its
first part is joined to the bone of the eye, and is, in fact, hard
and solid, and for this reason is called sclerotic, but the remaining part extends to the cornea. For this coat is not a complete one but lacks a portion of the sphere, and is filled with
fat and white flesh, as we see externally in eyes, and it is called
consolidativa or conjunctiva. We must bear in mind that in one
way there are said to be only three coats, but in another way
six; and both views are true and rational. For if we consider
the coats as whole ones, there are only three. If, however, we

consider the parts behind as distinct from the parts in the front both in name and fact, there are six. For three parts are posterior and three are anterior. Some also have maintained that they are fewer, and that, too, with elaborate argument; but we should not pay attention to them, because their interpretation is forced and deviates from sound reason. Some also have maintained that there are seven coats; but this is false, because they reckoned as a coat the spider-web structure, although it is not. Those who say that there are three coats call the whole first coat the uvea, and the whole second coat the cornea, and the whole third one the consolidativa. Hence authors on perspective call the whole first coat the uvea, and so I wish chiefly to employ the term in describing the method of vision. Therefore Alhazen says that the uvea has two openings, one anterior, and the other posterior, which is the opening of the nerve, at which the expansion of the concavity of the uvea begins, whence the extremity of the nerve with the whole cavity following as far as the anterior opening is the uvea in fact.

CHAPTER III

Concerning the humors of the eye and the weblike structure.

THIS coat contains in itself three humors and one web. For from the anterior part of that coat there begins a web small and fine like the web of a spider, and in this is contained a body that is called glaciale, crystallinum, or grandinosum [like ice, crystal, or hail], and this body is formed directly above the extremity of the nerve. But it has two parts; one is interior at the extremity of the nerve and is similar to melted glass, and on this account is called the vitreous humor. The other part is anterior and is like ice and hail and crystal, is whiter than the vitreous humor, and is called anterior glacialis, not having any other name of its own in the author* on Perspective. But it is called in other authors the humorlike crystal, ice, or hail, because it is similar to them, and the whole body contained beneath the web is so called from this part. Then toward the anterior part of the eye outside of the web a humor like the white

* Alhazen.

of egg fills the anterior cavity of the uvea, and on one side touches the anterior part of the glacialis, and on another side enters the opening of the uvea, and reaches to the cornea, so that the spherical convexity of this humor touches the concave figure of the cornea, and is called humor albugineus. There will then be the cornea, the humor albugineus, the humor glacialis, and the humor vitreus, and the extremity of the nerve, so that consequently impressions of things will pass through the medium of them all to the brain. Avicenna says in the fourth book on Animals that the retina conveys nourishment as a matter of fact to the parts of the eye, and contains the vitreous humor, as Constantinus states, and the author on Perspective agrees, maintaining that the lower part of the uvea contains the vitreous humor, and at the end of it carries blood in its veins and arteries well digested, with which the vitreous humor is formed and nourished, in order that the vitreous may be able to nourish the crystalline humor. For, as Avicenna says in the third book on Medicine, the vitreous humor is the nourishment of the crystalline humor. Constantinus also makes this statement. Hence, since the crystalline humor is quite white and clear, blood is not suitable for it as direct nourishment, but it needs a nourishment intermediate between blood and the crystalline humor, and of this kind is the vitreous humor, which is whiter than blood, and less white than the crystalline humor. Avicenna says that the humor albugineus is the overflow of the crystalline humor, and therefore is opposite in position as regards its nourishment, which is the vitreous humor, and for this reason the crystalline humor is between these. The vitreous humor fills the whole cavity of the nerve as far as the common section, and is thicker than the glacial humor. Each, however, is transparent, so that the impressions of objects may pass through in them. The crystalline humor is called the pupil, and in it is the visual power, just as in a subject that at first is changed, although not radically, since the common nerve is the radical organ, and there vision is completed, as far as the visual power can, as what follows will show.

THIRD DISTINCTION

In three chapters. The first is on the sphericity and central points of the vitreous humor and of the glacial humor, of the cornea, of the humor albugineus, and of the uvea.

CHAPTER I

WE must consider next the form of the eye and of its parts, and the location of the centers of its coats and humors: for these facts are quite necessary; without them the method of vision is not understood. The whole eye, then, approaches the form of a sphere, and the coats likewise and the humors owing to the admirable qualities of the spherical form, because it is less subject to obstacles than a figure with angles, and is simpler than other figures and is more spacious than other isoperimetric figures, as Alhazen, the author on Perspective, states. But in what precedes these properties and others were touched upon. The anterior glacial humor is the portion of a sphere different from the sphere of which the vitreous humor is a portion; for they are different bodies and of different transparency. Moreover, the anterior glacial humor is the portion of a larger sphere than is that of which the vitreous humor is a portion. Hence the bodies are not complete spheres, but are portions of different spheres, and therefore since these are intersecting spheres, they must have different centers. Since the cavity of the vitreous humor is toward the glacial humor, its center is beyond the center of the eye toward the anterior of the eye. Similarly the center of the anterior glacialis is in the depth of the eye. These centers are, however, on the same straight line that enters through the anterior opening of the uvea and through the opening that is at the extremity of the nerve, where the retina begins to expand. For these bodies are so arranged, according to the authors on Perspective, that from the opening of the bone, where the nerve enters, the nerve extends for some distance and is constantly more dilated, until it comes to the circumference of the whole glacialis, and is consolidated with its circumference. Then above the extremity of the nerve the whole glacialis is placed and is contained in the inferior part of the uvea, which

Optical Science

Alhazen calls the point of the cavity of the uvea, in the last part of which is the opening that is the extremity of the nerve, where the uvea begins. But the middle of the whole glacialis, namely, the vitreous humor, is in the orifice of the opening. For the extremity of the nerve contains the middle of the sphere of the whole glacialis, as Alhazen says, and this middle is the vitreous humor; and the uvea is consolidated with the circumference of the glacial sphere. The humor albugineus contained in the uvea touches the sphere of the anterior glacialis, and it fills the opening up to its contact with the cornea, not so as to touch the cornea in a point, but by the junction of surfaces, just as an interior sphere is contained by an exterior one. But since the convex surface of the cornea is continuous with the surface of the whole eye, and with the whole eye, as Alhazen states, they must have the same center. Since, moreover, the concave surface of the cornea is equidistant from the exterior convex surface, both surfaces of the cornea and the whole eye must have the same center, according to the book of Theodosius on Spheres: for equidistant spheres, one containing and the other contained, have the same center, for example, the spheres of the universe, as the starry heaven, and the sphere of fire, and similarly in the others; for the center of the universe is the center of them all. Since, moreover, the concave surface of the cornea and the convex surface of the humor albugineus, which is in the opening, are like an interior and an exterior sphere, the convex surface of the humor albugineus must have the same center with the aforesaid. But since the concave surface of the cornea does not touch the uvea in a point, nor is united to it as an exterior sphere to an interior one, but is united to it on the circumference of its opening, the cornea must cut the uvea, and therefore they will have different centers. Since the cornea is a larger sphere than the uvea, because it is continuous with the surface of the whole eye, and the uvea is contained below the sphericity of the cornea, the center of the cornea, therefore, must be further in the depth of the eye, as is clear to the sense in the case of spherical bodies so united. This fact is shown by Theodosius on Spheres, and Alhazen so states it.

Opus Majus

CHAPTER II

In which is explained a difficult doubt regarding the aforesaid.

BUT then there is serious doubt as to what fills the space between these bodies, where the smaller sphere deviates from the larger, and many for this reason think that the humor albugineus spreads itself below the cavity of the cornea, where the uvea is separated from it. But the objection is made that since the humor albugineus is concentric with the cornea, it will be contained in the cavity of the cornea, like a sphere joining it or equidistant; but it is not equidistant, since it touches it; therefore it will join this in its cavity, and will fill the space that is between the uvea and the cornea. But opposed to this statement is the fact that the author on Perspective does not so state it, but always says that it is within the uvea. The objections, therefore, are removed by the fact that the parts of the eye are not complete spheres, but portions of spheres, as is clear in regard to the parts of the glacialis and so, too, in regard to the others that precede these and serve them principally, as are the anterior of the cornea, and the humor albugineus in the opening of the uvea, and the anterior of the uvea. Hence we must take into account here only the sphericity of the portions; and therefore when mention is made of the sphericity of the cornea the statement has reference only to that portion which is necessary for vision, namely, that which is in the anterior part of the eye, but elsewhere is not spherical. Moreover, the uvea, although in the upper part spherical, is not so in the lower part; similarly the humor albugineus does not have a sphericity concentric with the cornea, except in the opening of the uvea, where it is joined to the cornea, for below the uvea it has concentricity with the uvea. Moreover, since such is the case, the humor albugineus cannot flow between the cornea and the uvea. For if the bodies were of complete sphericity, this result would follow, but such is not the case. But where the cornea and uvea are apart the consolidativa spreads itself, and fills up whatever there is to be filled between the consolidativa and the cornea, or the cornea and uvea giving up their complete sphericity dilate, and externally unite or internally or in both ways, and fill all that should be filled.

Moreover, since the anterior glacialis in its convexity cuts the uvea, similarly its center must be different from that of the uvea and farther within the depth of the eye: and since the whole eye, and the cornea, and the humor albugineus have a different center from the uvea and in the depth of the eye, just like the anterior glacialis, and these are required, that vision may take place in the glacialis, it is better, as Alhazen says, that the anterior glacialis should have the same center with them. Therefore the whole eye, the cornea, the humor albugineus, and anterior glacialis are concentric. But concerning the anterior glacialis it will be more definitely shown in what follows that it must have the same center as the cornea and the whole eye, when refraction in the vitreous humor is pointed out. In the meantime let what has been said suffice.

CHAPTER III

Concerning the center and sphericity of the consolidativa.

THE consolidativa is thought to have a different center from all these farther back in the depth of the eye. But the author on Perspective does not say this, but merely states in regard to the uvea and the vitreous humor that neither mutually nor with the others have they the same center, and in arguing that the center of the cornea and the center of the uvea are not the same he says that the sphere of the uvea is not in the middle of the consolidativa, but extends forward to a part of the visible surface of the eye itself, and the visible surface of the eye is a part of a larger sphere than the sphere of the uvea, wherefore the center of this visible surface will be farther back in the depth of the eye than the center of the uvea. But the surface of the cornea and that of the visible eye, as he assumes here and later explains, are the same. Therefore the center of the uvea and that of the cornea are not the same. From this it is argued by some that the center of the concave surface of the consolidativa and that of the cornea are the same, because through the elevation of the uvea from the middle of the consolidativa it is shown that the uvea has a different center from that of the cornea and of the whole eye. But it is to be noted that the exterior surface of the consolidativa is not concentric with the interior surface, as is evident; nor, moreover, is the interior surface completely spherical, because it fills the space where the cornea and the uvea are separated, for which reason it loses its true sphericity, and goes farther into the eye in that part than elsewhere, and therefore the cornea and the interior consolidativa are not concentric. But if both spheres, namely, the cornea and the consolidativa, were complete, the cornea would lie in the cavity of the consolidativa, and the interior of the consolidativa and the exterior of the cornea would be concentric. Moreover, since the exterior and interior surfaces of the consolidativa are not concentric, the exterior of the cornea and the exterior of the consolidativa will not be concentric. Since also the consolidativa does not have perfect sphericity on the exterior, as Alhazen states, for it tends in its anterior toward pointedness and therefore does not strictly have a center from which all lines drawn to the circumference are equal, for this reason neither on the outside nor on the inside is the body really spherical, and therefore a center is not assigned to it by Alhazen. It can, however, have a point similar to a center farther back in the depth of the eye than the center of any other part, as will be shown in the figure. If, however, we wish to remove all contention, we can say that the exterior surface of the consolidativa is not wholly spherical, just like that of the whole eye, because it is somewhat pointed in the anterior part, and thus the whole eye will not have the center of a sphere, nor will the exterior surface of the consolidativa. If the interior surface of the consolidativa were spherical, it would not fill the space that had to be filled between the cornea and the uvea. But either the cornea contracts itself at the surface of the uvea, and is deepened by losing its true sphericity, except in the anterior part that is opposite the opening, or the uvea elevates itself and passes into a protuberant form, externally losing its true sphericity. But although the centers are different in the parts of the eye, yet all are in the same line, which is perpendicular to the whole eye and to all its parts. This line passes through the middle of the opening of the uvea, and through the middle of the opening in the extremity of the nerve, on which the eye is formed. This line is the axis of the eye, by which the eye sees with certainty and by which it passes over the separate points of a visible object, so that it may make certain of each in succession, although it grasps at the same time and at once with full certainty a visible object or a part of a visible object. For since this line is perpendicular to the eye and to all its parts, an impression coming along it is strongest, because approach along the perpendicular is the strongest, as was demonstrated in what was said on the multiplication of species. This arrangement is a necessary one, in order that the eye may grasp most strongly and with the utmost certainty what it should.

I shall draw, therefore, a figure in which all these matters are made clear as far as is possible on a surface, but the full demonstration would require a body fashioned like the eye in all the particulars aforesaid. The eye of a cow, pig, and other animals can be used for illustration, if any one wishes to experiment. I consider this figure better than the one that follows, although the following one is that of the ancients. For it is impossible that the center of the vitreous humor should be below the sphere of the anterior glacialis, because in that case right will appear left and the reverse, as will be shown below: nor yet on the surface of its body, because in that case an impression on the right would go too far to the right, and one on the left too far to the left, and they would never meet in the common nerve, wherefore the center will lie outside toward the anterior part of the eye. Since, moreover, the opening of the uvea is small, and the anterior glacial opening is less, since it is farther in, concentric with the humor albugineus in the opening, the vitreous must cut a very small portion from the glacialis, *cfd* in the figure, so that it can scarcely be drawn by the hand of man, for to this portion corresponds *mo,* the opening of the uvea, which is here larger than the opening of the uvea in the eye of any man of this day. The size of the opening is determined by the boundary lines of the visual pyramid, which is *abl.* For let *al* be the base of the pyramid, which is the visible object, the impression of which penetrates the cornea under the pyramidal form and enters the opening, and which tends naturally to the center of the eye, and would go to it if it were not met first by a denser body by which it is bent, namely, the vitreous humor, *chd.* For this reason, therefore, I have so placed the center of the vitreous humor and have so drawn its sphere; and it is evident that its sphere is less than the sphere of the anterior glacialis. But in the eye there are not whole spheres, but only small portions of them, like the portion of the sphere of the anterior glacialis, *cfd,* and the portion of the vitreous humor, *chd;* I have completed, however, the spheres in the figure to show the centers and the portions. The uvea, moreover, is drawn in a complete sphere, except in its opening, *mo,* and yet it is not in the eye completely spherical, as has been

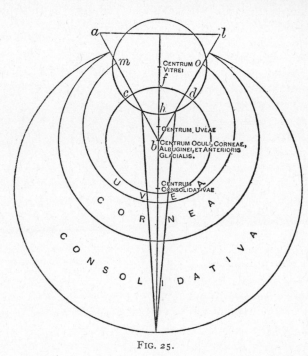

FIG. 25.

stated, but is so in its anterior part, in which is the opening, because sphericity is not required for vision except in that place; elsewhere it is of irregular form, in order that a void may not exist between the uvea and the cornea; and the lines *c* and *d,* which are drawn toward the interior of the eye, are in the sides of the nerve of the uvea, and between these lines is the opening of the uvea, which accordingly is toward the interior of the eye. Above this opening the vitreous humor is formed, as is apparent; for the aperture of these lines terminates at the extremities of the portion of the vitreous humor,

and its distance is between *c* and *d,* and this distance between
the sides of the nerve is filled with the vitreous humor as far
as the common nerve in the surface of the brain. This nerve,
however, in which is this path of the vitreous humor, spreads
and expands in the circuit of the humor vitreus, glacialis, and
albugineus, as far as the anterior opening of the uvea, *mo,*
which is opposite to its own interior opening, which is *cd.* Then
follows the cornea, and then the consolidativa, as indicated in
the figure.

FOURTH DISTINCTION

In four chapters. The first chapter is on the properties of the cornea, the humor albugineus, and the uvea.

CHAPTER I

THE coats and humors, according to Alhazen, have their admirable qualities, from which follow the benefits of vision, as he himself shows. The first function of the cornea is the closing of the opening in the uvea, preventing the escape of the humor albugineus; it is, moreover, transparent, so that the impressions [species] of light and color may pass through it, as was verified before in the multiplication of species. It has strength, moreover, so that it is not quickly destroyed. Since it is exposed to the air, and could easily be destroyed by smoke and dust and the like, it has for this reason four coats, as explained above. The humor albugineus is transparent, so that impressions may pass through it and beyond. It possesses moisture, in order that it may always keep moist the humor glacialis and the spiderlike web, which is very thin and for this reason could be destroyed by excessive dryness. The uvea is usually black, in order that the humor albugineus and the glacialis may be obscured, so that feeble impressions of light and color may appear in it, since feeble light is very apparent in dark places, and is concealed in places full of light. It is somewhat strong, in order that it may retain the humor albugineus and prevent any of it from exuding. It is also thick so as to be obscure. In the eyes of human beings, however, it is sometimes found to be gray, and frequently so in the eyes of horses. This is due to the fact that the natural heat was not able sufficiently to assimilate the substance of the uvea and of the humors, and for this reason they are somewhat white, because the weak action of the assimilating heat in moisture is the cause of whiteness. Or it sometimes happens from the complete assimilation of the moisture and the victory of the dryness, as is evident in the leaves of the trees in autumn. This grayness either can be due to the uvea, for if the uvea is gray, the eye is gray; if black, the eye is black. Or the grayness can be caused by the humors, since if the moistures are placed near the exterior, and the crystalline is of large size, and the albugineous is moderate-sized, the eye will be gray, unless the opposite happens from the coat. If the moistures are dark, and the crystalline lies toward the interior of the eye and is small, and the albugineous is large, so that it causes darkness, just like very deep water submerging and covering things, the eye will be black. Aristotle held this view, and Avicenna in the nineteenth book on Animals.

CHAPTER II

Concerning the properties of the anterior glacialis.

THE anterior glacialis has many properties. For the first and chief of these is the fact that in it alone is the visual power, according to Alhazen and the other authorities. For if it is injured, even though the other parts are whole, vision is destroyed, and if it is unharmed and injury happens to the others, provided they retain their transparent quality, vision is not destroyed; for while the transparent quality through the glacialis remains continuous with the transparent quality of the air, vision is not destroyed, provided the anterior glacialis itself is uninjured. Moreover, the anterior glacialis is moist, so that it may more quickly respond to the impression of light and color, for very dry substances do not easily receive impressions; and it is of delicate structure, since such a structure in a body causes delicacy of perception. It is somewhat transparent, in order that it may receive the forms of light and color, and that they may pass through it to the common nerve; and it is somewhat thick, so that it may retain in it impressions for some time, in order that they may become apparent to the visual power and permit the exercise of judgment. For if the transparent quality were too great, the impressions would pass through, and would not remain so that a judgment could be formed. Hence it must be somewhat thick, in order that it may experience a feeling from the impressions [species] that is a kind of pain. For we observe that strong lights and color narrow vision and injure it, and inflict pain. But every action of light is of one nature and of color likewise, except that one is stronger, another weaker. Therefore vision always experiences a feeling that is a kind of pain, although it does not always perceive this, that is, when the impressions are moderate. But a painful feeling would not exist in a body unless it be fairly dense, because if it were of too great rarity the impression would not remain until it could cause the action of pain. Its surface forms part of a larger sphere than that of the vitreous, so that its surface is equidistant from the anterior surface of vision, that they may have the same center, which is the center of the whole eye and of the cornea and of the humor albugineus. These bodies aid it mainly in the act of vision, and more so than the uvea. The surface or portion of the anterior glacialis is less than half of its sphere, for otherwise it would not follow that its center is farther within the depth of the eye, as has been assumed.

CHAPTER III

*On the properties of the vitreous, the weblike struc-
ture, the optic nerve, and the consolidativa.*

THE vitreous humor is thicker than the anterior glacialis, since the ray that is not perpendicular must be refracted between the perpendicular drawn from the point of refraction and the direct path. Concerning this refraction sufficient mention was made in a preceding part on the multiplication of light. Unless refraction took place thus, vision would never be completed, as will be explained below. The color of the vitreous is whiter than that of blood, and not so white as the anterior glacialis, because the vitreous is its nourishment, as explained above. It is the portion of a smaller sphere, so that the center of this sphere is different from that of the anterior glacialis, since this is necessary owing to the refraction noted above. Its noblest property is the fact that the perception that is in the anterior glacialis is continued in it through the whole optic nerve to the point of ultimate perception, which is in the anterior part of the brain, as Alhazen says. These two humors are wrapped around by a web, since humors unless retained would flow somewhere and would not retain one shape. This web is very thin, so as not to hide the ray, and is spherical, because it contains the portion of a sphere, although there are other reasons for this, as for the whole eye and its parts. The nerve, moreover, as Alhazen says, on which the eye is formed is entirely the optic, so that the impression may be transmitted in it to the brain, and the impression of the visible object and the natural heat due it and the force of first perception may come freely to the eye, and therefore the term optic is the same as concave. The consolidativa is exterior, so as to assemble and preserve all the parts; and is somewhat moist, in order that it may adapt itself better to the positions of the coats in it, because more quickly and easily they assume the form of their position in it owing to its softness than if it were hard; and in addition it is moist, so that dryness may not quickly happen in the coats. It is somewhat firm and strong, so as to preserve the positions and forms of the coats, in order that they may not be altered quickly; and it is white, that by its means the form of the face may be beautiful.

Chapter IV

Concerning the eyelids, the lashes, and the whole eye.

THE eyelids are to protect the eye during sleep and to enable the eye to rest when fatigued by a strong impression. And although the impressions are moderate even, the eye needs the means of closing furnished by the eyelids, in order that it may not work continuously. In a similar way smoke and dust and other things harm the vision, for which reason it needs a means of closing, and therefore the lids have a quick motion, in order that they may swiftly close over the eye when harmful things approach. The lashes are to moderate the light when vision takes place, and for this reason when looking one unites them and draws them together, so as to look from a narrow opening when the strong light would harm him. Creative goodness has supplied two eyes, so that if accident or injury should happen to one of them, the second might remain. Another purpose is to add beauty to the form of the face. Both eyes, moreover, are alike in their arrangements, in their coats, and in the forms of their coats, and in the position of each coat with respect to the whole eye; and both have a similar position with respect to the common nerve and the brain. Moreover, although the general reasons for the roundness of the eyes and of their parts were given above in the properties of the sphere, yet it was especially necessary that they should be round for two reasons, namely, owing to the swift motion of this form, enabling the vision to pass at our will from one visible object to another, and from one part of the same visible object to another part, in order that anything may be perceived with full certainty by a swift motion of this kind. But of all figures the sphere is best adapted to motion. It was necessary also that the eyes should be round and the parts likewise, for if the surface of the eye were plane, the impression [species] of an object larger than the eye could not fall perpendicularly on it, because perpendicular lines to a plane tend to different points and at right angles in each case, as shown in the figure. For the lines can fall perpendicularly on the eye *fg* that come from the visible object *cd,* which is equal to the eye, but from the points *a* and *b* the ray cannot come perpendicularly, but at oblique angles. But sensible action, and such as is required in seeing, does not take place except when the ray falls perpendicularly on the vision. Since, therefore, the eye sees large bodies, as almost a fourth part of the heavens in one view, it is evident that the eye cannot be of a plane figure nor of any other figure than that of a sphere, since on a small sphere perpendiculars infinite in number coming from a large body can fall, and they tend to the center of the sphere, and thus a large body can be seen by a small eye, as is shown in the figure.

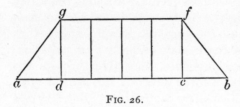

FIG. 26.

FIFTH DISTINCTION

In three chapters. The first chapter shows that impressions
[species] of light and color are required for perception.

CHAPTER I

AS we now understand those things that need explanation
on account of the mode of our vision, we must pass on
to a consideration of the mode itself and how vision
takes place. First we must determine what is required for rectilinear vision. The first requisite here considered is, that vision
needs the impression of a visible object, for without this there
can be no vision. Accordingly Aristotle says in the second book
on the Soul that in every case the sense receives the impressions
of sensible things, so that there may be an act of sensation.
Moreover, the passive must resemble the active through the
active; but vision is a passive force, and for this reason must
resemble the active, which is the visible object. But there is
no similitude of the active except the impression, as all know.
Moreover, an object makes an impression [species] everywhere along all diameters. But when there is an obstacle between the impression of the object and vision, vision does not
take place. But when every impediment is removed, so that the
impression comes to the eye, the object is seen. Wherefore
vision must happen by means of an impression; but especially
by means of the impression of light and color. For it is evident
that colors have their effect on vision from the fact that when
one views a thick growth of vegetation on which the light of
the sun falls, and continues gazing at it, if he then removes his
vision and turns it to a dark place, he will find in that dark
place the form of that light tinged from the green of the
vegetation. And if under this condition he looks at visible
objects that are white in the shadow, and in a place where the
light is weak, he will find the colors of the objects mixed with
green. If, moreover, he closes his eye and looks in it, he will
find in his own eye the form of the light with green. In the
same way he will find a change of this kind if he looks at the
color blue or purple, or at any other strong color, as any one
can prove by experiment. Therefore color must have an effect

[449]

on vision. But light more so, since in accordance with the diversity of light falling on the vision and on visible objects is the diversity of the image in individual objects. For a very bright light hides other visible objects, and even injures and oppresses vision and weakens the action of sight. But a very weak light does not change vision as it should, nor does it reveal objects. A moderate light greatly strengthens vision in its action and reveals objects sufficiently. Wherefore the species of light is especially essential for vision. And again we see that in accordance with the diversity of the fall of the same light on the same object the aspect is changed, and the color appears different to the vision, as in the case of the dove's neck when it turns the neck in different positions to the light, and so too in the case of the peacock's tail. In the same manner many things, as, for example, the scales of fish, or decayed oak, and certain worms, and the bird that is called noctiluca [shining by night]; when the light shines on them, their light is hidden and a color is seen; but when they are in darkness, their light is apparent. It is clear, then, that the species of light is especially essential in vision. Without contradiction we find by experiment that without light nothing is seen; for the extrinsic light of the sun, or of the stars, or of a fire must be present in the air, or the light belonging to the eye and multiplied by it, as is the case in the eye of the cat. Wherefore the species of light must always be necessary for vision.

CHAPTER II

Showing that vision is not completed in the eye,
but in the common nerve.

WE must understand that vision is not completed in the eyes, according to the teaching of the authors on Perspective. For two different species come to the eyes, and a difference in the species causes a difference in the judgment, since by the different species will one object be judged to be two. A similar result follows through a difference in the one judging. For in two eyes there are different judgments. Therefore one object as viewed will be considered as quite different. Therefore there must be something sentient besides the eyes, in which vision is completed and of which the eyes are the instruments that give it the visible species. This is the common nerve in the surface of the brain, where the two nerves coming from the two parts of the anterior brain meet, and after meeting are divided and extend to the eyes. Therefore the visual faculty is located there, as in a fountain, and since in this case the fontal faculty is a single one, to which the faculties of the eyes are continued through the medium of optic nerves, an object can appear as single, as far as concerns this cause. But it is, moreover, necessary that the two species coming from the eyes should meet at one place in the common nerve, and that one of these should be more intense and fuller than the other. For naturally the two forms of the same species mingle in the same matter and in the same place, and therefore are not distinguished, but become one form after they come to one place, and then since the judging faculty is single and the species single, a single judgment is made regarding one object. A proof of this is the fact that when the species do not come from the two eyes to one place in the common nerve, one object is seen as two. This is evident when the natural position of the eyes is changed, as happens if the finger is placed below one of the eyes or if the eye is twisted somewhat from its place, both species do not then come to one place in the common nerve, and one object is seen as two. This happens in the case of him who does not have the position of his eyes similar with respect to the common nerve, and for this reason the species of his eyes, unless he takes diligent care and rectifies their position, will come to different places in the common nerve, and therefore one thing frequently appears to be two. But naturally eyes that are well formed and healthy have a position similar with respect to the common nerve, and therefore the two species come to the same place in it and become one, so that thus through one species and one perception one judgment is formed regarding a single object. Experience teaches that when the common nerve is injured vision is destroyed in the eyes, and that the faculty is not destroyed in the common nerve owing to an injury to the eyes. When the common nerve is cured, vision is restored in healthy eyes; and when the eyes become well, vision is again restored, because the faculty in the common nerve was preserved, and is not destroyed in the common nerve.

Opus Majus

CHAPTER III

On the ultimate perception.

BUT since Alhazen says that this ultimate perception is in the anterior part of the brain, some one might think that it is the common sense and the imagination or phantasy which are in the anterior brain, as was stated above: especially as it was there said that a judgment concerning any sensible object is not completed before the impression [species] reaches the common sense. But it is necessary to state that the ultimate perception can be the origin of all the senses, and in this signification we are not speaking here of the ultimate perception: for this is the common sense in the anterior part of the brain. The ultimate perception is taken otherwise in the case of the special sensations of seeing, hearing, smelling, or the others, when some particular sense is mentioned; and thus the ultimate perception is the common nerve in vision with respect to the two eyes, which are the instruments that are first affected by a visible object. The same is true of the small pieces of flesh similar to the nipples of the breasts; for they are the instruments that are first affected by an odor, and the nerve to which they are continued in the anterior part of the brain is the radical and original instrument of the sense of smell. As to his statement that the ultimate perception is in the anterior part of the brain, we must note that this anterior part of the brain is not taken as the first cell of the brain, but as the place near it, namely, in the opening in the skull where the nerves meet; for since it is before and near the brain it is called the anterior part of the brain. The same is true regarding the olfactory process; for it begins at the middle of the anterior brain and extends between the two nipples [olfactory bulbs] near the brain, and closer than the visual nerve, because it is very necessary for an animal that the brain be strengthened by odor. This is especially true in the case of man, because he has a larger brain in comparison with his body than any other animal, as Aristotle says in the book on Animals.

Thus it is manifest that the eyes not only judge concerning a visible object, but that the judgment is begun in them and is completed by the ultimate perception, which is the visual faculty with its source in the common nerve. In a similar way it is evident that the eyes perceive and not only the common nerve. But since the eyes are adjusted to the radical faculty, and from it flow the forces to the eyes, and the sensitive force is continued through the whole nerve from the common nerve to the eyes, as Alhazen says, therefore the visual act is a single and undivided one, which is performed by the eyes and the common nerve. And although he says that the eye is the instrument of the ultimate perception and is the medium between it and the visible object, yet the eye of necessity has judgment and the power of sight, although its judgment is incomplete. For the angle by which the size of an object is known does not exceed the glacialis, and the arrangement of the object seen is made to accord with the object itself on the surface of the glacialis. It is by this arrangement that the object is distinguished and known. This is the statement that is forthwith made.

SIXTH DISTINCTION

On the removal of difficulties in the theory of vision, in four chapters.

CHAPTER I

*In which is removed chiefly the difficulty that seems
to arise from the smallness of the pupil.*

WE must consider, then, as was verified in what precedes, that the natural action is completed by a pyramid whose vertex is in the patient [object receiving the action] and whose base is the surface of the agent. For thus does the force come from the whole agent opposite to the patient, as has been stated before, so that the action may be vigorous and complete; and therefore in vision there is the requirement that the impression [species] should come from the whole surface of the agent. But although in the natural change produced in the objects acted upon it is required that separate pyramids come to the individual parts of the body acted upon, because each point of this body must be affected, yet in the change produced the chief requirement is that one pyramid come from the agent, and the vertex fall on the eye. This pyramid falls perpendicularly on the eye, so that all of its lines are perpendicular to the eye. For the chief requirement is that vision should perceive distinctly the object itself both with certainty and sufficiency, and this can be done by means of one pyramid in which there are as many lines as there are parts or points in the body seen. Along these lines the separate impressions come from the individual parts to the anterior glacialis, in which is the visual force. And those lines will terminate at the individual parts of the glacialis, so that the impressions of the parts of the thing seen are arranged on the surface of the perceiving member just as the parts are arranged in the thing itself, so that the judgment in regard to the separate parts may be distinct and not confused. Those lines, moreover, are perpendicular to the eye, in order that stronger impressions may come, so that it may be possible to see with perfect vision and judge concerning the thing as it really is. For the eye either does not judge at all, or forms an imperfect judgment by means of those lines alone that are not perpendicular, owing to the weakness of the impression coming by their means, although those lines converging with the perpendiculars will act more fully in securing a perception of a visible object, as will be shown below. The requirement of perpendicularity in lines and species for effective action has been expained at sufficient length in what precedes on the multiplication of species.

But we must now verify the fact that on the surface of the glacialis, although it be small, the distinction of any visible object whatsoever can be made by means of the arrangement of the species coming from such objects, since the species of a thing, whatever be its size, can be arranged in order in a very small space, because there are as many parts in a very small body as there are in a very large one, since every body and every quantity is infinitely divisible, as all philosophy proclaims. Aristotle proves in the sixth book of the Physics that there is no division of a quantity into indivisibles, nor is a quantity composed of indivisibles, and therefore there are as many parts in a grain of millet as in the diameter of the world, as is shown in the figure. If a triangle or pyramid has a large base, *abc,* and a very short line, *ed,* subtends its vertex, it is evident that from any point of the line *ab* a line can be drawn to *c,* likewise from its other points and from all its parts, because an infinite number of lines can terminate at a point. This fact is well established. If, therefore, all those lines extend to *c,* then they pass through the points of the

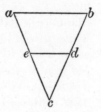

FIG. 27.

line *de;* since, therefore, they do not meet before *c,* they will pass through different points in the line *de,* because if all or some of these lines passed through the same point, the lines would meet before *c,* but it has been assumed that they do not meet. For if there were a meeting of all the lines or of some of them in some point of the line *de,* then without doubt

FIG. 28.

after the meeting they would separate one from another to infinity, and would never meet in *c,* as is evident to the sense in this shorter pyramid, *fgh.* Since, therefore, the species of an object seen, of whatever size it may be, can be arranged on the surface of the glacialis owing to the divisibility of quantity which continues to infinity, and which assumes as many parts in a small body as in a large one, no confusion happens when a large species comes to the small surface of the glacialis.

Chapter II

In which there is removed a second difficulty due to the meeting of oblique rays with the perpendicular ones.

But we must remove another difficulty that can be imagined from another source. For from any part of an object seen come forth species in infinite number, as explained in the laws of multiplications. Therefore to any part of the glacialis there comes the species from the whole object, and separate pyramids, the vertices of which are in any point of the eye and of the cornea and of the opening of the uvea, and the base of all these pyramids is the object seen. Therefore any point of the cornea and of the opening of the uvea will have species of all the parts confused in it; wherefore the judgment will become confused. We must not say that any point of the eye is infinitely divisible, in order that we may fall into the sophistry given above, since we here accept a point of the pupil or a part as the least sensible portion in the division of the parts of the perceiving member in accordance with the division of the parts of the thing seen. And therefore, excluding this sophistry, we can say that although in reality the vertex of one pyramid from the whole thing comes to every point of the eye and the cornea, and that although the species of all parts are there mingled, yet to one point of the eye or cornea and opening of the uvea a species does not come perpendicularly except from one point of the thing seen, although to the same point an infinite number of species come falling obliquely at unequal angles. Therefore since the body of the eye is denser than the air, according to the laws of refraction determined above, all lines falling obliquely are refracted at the surface of the cornea. And since the species is weakened by falling at oblique angles and likewise by refraction, and since the species falling

perpendicularly is the strong one, therefore the perpendicular species conceals all the oblique ones, just as a larger and stronger light hides many weak lights, as, for example, the light of the sun hides the countless lights of the stars, whence to the point *b* there comes a perpen-
dicular from *c* itself, and to the same *b* comes *ab* not perpendicular, since it does not fall to the center of the eye, and therefore the species of *a* itself is concealed, although from the point *b* the species of *a* itself may be able to come to the glacialis by the refracted line *bd;* and therefore the judgment is in accordance with the perpendiculars. And since perpendicular species are distinct and arranged on the surface of

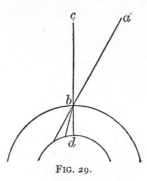

FIG. 29.

the vision, therefore a distinction takes place. The pyramid, therefore, coming perpendicularly produces both a strong vi-
sion, so that by reason of its strength forms falling obliquely are hidden, and nevertheless a distinct vision, so that it excludes the confusion that seems to happen from an infinite number of rays falling obliquely which meet each point of the pupil. This pyramid is called the visual and the radiant one, by which vision is chiefly caused.

I say this because rays coming from a point of an object from which a perpendicular ray comes to a point of the eye, al-
though they do not fall to that point directly, but to other points, yet can extend from the other points to which they fall, by refraction in the coats of the eye, to the same place in the glacialis and the common nerve to which the perpendicular species comes from the same point in the object, from which those oblique rays come; so that there is a fuller vision of any part of a visible object, since it is seen by means of its own direct rays and by means of the refracted ones. But concerning this matter mention will be made in what is to be said in regard to refraction. Moreover, for another reason I have said that vision takes place chiefly by means of the radiant pyramid; for since this pyramid alone is perpendicular to the eye, and falls to the opening of the uvea, and is directly opposite to the center of the eye, it produces for this reason a good vision and

the principal one; and yet species can come outside of this pyramid to the eye which will fall not perpendicularly on the cornea, and will all be refracted, so that in this way vision is produced by them; but the vision will be weak, because things seen not perpendicularly are not clearly apparent to the eye. Therefore we can here consider two pyramids: namely, the principal one, which falls to the opening of the uvea, or the greater one, composed of this pyramid and of the rays coming from either side of the opening on the cornea. This whole pyramid so formed is not called the visual pyramid, or the radiant pyramid, although the eye sees by means of it, but it sees principally and clearly all that falls under the visible pyramid, and other things obliquely and weakly, namely, those things that fall outside this pyramid. Hence a thing can be so large that some part of it will fall in the visual pyramid and be well seen, and other parts on the sides will fall without the pyramid on the eye, and will be seen imperfectly. Or it may happen that a thing of moderate size falls in the visual pyramid and other different things will be seen on the sides. Or it may happen that several small objects will fall in the visible pyramid and others fall in like fashion at the side. But that which falls in the visible pyramid and nothing else will always be seen principally and clearly. But with greatest clearness will that be seen at which the axis of the visual pyramid terminates. For that axis is perpendicular to all the coats and humors, and passes through all the centers; and therefore the species which comes along it is strongest and fullest, and causes certainty of vision. But a discussion of this matter will be given below.

CHAPTER III

In which a third difficulty due to the mixing of species in the air is removed.

BUT up to the present time there is no small doubt in regard to the removal of the third difficulty, which requires full discussion in the treatise on the generation, multiplication, corruption, and action of species. Without this treatise perspective cannot be understood. But, however, this doubt ought here to be set forth owing to the requirement of vision somewhat more briefly, that it may not increase too greatly our confusion in the mode of our vision. For as a matter of fact the species of colors mingle at every point of the medium, since from extreme colors an intermediate is formed, and from two species of the same specific nature one is formed. For opposites, that is, extremes, according to the statement of Aristotle in the tenth book of the Metaphysics, produce an intermediate, as, for example, white and black; and two white colors blend into one when they are in the same subject; for in the same place and subject they cannot be distinguished, but become one. But what is true of colors is also true of the species of colors, for the species is of the same nature as that which produces it, and therefore any species of color is of some genus of color, since the species of white cannot be derived from substance or from any predicable [of substance] other than quality; nor of this, from any genus other than color; nor of this, from any species, however specialized, other than white, not from black, say, or from green. Hence it remains true of white [as formerly of color] that any particular species of it, being like white, will be an individual case within the special class [of colors] to be called white. From which follows that just as in the same subject white is commixed with black, so species of white with species of black. And if this is true, then a mixed species comes perpendicularly from every point of the air to the eye, and the whole radiant pyramid will be mixed from its point of mingling in the air, and this is a necessary conclusion.

Many philosophers hold that in this view there is difficulty, and say that species have a spiritual existence in the medium and in the sense, and Aristotle and Averroës maintain this in the second book on the Soul. And because they have a spiritual existence and not a material one they therefore do not observe the laws of material forms, and for this reason do not mix, because due to a material existence material forms mix. Therefore they maintain that different species of light in the medium and countless sources of light are found at the same point of the air and are distinguished, so too the species of color and all similar species of things, and for this reason vision is able to see things distinctly. This error is a very serious one, for it contains many false and absurd things, and arises from the fact that they believe that they must maintain the distinction of vision, which they think cannot exist unless the species are wholly distinct in the air. First, then, I shall preserve the distinction of vision, so that it may be seen that it is not necessary to err in this way. Then I shall remove the error more easily, and I shall explain the authors who seem to be at variance.

I say, therefore, that species have a material and natural existence in the medium and in the sense; and that opposite species mingle in a real mixture, as, for example, the species of white and black and of intermediate colors, and that the species of two white colors and of two lights become one, and the same is true of the other species of the same categorical species. A mixed species will come to the eye from the place where the species mix, and the whole pyramid will be mixed. But the species of a visible object has a principal and primary multiplication, but the others have an accidental. Moreover, the principal or primary multiplication is straight, refracted, and reflected, and comes from the agent, as we have shown above. But the accidental or secondary does not come from the agent, but from the principal species; just as is the case with light which comes to the corners of a house from a ray of the sun through a window; and this is so weak that it has no comparison with the principal one, nor does it direct the eye to the object from which the multiplication comes. Hence a man in the corner of the house with the secondary species of the solar light in his eye does not see the sun but the ray falling through the window. If, however, he applies his eye to the principal ray, he will see the sun distinctly. I say, therefore, that just as the perpendicular ray hides all the oblique rays that terminate with it, so the principal ray hides all the accidental rays. Hence at the point d there is a real mixture of the white, black, and red, and from this point comes a mixed species to the eye along the line de. But in the line de there is no principal multiplication except from the visible point b itself, nor is there one from a or c, but merely an accidental and secondary one; because a multiplication similar to a and c does not come except from their species, not from the points themselves. But the principal multiplication hides all accidental ones, just as the perpendicular ray hides all oblique ones conterminous with it. Thus the whole pyramid is mixed everywhere, but no mixture as regards the principal multiplication comes to the eye.

This conclusion is confirmed by the fact that when different colors have the same principal multiplication, a mixed color appears to the eye; as when glass or crystal or some other transparent colored body is placed before the vision, and another dense body is behind the transparent one in a direct line with it and the vision, the species of both bodies enter the sight in the same place as regards the principal multiplication, and therefore a mixed color appears. Therefore, on the contrary, a single color will appear, when one color multiplies itself along the principal line, and another accidentally, although in the same place. If, therefore, philosophers should consider this distinction of vision, they would never maintain that species do not

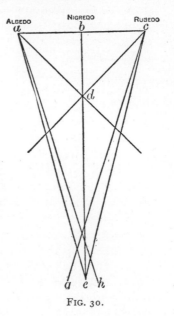

FIG. 30.

mix in a medium, because owing to the distinction of vision, which they do not know how to preserve, they fall into that error. And if it should be said that just as those species mingle in a mixture of principal multiplications at any point in the air, so do they also in the eye; therefore there will then be complete confusion, because a mixture will take place there real in character and principal as regards multiplications; the reply to all this must be that a real and principal mixture can take place at any point of the eye; but only one species at one point will be perpendicular, which falls to the center of the eye, and all others will be oblique, as are *ah, cg,* and therefore will be hidden, and a judgment will not be formed concerning these but concerning the perpendicular one, which is *be,* and by means of it concerning the thing itself, which is *b.*

Opus Majus

Chapter IV

In which a real mixture of species is proved at any point of the medium, with the removal of cavilings to the contrary.

But when they say that species has a spiritual existence in a medium, this use of the word spiritual is not in accordance with its proper and primary signification, from spirit, as we say that God and angel and soul are spiritual things; because it is plain that the species of corporeal things are not thus spiritual. Therefore of necessity they will have a corporeal existence, because body and soul are opposed without an intermediate. And if they have a corporeal existence, they also have a material one, and therefore they must obey the laws of material and corporeal things, and therefore they must mix when they are contrary, and become one when they are of the same categorical species. And this is again apparent, since species is the similitude of a corporeal thing and not of a spiritual; therefore it will have a corporeal existence. Likewise it is in a corporeal and material medium, and everything that is received in another is modified by the condition of the recipient, as the book on Causes states, also Boetius in the fifth book on Consolation. Therefore it must have a corporeal existence in a corporeal medium. Moreover, it produces a corporeal result, as, for example, the species of heat warms bodies, and dries them out, and causes them to putrefy, and the same is true of other species. Therefore since this produces heat, properly speaking, and through the medium of heat produces other results, species must be a corporeal thing, because properly speaking a spiritual thing does not cause a corporeal action. And in particular there is the additional reason that the species is of the same essence as the complete effect of the agent, and it becomes that when the agent affects strongly the patient [thing acted on]. Since at first, when wood becomes warm, while it still remains wood it has the species of fire, and later the action becomes stronger, and the species is changed into complete fire, when the fire has destroyed the specific nature of the wood, and flame is produced and charcoal. The species does not, therefore, differ from the charcoal and the flame, except as the incomplete differs from the complete, the embryo from the child, and the child from the man. But it is agreed that the complete is material; therefore also the incomplete, wheresoever we observe these things, because the incomplete becomes complete. It is manifest, therefore, that the species of corporeal and material things will have always a material and corporeal existence, whence it is madness to think otherwise.

When, therefore, Aristotle and Averroës say that the species has a spiritual existence in the medium and in the sense, it is evident that spiritual is not taken from spirit nor is the word used in its proper sense. Therefore it is used equivocally and improperly, and this is the truth. For it is taken in the sense of imperceptible; for since everything really spiritual, as, for example, God, angel, and soul, is imperceptible and does not fall under the sense, we therefore convert the terms and call that which is imperceptible spiritual. But this is homonymous, and outside the true and proper meaning of a spiritual thing. Hence the species of things do not fall *per se* under the strong and distinguishing sense; for since nothing is visible *per se* unless it be dense, because this alone can terminate vision, light or the species of color in transparent air is not visible *per se,* but becomes so *per accidens,* because no doubt there is something denser than the air, at which vision terminates, and thus perceives that there is a transparent quality in the medium, at which vision is not terminated, and consequently the clearness of light is apparent in it. And similarly when a ray falls through a window, it is seen *per accidens* owing to the fixed shape of the window, by which the light is shaped, and owing to the opaque places everywhere, so that thus an opposite placed beside its contrary becomes more easily apparent. Similarly when a solar ray passes through glass or through a highly colored cloth, the species of the color is apparent on an opaque body. But this takes place doubly *per accidens,* both because of the excessive clearness of light with respect to color and with respect to an opaque body, which intercepts the light. And in the bodies of the stars the species of the solar light is seen, not because of this light, but owing to the density of the body of the star, a density that terminates vision; and a dense body is the cause of illumination, as was noted above. In these cases, therefore, the species is seen *per accidens,* and likewise at times because of excessive weakness of vision and because of negligence in looking, as in certain cases will be explained below. And since it is only *per accidens* (as from defect of vision or negligence in looking) that species can sometimes, as it were, by chance be perceived in a measure, they are not for this reason said to be visible and perceptible in the simple and absolute use of the word. The same principle applies to the species of objects perceived by taste, smell, and the other senses; perception of them is gained neither *per se* nor *per accidens,* and therefore the species are imperceptible. And because they are imperceptible they are called spiritual; but this spirituality does not contradict corporeality nor materiality in material and corporeal things.

That, moreover, species do unite into one, and that one species is really formed from several, is shown by Alhazen the author on Perspective and by Ptolemy, who makes these statements, and by what has been said concerning the first part of the act of perception. For in it the two species coming from the eyes must become one, so that the object seen may appear as one and not as two. Alhazen says in the first book that lights mix in the medium; and Ptolemy in his third book clearly teaches a mixing of the species. But as to the fact that Alhazen wishes to prove by experiment that lights do not mix in the air, when three candles are placed opposite an opening; for then the lights appear distinct beyond the opening, and therefore also in the opening, as he seems to say; we must state that in one way there is understood to be a real mixing, and in another way there is said to be a distinction. For in fact they do mix in the opening: but since light travels along a straight path, while it is being multiplied in the same medium, therefore the light of each candle, just as it passed along different straight lines before the opening, so must it continue to do beyond the opening as regards the principal multiplication, and therefore the primary and principal paths are divided beyond the opening just as they were before it. But an accidental multiplication of the two candles occurs with the principal multiplication of the third candle, and thus there is a mixing beyond the opening. But since an accidental multiplication is not taken into account with a principal one, nor does vision form a judgment in regard to the former, because it is hidden by the principal one, therefore no confusion is apparent to us, nor is there a mixing in the places where the lights of the candles fall. There is then a mixing in the case of the lights, namely, of the accidental light with the principal; and the author [Alhazen] says that there is no appearance of mixing, because it is hidden, and he says that there is no mixing of the principal multiplications in the places where they fall; and I grant this; and yet there is a mixing there, which I mentioned in regard to the opening. I say that light considered without restriction as it is in the opening must mingle in a natural mixing and become one undivided light, and he does not deny this. But if we consider the lights as regards their relation to the straight principal paths divided after the opening, just as they were before it, they are thus said to be divided and not to mix. Hence speaking without restriction they do mix, but with respect to the different principal paths, into which it is stated that they must be now distributed in the opening, they are divided and distinct. But distinct existence in this way is not understood in the ordinary sense of the term, nor is it opposed to a real mixing without restriction, because this has to do with effect and not with mode of existence; for they are said to be distinct in the opening solely because they make after the opening distinct paths, just as the sun is said to be hot because it produces heat, not because it is formed by heat. Whenever, therefore, any of the sacred writers, or of the philosophers, or of the men of science in the past say that the species of light and color or other species at the same time are distinct in a medium, this statement must not be understood without qualification, but it is made because the species make distinct principal paths beyond the place of mixing, just as they did before it.

SEVENTH DISTINCTION

*In four chapters. First there is removed the error of vision which
would result if the vitreous and the lens [glacialis]
were of the same nature.*

CHAPTER I

HAVING removed the difficulty in seeing, we must now
show how other inconsistencies may be avoided. For
if the rays of the visual pyramid meet at the center
of the anterior glacialis, they must be mutually divided, and
what was right would become left and the reverse, and what
is above would be below, and thus the whole arrangement of
the visible object will be changed, as is easily apparent in the
figure: and thus the species of the right part of the object will
not come to its place, but to the opposite side, and the same is
true with regard to the left, and with
regard to other differences of positions.
In order, therefore, that this error may
be avoided and the species of the right
part may pass to its own side, and the
left to its side, and so too of other positions, there must be something else between the anterior of the glacialis and
its center to prevent a meeting of this
kind. Therefore nature has contrived to
place the vitreous humor before the center of the glacialis, which has a different
transparency and a different center, so
that refraction takes place in it, in order
that the rays of the pyramid may be diverted from meeting in
the center of the anterior glacialis. Since, therefore, all rays
of the radiant pyramid except the axis, which passes through
all the centers, are falling at oblique angles on the vitreous
humor, which is of a different transparency, all those rays must
be refracted on its surface, as was shown above in refractions.
Since, moreover, the vitreous humor is denser than the anterior
glacialis, it follows, therefore, that refraction takes place between the straight path and the perpendicular drawn at the

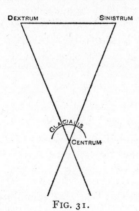

FIG. 31.

point of refraction, as has been shown in the multiplication of species. Wherefore of necessity the ray *mq*, when it reaches the point *q* on the surface of the vitreous humor, which is *gdf*, does not pass by the straight path to *a*, center of the anterior glacialis, which is *ghf*, but will be refracted at the point *q*, between the straight path, which is *qa*, and the perpendicular drawn from the point of refraction, which is *q*, into the vitreous humor. This perpendicular is *bl*; for *bl* goes to the center of the vitreous humor, which is *b*. Thus the right species will always go according to its own direc-

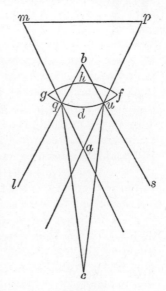

tion until it comes to a point of the common nerve, which is *c*, and will not go to the left. In the same way the ray *pu* will not pass to *a*, the center of the anterior glacialis, but will be refracted between the straight path, which is *ua*, and the perpendicular *bs* drawn from the point of refraction, which is *u*, and thus the ray *pu* will pass to a point of the common nerve at *c*, and will always be to the left. The same is true of the species coming from all other parts, because they will always travel along the paths that are due to them, and through the location they should have, so that no error may happen. Since the nerve is filled by a similar vitreous humor as far as the common

FIG. 32.

nerve, there is, therefore, no other refraction, but the species travels uniformly without refraction, nor does it change its straight path in any manner except in accordance with the tortuosity of the nerve. And in this fact we must wonder at the power of the soul's force, in that it causes the species to follow the tortuosity of the nerve, so that it flows along a tortuous line, not along a straight one, as it does in the inanimate bodies of the world. For while it is in an inanimate medium it always travels along straight paths, as stated above: but owing to the necessity and nobility of the processes of the soul, species in an animated medium keeps to the path of the medium and disregards the common laws of natural multiplications, rejoicing in the special privilege of the soul. Thus, therefore, we must consider that the species of the thing seen is necessary to vision, and we must also consider how it falls upon the vision and all its parts.

CHAPTER II

In which it is shown that the species or force of the eye radiates to the visible object because of the act of seeing.

WE must now consider whether the species of vision is necessary for the act of seeing. It is clear, moreover, that a species is produced by vision just as by other things, because accidental qualities and substance inferior to vision are able to produce their own forces; much more therefore has vision this power. This fact is evident also for this reason, because the eye is seen by itself, as by means of a mirror, and can be seen by another. But nothing is seen except by means of a species coming from the object seen. But whether this species, or force of vision, or visual rays come from the eye to the thing seen has always been a doubtful matter with scientists. But Aristotle settles this question on his own authority in the ninth book of the De Animalibus, saying that vision is nothing else than the visual force touching the object seen. Ptolemy also in his book on Optics, that is, on vision or in his theory of perspective, previous to the teaching of Alhazen, which Alhazen expounded as received from Ptolemy, maintains throughout his whole work that visual rays come from the eye to the object seen. Tideus also in his book on Aspects affirms this, and states that sight never determines the distance between itself and the object seen, nor the size of the object seen, nor the position and situation of it, unless the visual rays pass to the object seen and rest upon it, and grasp its surface and contain its extremities. This likewise Jacobus Alkindi asserts in his Science of Optics, also Euclid and all other authorities. If we wish, moreover, to confirm this by the sacred writers, we shall state that they agree in this view, Augustine in particular; for he maintains in the sixth book on Music that the species of vision comes and is propagated in the air to the object. Hence just as an inanimate object produces its own inanimate species, so does an animate thing produce a species that has in a measure the force of the soul [*anima*]. For just as an inanimate thing has a relationship to its species, which is similar to it, so is an animate thing related to a species similar to it. A medium, however, which is inanimate will not because of this fact be animate, but will be made like an animate one through its likeness now received.

CHAPTER III

In which objections are removed.

IF, moreover, Alhazen, and Avicenna in the third book on the Soul, and Averroës in his work on Sense and the Sensible are cited as opposed to this view, I reply that they are not opposed to the generation of the species of vision, nor to the part it plays in producing sight; but they are opposed to those who have maintained that some material substance as a visible or similar species is extended from the sight to the object, in order that vision may perceive the object itself, and that it may seize upon the species of the object seen and carry it back to the sight. For this was the opinion of some of the ancients in this matter, who did not yet possess definite knowledge of vision. We must state, then, that the philosophers mentioned above, Alhazen, Avicenna, and Averroës, are opposed only to this view, as is evident from their text. But nevertheless the majority is imbued with the contrary notion, owing to a passage of Aristotle in the Topics, because what one hears from his youth he accepts as a matter of habit, so that he is unwilling to receive anything else. For Aristotle in the book of the Topics, since he is giving the art of proof for every problem, states examples, which are the arguments of philosophers on matters concerning which there was doubt and which are discussed in common among them, as is evident from that book. Therefore that famous instance, that vision is the result of internal reception and not of external transmission, he cites in accordance with well-known opinions. For the Stoics held this view, as is shown by Boetius in the fifth book on Consolation in that verse, "Quondam porticus attulit obscuros nimium senes, etc." And in the book of the Priores he says that we do not always cite examples because they are true, but that he may assent who learns. Aristotle, therefore, does not assert that vision is not the result of external transmission, but makes the statement in accordance with the general opinion, and as an example, not as a truth. As to the fact, also, that in the second book on the Soul he strives to show that in general sensation belongs to the class of passive faculties and does not teach that sensation is active, we must state that this was necessary owing to the position of his master Plato and of many Platonists. For it was the common belief among them that vision was only active, and that it emitted a visible species for viewing all visible objects, whence according to them vision sends suddenly to the stars a visible species which views them and returns to the sight their species. Therefore Aristotle, who wished to verify all things as far as the possibilities of his age permitted, rejects both opinions regarding vision; namely, that of the Stoics, who maintained that it is passive only, and that of the Platonists, who held, and erroneously so, that it was only or principally active. But one of these views, namely, that of the Stoics, he refutes in his book on Animals, and the other, that of the Platonists, in his book on the Soul, just as it suited his purpose. But those versed in the philosophy of Aristotle and particularly in perspective think that vision is active and passive. For it receives the species of the thing seen, and exerts its own force in the medium as far as the visible object. Since the multiplication of species is instantaneous for every distance, as most people reckon, or rather it does require time, but an insensible amount, this time escapes perception owing to its brevity.

Chapter IV

In which the true theory is given.

THE reason for this position is that everything in nature completes its action through its own force and species alone, as, for example, the sun and the other celestial bodies through their forces sent to the things of the world cause the generation and corruption of things; and in a similar manner inferior things, as, for example, fire by its own force dries and consumes and does many things. Therefore vision must perform the act of seeing by its own force. But the act of seeing is the perception of a visible object at a distance, and therefore vision perceives what is visible by its own force multiplied to the object. Moreover, the species of the things of the world are not fitted by nature to effect the complete act of vision at once because of its nobleness. Hence these must be aided and excited by the species of the eye, which travels in the locality of the visual pyramid, and changes the medium and ennobles it, and renders it analogous to vision, and so prepares the passage of the species itself of the visible object, and, moreover, ennobles it, so that it is quite similar and analogous to the nobility of the animate body, which is the eye. But since this theory is doubtful to many, therefore besides the verifications now given I shall adduce diverse true and certain experiences, as they shall appear in different places below in regard to other conclusions, which necessarily accompany this view of the subject. Concerning the multiplication of this species, moreover, we are to understand that it lies in the same place as the species of the thing seen between the sight and the thing seen, and takes place along the pyramid whose vertex is in the eye and base in the thing seen. And as the species of an object in the same medium travels in a straight path and is refracted in different ways when it meets a medium of another transparency, and is reflected when it meets the obstacle of a dense body; so is it also true of the species of vision that it travels altogether along the path of the species itself of the visible object. And although the species of the eye lies in the form of a pyramid, whose vertex is in the eye and whose base rests on all parts of the object seen, yet from the surface of the glacialis there are pyramids in an infinite number, all of which have one base, and the vertices of these pyramids fall upon the separate points of the thing seen, so that thus all parts of the visible object are seen with such intensity as is possible. Nevertheless one pyramid is the principal one, namely, that one whose axis is the line passing through the center of all parts of the eye, which is the axis of the whole eye; for that pyramid attests all things, as was stated above and will be explained more fully.

Opus Majus

Although the species of visible things, as those of light and of color, mix in a medium, that is, several lights unite to form one, and several colors mix, as has been stated, and this species of an object and the species of vision lie in the same undivided place; yet is there no confusion of these species, or mixing, nor is one thing formed out of them, since they are not of the same species or of the same genus; because the pupil does not have color, nor do color and light have the force of the soul. Moreover, the species of the eye is the species of an animate substance, in which the force of the soul holds sway, and therefore it bears no comparison to the species of an inanimate thing, so that one thing should result from them, just as there is no such result from whiteness and sweetness in milk; and much less so in the case in point, because there is a much greater distinction between the animate and the inanimate, than between the two inanimate.

EIGHTH DISTINCTION

In which we are shown that besides species there are nine conditions required for vision. The distinction contains three chapters. In the first it is shown that light and a proper distance are required for vision.

CHAPTER I

AFTER these things we must consider that besides species nine things are required for vision, as the authors on Perspective show. One of these is light, because nothing is seen without light. For light in the first place is the visible thing, then color and the rest of the twenty things which I enumerated before, and all other things are seen with the participation of these, but no one of them is seen unless it is bathed in light. The reason for this is thought to be found in several ways, namely, either because color does not have a real existence in darkness, according to Avicenna in the third book on the Soul, or if it has, it is not able to produce its species in darkness, according to Alhazen, or if it can, it will not affect vision, nor will it change it, so that an act of vision takes place, according to the same Alhazen. The first supposition Ptolemy proves false in the second book on Perspective as follows: For if such were the case, any two things having the same position with respect to light and vision would seem of like color, the reverse of which we see in different things quite generally, and in the same thing at different times, as in the chameleon, which changes its color in accordance with the difference of those things that approach it, and in the case of him who turns red from shame and becomes pale from fear; although the thing always has the same position with respect to the light. The second supposition is shown to be false by comparison with every other active thing that produces species in darkness and in light. The third supposition is the true one, and with reason, because the first and principal visible thing is light, and therefore nothing can be seen without its help; just as in the other senses we smell nothing without the aid of the sense of smell, nor do we touch without the aid of the first four qualities, which are hot, cold, moist, dry.

The second thing that is required for vision is distance. For in general a sensible object placed on the organ of sense is not perceived, as Aristotle states in the second book on the Soul. The reason for this is that every sense acts by external transmission, that is, by emitting from itself its own force into the medium, so that the sensible species is returned more fitted to the sense, and receives a nobler essence from the species of the sense, so that it may be more conformed to the sense. Moreover, we find this in all the senses. For we have shown this above in regard to vision; and the like is true in the other two senses that have an extrinsic medium, namely, the sense of smell and hearing, since Aristotle says in the nineteenth book on Animals that forces are produced by the sense of smell and by hearing, just as water from canals. Similarly also regarding the senses that do not have an extrinsic medium, but an intrinsic one, namely, touch and taste. For concerning touch Aristotle says in the second book on Animals that its medium is flesh and its instrument is nerve. But in the twelfth book on Animals he maintains that the flesh perceives in touch, just as the eye in vision. Avicenna, moreover, in the first, second, and third books on Animals maintains that the skin and the flesh perceive. Therefore the sensitive force which is in the nerve scatters its force in the medium of touch, which is the flesh and the skin. But taste is a kind of touch, as Aristotle says in the second book on the Soul, and has an intrinsic medium, as touch has. Therefore the force of taste, which is in the nerve, emits its species into the flesh and skin of the tongue, nay, what is more, into the palate and other parts of the mouth, so that in a measure those parts seem to perceive the savor.

To what distance we can see on a plain of the earth's surface and on mountains the author on Twilights shows, saying that we see on a terrestrial plain about three miles; and on a very high mountain, the greatest height of which is eight miles, we shall see even on a plain of the earth's surface only about 250 miles; and the gibbosity of the earth restricting vision causes this.

Optical Science

CHAPTER II

*Concerning the third condition which requires that the
visible object confront the eye.*

THE third condition is that the visible object confront the eye.
For this is required in vision effected along straight lines, the
kind of vision here under consideration, although by reflection
and refraction a thing can be seen without confronting the
eye. But this is a remarkable fact, since we hear and smell in
all directions, and feel in front of us the heat of a fire placed
behind us, if it is large and strong; and vision, which is a
nobler sense, does not act in this way. Moreover, the cause of
this thing is quite hidden and still strange and unperceived by
scientists. For Aristotle in his book of Problems should have
informed us in regard to this matter, for he touches upon it
there among his other secret problems. But either a bad translation or error in the Greek edition, or some other reason hinders us in this particular.

It is certain, however, that we hear in every direction sounds
without refraction and without reflection, as, for example, one
speaking hears his own voice; but it is impossible that this happens by an accidental multiplication, because an accidental
species does not cause us to perceive an object, as has been explained above. Nor does it take place by refraction, since there
is only one medium; nor is there present a dense body, from
which reflection takes place; wherefore the action must be
along straight lines produced to the ear, therefore there must
be a real sound and not merely the species of sound opposite the
ear, and there must be a multiplication into it; but the first
sound cannot strike the ear. Therefore a real sound must be
produced opposite the ear; and the way in which this is true I
shall describe. For sound is produced because parts of the
object struck go out of their natural position, where there follows a trembling of the parts in every direction along with
some rarefaction, because the motion of rarefaction is from the
center to the circumference, and just as there is generated the
first sound with the first tremor, so is there a second sound with
the second tremor in a second portion of the air, and a third
sound with the third tremor in a third portion of the air, and

so on. Moreover, because these tremors are violent and especially so in the air, which is easily moved, and when it is put in violent motion retains the impression of the motion, therefore the second sound and successive ones for a good distance are not merely the species of sound, but a real sound possessing at any rate more than the species. Moreover, since this is a fact, for this reason a sound similar to the voice multiplied from the mouth to the surface of the ear can be generated by tremors of this kind in the air produced in every direction to the ear, not by an accidental generation but by a principal one, since the reason for this is found in the tremor mentioned, which causes the air to vibrate to the ear, and produces a real sound in it, and in every direction. Moreover, a sound made in the ear or near it, and in a straight line with it, is not the species of a species, but is sound itself produced by the tremor. Moreover, a proof that sound in the parts of the medium of the air from the first place of its production is not merely the species of the sound, but has more of the nature of the object, is the fact that sound is more violent than other sense perception, because sound suddenly confuses the hearing and destroys it, when it is very loud.

Odor not only produces a species, but from the odorous body a vapor goes forth, which is a subtle body diffusing itself everywhere in the air, and when it comes opposite to the nostrils it multiplies its species to the organ of smell, and therefore that vapor has real odor, just like the first odorous body: and for this reason not only the species, but the real odor is found here in the opening of the nostrils, not, however, the first odor, but the second, which is in the vapor.

Now the four qualities, as stated above in the laws of multiplications, are able to complete their species like the four elements, because of the necessity of generation. For we see that fire not only generates its species, but also a real and perfect fire, in flame and charcoal; and thus the heat of fire, having more than does mere species, is able to generate real heat, and this can take place everywhere in the air. Therefore it can reach to the opposite part of an animal which is not exposed to the fire, namely, when it comes outside the shadow of the fire, which the exposed object makes as far as the point *a,* and

Fig. 33.

then is able to produce a species on the surface of the object not exposed to the fire by the line *ab*. But cases of this kind do not happen in those things ordinarily seen, and therefore an object must confront the sight.

CHAPTER III

Concerning the sensible magnitude of the visible object.

THE fourth condition required for vision is that the object be of a magnitude perceptible by the sense. For the object can be so small that it will not be visible. The reason for this is that the species coming from the parts of the visible object must be arranged distinctly on the surface of the lens, and in addition sensibly as regards the sentient faculty. But when the object is too small, the species coming from the individual parts of the object to the parts of the sentient organ, although distinguished according to the position of its magnitude, as its surface is infinitely divisible, are not, however, distinguished as regards sensation, but are confused because of too great proximity on the small part of the sentient organ which the visual pyramid occupies.

Joined, moreover, to this consideration is that of the maximum magnitude that we can see by means of the visual pyramid. This question is one of great doubt, namely, How much in extreme magnitude can be seen by the eye? Men versed in the problems of perspective estimate that the eye on the surface of the earth, as we now see, cannot see a fourth part of the heavens by means of the radiant pyramid. But if the eye were at the center of the earth, it would see a fourth part of the heavens under that pyramid; since they maintain that the pyramid contains in the eye a right angle, because by that angle is subtended the side of a square that can be described in the sphere of the uvea, namely, because the portion of the uvea in which the opening is can take the side of a square, and to the side of a square a right angle corresponds. Since this is a fact according to the opinion of those men, they think that in the portion seen of the heavens the side of a square can be contained, and for this reason the whole fourth part would be seen if the eye were at the center of the earth. But if this be a fact, then without doubt a fourth part cannot be seen by an eye that is on the surface of the earth, by the twentieth proposition of the Elements of Euclid. For according to this proposition, if from the extremities of the base of a triangle two lines are drawn beneath the triangle they will contain a larger angle, as is evident in the figure. Therefore the vertex of a pyramid coming on a fourth part of the heavens to an eye on the surface of the earth would contain an obtuse angle. Since, therefore, the angle of the pyramid according to these men is a right angle, the pyramid itself will not have a quarter of the heavens as a base, since the eye is on the surface of the earth, but will have less than a fourth.

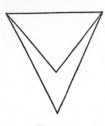

FIG. 34.

But the supposition that the radiant pyramid contains a right angle has neither authority nor experience nor proof up to the present time, and therefore is rejected with the same facility with which it is proved. Moreover, the reason for this assigned in the side of a square described in the sphere of the uvea cannot stand; because the sphere of the uvea and the anterior glacialis are not concentric, and therefore a right angle in the sphere of the glacialis will not correspond to the side of the square in the sphere of the uvea, nor will the portions of the glacialis and the uvea be similar, and therefore the portion of the sky will not be similar to the portion of the uvea in which the side of the square is drawn; which, however, would be necessary. Moreover, I am here calling portions similar which have portions proportional with respect to their spheres when they are cut by the same diameters of the earth, as is evident in the figure. For let the sphere of the heavens be *aci,* the sphere of the glacialis concentric with it *do,* and let the sphere of the uvea, whose center is different toward the anterior of the eye, namely *t,* be *efg.* It is evident, therefore, that *ac,* a fourth of the heavens, and *do,* a fourth of the glacialis, are similar, and will have the same right angle, namely, *ohd;* but *eg,* the fourth of the uvea, does not have that angle, since it faces the angle *ghe,* which is part of the right angle *ohd,* but the portion is larger than that fourth is, namely, *ef.* Therefore the side of the square described in a quarter of the uvea cannot face the right angle of the pyramid and of the gla-cialis, and therefore the angle of the pyramid cannot be closed by that side. But if it should be so closed, it will be acute, not right, as is evident to the sense in the angle *ghe,* since it is part

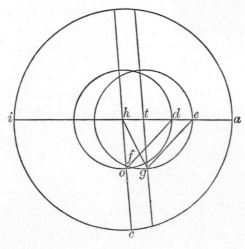

FIG. 35.

of the right angle *fhd* and *ohd,* which are identical. But it would be better to say that the portion of the anterior gla-cialis is a fourth of the sphere; for thus the angle of the pyra-mid would be a right angle, because that whole portion, how-ever small it may be, is occupied by the angle of the pyramid, because it as a whole is the organ of vision, and not merely some part of it. Then, moreover, the side of the square de-scribed in the glacialis is subtended by the right angle of the pyramid; and similarly in the portion of the albugineous humor, which is in the opening of the uvea; and in the same way in the portion of the cornea, for they will then be fourths of their spheres, because they are concentric with the glacialis. More-over, since the heavens would be concentric with them, if the center of the eye were at the center of the earth, the fourth part of the heavens would then correspond to them, together with the side of the square described in it, and thus a fourth part of the heavens would be seen. But there has been no verification of the statement that the portion of the anterior glacialis is a fourth of its sphere, and therefore we have no proof that an eye at the center of the earth would see a fourth of the heavens, nor by this method or proof can we be certain that an eye on the surface of the earth will see less than a fourth, nor how much less.

But experiment proves that the eye cannot see a fourth part of the heavens on the surface of the earth. For if one views a star that is above his head, and stands in a level space, he will not be able to see as far as the earth, however much he tries; but a fourth part of the heavens extends from the zenith to the earth. Therefore he will not see a fourth part. But he will see, however, a little less, since if on fixing his eye he bends his head a little he will see the earth, and he will not see the star. There is no other reason for this than the arrangement of the eye, because the pupil is so situated, and the opening of the uvea so arranged, that he cannot see more. This is manifest, because one person owing to the arrangement of his eye will see more of the quarter and another will see less. For he who has the opening of the uvea small, and the pupil deep set will see less of this fourth, and where the arrangement is the opposite, one will see more, as is shown in the figure; so that if the pupil is at the point *a* and the chord of the opening is *bc,* one will see less than if the pupil is at *d,* because the lines *db* and *dc* diverge more than *ab* and *ac*. Similarly, if the opening is greater with nearness of pupil more will be seen, as is evident by the lines *df* and *dg,* which separate more widely; and this is the definite reason in this case. Therefore those suppositions given above have no basis in fact.

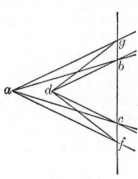

FIG. 36.

NINTH DISTINCTION

*In four chapters. The first deals with the density
and rarity of the object.*

CHAPTER I

THE fifth condition is that the visible object, which we commonly call the object of vision, must exceed the density of the air and of the heavens, as Alhazen shows. For this reason we see clearly water, because it is denser than air, and vapors, and clouds, and glasses and transparent objects of this kind, which have little density as compared with those things that have perfect density. But, however, we should know that Ptolemy says in the second book of the Perspective that we see the air or the celestial transparent body far off and within a considerable distance although not within a distance near at hand; for much of a transparent body is accumulated in a great distance and has the same effect on vision as that which is perfectly dense within a small distance. Much, therefore, of a transparent object accumulated in a great distance becomes shaded, just as we see in the case of deep water, through the medium of which we cannot see the ground as we can through water not too deep. For the parts of deep water cast forward a shadow on those that succeed them, and a darkness is produced that absorbs the quality of the rarity, so that in this way the whole body of water appears like some dense body, and the same is true of the air or celestial transparent medium at a distance, for which reason it is rendered visible, but not so at close range.

But there is also another reason, namely, that vision is terminated at a distant transparent object. For as Alhazen says in the seventh book, the rarity of bodies in the world is limited, and for this reason all of them have some density and rarity, although not very perceptible especially when near; for the species of vision is emitted from the sight to the visible object, and is weakened in distance, so that although on account of its strength it penetrates the air near at hand, but does not penetrate, however, the transparent celestial medium at a distance; and therefore vision is terminated at it. But Avicenna says in the third book on the Soul that that is really visible which terminates vision, and therefore this transparent celestial medium is really visible at a distance. I offer an example in the case of air filled with vapor and cloud in winter, which is seen at a distance but not near at hand, and when the air filled with vapor is uniform in density and rarity. But from a great distance it is seen because it can terminate the species of vision and resist it; and thus it becomes visible, a visibility it cannot have near at hand owing to the strength of the species of vision. Nor is there deception of vision, because that air filled with vapor becomes an object of vision. The explanation of this according to Avicenna lies in the fact that it is able to terminate vision. Likewise I say here that air, or the sphere of fire, or the heavens, near and remote, is of similar rarity as far as perception is concerned; but it has, however, some density of its own nature, and this density is able in a great distance to terminate the species of vision, which it cannot do in a short distance, and therefore it will be quite visible at a distance, but not near at hand. Alhazen's statement, therefore, that a visible object must exceed the density of the air, and the fact that he calls air wholly transparent as far as the stars, are to be understood in the case of the usual visible objects which can be seen within the required distance and strength of vision. Why a color appears approaching black, namely, blue, is explained in the same way as in the case of deep water, where in a like manner that color appears owing to shadows projected by particles. Darkness is caused by these shadows, which is similar to blackness. This is what takes place in the air or medium between us and the last heaven. If some celestial body were a dense body, we could then say that that body would be visible chiefly because it terminates vision, and that the whole transparent medium between the object and the eye would not be perceived, except for the fact that vision perceives that it is not terminated before its species reaches that dense body. Moreover, it is thought by learned astronomers, who are ignorant of theology, that the starry heaven is everywhere dense. But there is another view, namely, that that which is seen beyond is the heaven of water. For it has a color like the water of the sea, and we see that heaven through the medium of all the eight heavens that are on this side of it. For there is no doubt in the minds of theologians and those philosophizing in accordance with theology that the ninth heaven is of water; and then beyond it is the tenth. But concerning these the discussion belongs elsewhere.

But an objection is raised in regard to the ray or luminous air falling through a window that it is quite visible, and yet that portion of the air is rare, and rarer than that outside the path of the light, because light rarefies air as it generates heat; for heat is not generated except from rarefaction. Here, moreover, some have attempted to show that density is not required in luminous bodies, whence they judge that the stars are not dense, nor are the spheres. But owing to the excessive brilliancy of the light they say that vision cannot penetrate them, but is beaten back or fails from the excess of splendor. But the example of the ray falling through the window is clearly explained, as stated above. For it is not of itself a visible object nor does it terminate vision, but the dense body surrounding it terminates vision, and not the ray; for if there were not a dense body beyond it, it would not be seen, just as the luminous air outside is not seen, unless it be terminated by the density of some portion of the heavens. The air in the window is rendered more perceptible, because its shape is determined by the parts of the window and by the ground on which it falls. It is not, therefore, a visible object except in a secondary and not a primary sense, nor is this of which we are speaking here a visible object, which, namely, has the power of itself by means of the necessary distance to terminate vision. Moreover, just as the wrong understanding of this example is now removed, so must we now have the right view regarding that which they attempt to prove by the example just quoted in regard to luminous bodies. For after the antecedent is shown to be false, we need not believe the consequent. We have stated above in the sections on mathematics that the spheres are not luminous, but that a star is so solely on account of its density, as Averroës says, and as was stated in that place. Moreover, although too great brilliancy confuses vision, as is evident when we gaze on the sun in its full strength, yet this does not exclude density in the sun, because density is the cause of illumination, as Averroës states, and the moon and the fixed stars when viewed do not confuse vision from excessive splendor. Therefore vision would penetrate them, unless their bodies possessed density.

Now from this chapter it is clear to him who gives it due consideration that vision must take place by means of its species emitted to the visible object. For if a single continuous transparent medium in extreme distance terminates vision, and does not terminate it owing to a perfect density, which independently is perceptible in every distance, but terminates it because of the weakness of the species of vision, which fails at a too great distance, then vision must be produced by sending forth its species; that is, by emitting its species owing to the act of seeing.

CHAPTER II

Concerning the rarity of the medium.

THE sixth condition required for vision is rarity of the medium. For if a dense body is placed between the sight and the visible object, the species cannot pass through from one side to the other, and thus of necessity vision is cut off. But some, possessing an excellent understanding of many things in the science of Perspective, raise an objection in regard to a flame placed between the sight and a visible object impeding vision; and the flame, as they say, is a very rare body, because Alhazen says in the third book that the rarity of flame deviates from the mean. Therefore a rare body hinders vision more than a dense one. This, however, is a great error, for of necessity flame is denser than air, because Aristotle says in the second book on Generation that flame is a glowing terrestrial vapor; and therefore the deviation of rarity from the mean can be understood, either through a change to an extreme deficiency, or to an extreme excess, because the mean is midway between the two, just as liberality is between prodigality and avarice. And therefore just as avarice deviates from the mean of liberality through a lack of this quality, so does flame deviate from the mean of rarity by a lack of it, not by an excess. This, moreover, is Alhazen's meaning, for he so explains himself in what follows. If then an objection be raised regarding the lynx, which sees through the middle of a wall, as Boetius in the third book on

Optical Science

Consolation imputes to Aristotle, we reply that although this be true of the sight of the lynx, it is not true, however, of human vision with which the science of Perspective deals. For we are here discussing the latter vision.

But if we assume that there is a vacuum between heaven and earth, there would be neither a dense body nor a rare one. And yet Democritus thought that an eye on the earth could see an ant in the heavens, as Aristotle states in the second book on the Soul. Moreover, vacuum does not possess some nature by which it should impede species, or resist it, because no form of nature exists in a vacuum, as Aristotle says in the fourth book of the Physics. Therefore species will not pass through from heaven to the eye, and thus we should see the stars without a rare medium and without a dense one. But we must here state that we should not see anything if there were a vacuum. But this would not be due to some nature hindering species, and resisting it, but because of the lack of a nature suitable for the multiplication of species; for species is a natural thing, and therefore needs a natural medium; but in a vacuum nature does not exist. For vacuum rightly conceived of is merely a mathematical quantity extended in the three dimensions, existing *per se* without heat and cold, soft and hard, rare and dense, and without any natural quality, merely occupying space, as the philosophers maintained before Aristotle, not only within the heavens, but beyond.

The seventh condition required for vision is a sensible time. For Aristotle says in his book on Memory and Reminiscence that our whole intellect is concerned with continuity and time; much more so, therefore, is sensation. For the action of the intellect is spiritual, and the act of sensation is corporeal. But if a thing is brought suddenly before the eyes it is not seen distinctly and perfectly, and therefore a sensible time is required for vision in which the judgment of vision may be made. Whence Ptolemy in the second book of the Optics says that things which pass through the visual pyramid are thought to move swiftly, like the embers of fire and things passing through holes and narrow places, to which the vision penetrates. For since they pass through the pyramid in a short time, they are thought to move swiftly. But such is not the case.

Opus Majus

Chapter III

*Showing that the species of vision and of the visible are
produced in time.*

BUT here a very great doubt arises in regard to the species of
sight and of the visible object, whether they are produced suddenly and instantaneously, or in time; and if in time, whether
they require a sensible and perceptible time or not. Alkindus,
moreover, tries to show in his book De Aspectibus that the ray
passes through in a wholly indivisible instant, and cites in support of his view quite a curious and probable reason, when he
says, "If the species, as for example the light of the sun when
it rises, is produced in a particle of time in the first section of
the air, then if the time is doubled in the second section of the
air, and tripled in the third, and so when the light reaches the
west, there would result a time made up of many parts which
would be large in comparison with the first particle of time;
and although the first particle would be imperceptible, yet the
whole time owing to its magnitude incomparable, as it were,
with respect to the first particle, will be perceptible." Aristotle,
moreover, says in the second book on the Soul that although in
a small distance the multiplication of light might be able to
escape our sense, yet it would not be able to do so in so great
a distance as that which separates east and west. Therefore, if
the species required time this would be perceptible to the sense.
Therefore the species will not be produced in time but instantaneously. Aristotle says in the book De Sensu et Sensato that
the explanation in regard to light differs from that in regard to
other things of perception, and in regard to these others he
teaches that their multiplications take place in time. Therefore
the multiplication of light is instantaneous.

All authorities make this statement except Alhazen, who attempts to prove this view false in the second book, arguing as
follows: "Let us take the last instant at which the light is at
the terminus *a quo* and the first at which it is at the terminus
ad quem." Since therefore the instants are different, as he
strives to prove by experiment, there will be a time between
them; and he says that every change takes place in time, but
the medium and the eye are changed by species. But these rea-

sons of Alhazen do not have any weight, because the first is explained elsewhere. For it is not necessary to give always a last instant of an existing thing at the terminus *a quo,* just as universally happens in the generation of permanent things, but it is necessary to give the first instant of the terminus *ad quem,* as Aristotle teaches in the eighth book of the Physics. Whence when Socrates becomes white from non-white, it cannot be said now at last is he not white, taking *now* as an instant, but now first is he white; for he is not white during the whole time measuring the change, and he becomes white at the end of this time, namely, at the instant which is its terminus, as Aristotle teaches, and as is certain, although it is too difficult to understand unless well explained; but this is required elsewhere. His second reason has no weight; for all holding the opposite view say that the multiplication of light is not a successive and temporal change.

A sound argument, however, for the view of Alhazen can be drawn from the statements which he makes in the seventh book. For he there teaches that from the same terminus the perpendicular ray reaches more quickly the terminus of the space than the ray that is not perpendicular. But quicker and slower belong only to time, as Aristotle says in the fourth and in the sixth book of the Physics. And this is demonstrated without possible contradiction. For no finite force acts instantaneously, as Aristotle says in the sixth book of the Physics; and he proves this, because in that case a greater force would act in less than instantaneous time, which is impossible. But the force of the eye, and of its species, and of everything created is finite. Therefore no force can act instantaneously. Moreover, in the eighth book of Physics at the end he maintains that a finite force and an infinite one cannot act in the same and equal period of time, since in that case they could have equal results, and thus in turn the forces themselves would be equal. But it is the property of an infinite force to act instantaneously. Therefore a finite force cannot produce any result in an instant, wherefore it must require time. Moreover, an instant has the same relation to time as a point to a line. Therefore, interchanging terms, an instant has the same relation to a point as time has to a line; but the passage through a point is in an instant. Therefore the passage through the whole line is in time. Therefore species passing through linear space, however small, will pass through in time. Moreover, before and after in space are the cause of before and after in making translation over space and in duration of time, as Aristotle says in the fourth book of the Physics. Therefore since space through which species is carried has a before and after, passage of the ray must have a before and after both in itself and in duration; but before and after in duration exist only in time, since this condition cannot exist in an instant. If, moreover, it be said that this is true of those things that have a corporeal existence in a medium, not concerning those things that have a spiritual existence, as it is assumed here, evidently the objection has no weight, owing to what has already been said. Again if it be said that this is true in regard to those things that are measured by parts of space, but that species is not so measured, as they assume, this objection also has no weight, because that second statement is not made except on account of a spiritual existence. Since, therefore, the species of a corporeal thing has a really corporeal existence in a medium, and is a real corporeal thing, as was previously shown, it must of necessity be dimensional, and therefore fitted to the dimensions of the medium.

But if at the same instant it were throughout the whole medium, it would then be at the terminus *a quo,* and at the middle point of the space, and at the terminus *ad quem,* namely, at one and the same time. But this is in many ways impossible. For, in the first place, it follows from this that a created thing would be at one and the same time in several places, and by this reasoning if in several places, then also in an infinite number, as has already been shown in the chapter on matter. It would therefore have an infinite power and would be God, or equal to God. In the second place, the argument is drawn from this that while the thing is at the terminus *a quo* it is wholly quiescent, nor does it suffer change in any way; and when it is at the terminus *ad quem* the change has already been effected, and the change takes place between these termini. Therefore at the same instant the species would be quiescent before its passage, and the change would be effected, and would take place actually through the whole space. Therefore at the same time it would be changed, and would not be changed, which are contradictory, as Aristotle argues reducing the matter to an impossibility in another case in the sixth book of the Physics.

But there is still another reason for this, namely, since the multiplication of light does not depend on some other motion, we may assume, therefore, that the heavens are at rest and that there is no motion, for in a stationary heavens the multiplication of light can take place excellently, and will be accomplished at the end of the world, if the heavens shall be stationary, as is assumed. If, therefore, the multiplication of light is instantaneous, and not in time, there will be an instant without time; because time does not exist without motion. But it is impossible that there should be an instant without time, just as there cannot be a point without a line. It remains, then, that light is multiplied in time, and likewise all species of a visible thing and of vision. But nevertheless the multiplication does not occupy a sensible time and one perceptible by vision, but an imperceptible one, since any one has experience that he himself does not perceive the time in which light travels from east to west.

Chapter IV

Concerning the removal of objections to the truth.

Moreover, to this statement made by Jacobus Alkindi we must reply that, just as the first period of the time is imperceptible, so also is the double of it, and the triple, and the thousandth multiple: whence the whole time is imperceptible, although it has many parts which taken together make an imperceptible whole, for this motion of the species is of such great velocity that it can traverse in an imperceptible time a very great distance. Aristotle's statement is true according to his understanding of it, for he is arguing in that place against Empedocles, who maintained that light is a body and the flow of a body, just as water flows from a spring; and it is not possible that a body should change its position wholly from east to west, so that it would not be perceived owing to the great distance. But the species is not a body, nor is it changed as regards itself as a whole from one place to another, but that which is produced in the first part of the air is not separated from that part, since form cannot be separated from the matter in which it is, unless it be soul, but the species forms a likeness to itself in the second position of the air, and so on. Therefore it is not a motion as regards place, but is a propagation multiplied through the different parts of the medium; nor is it a body which is there generated, but a corporeal form, without, however, dimensions *per se,* but it is produced subject to the dimensions of the air; and it is not produced by a flow from a luminous body, but by a renewing from the potency of the matter of the air, as we stated above when the question was discussed in regard to the generation of species. Moreover, if we inquire still more carefully why we do not perceive this generation of light take place successively in the particles of the air, the answer can be given that light in the air is not an object, but a species with a weak and in a manner imperceptible existence as regards itself, and its subject between the east and the west is imperceptible, namely, the air itself, and for this reason the sense is not able to perceive a successive generation of this kind.

Moreover, as regards Aristotle's statement that there is a difference between the transmission of light and that of the other sensory impressions, we must say that many are deceived in this particular; for his statement is true, but this difference is not to be understood as consisting in the fact that light is transmitted instantaneously and the other impressions require time; nay, we must understand that, although light has a succession in its transit, it does not, however, have so great a one as sound and odor, of which he is speaking in this place. For sound has the motion of the displacement of the parts of the body struck from its natural position, and the motion of the following tremor, and the motion of rarefaction in every direction, as was stated before, and as is evident from the second book on the Soul; and these are the three local motions of the particles of the air, as well as of the body struck, no one of which motions takes place because of the multiplication of light. For although the air must be rarefied for light to produce heat, yet rarefaction is not necessary because of the multiplication of light itself, since in celestial spaces light is multiplied, where rarefaction and the generation of heat are not possible. Since, therefore, there is no succession on the part of light except the succession itself in multiplication, but in the multiplication of sound a threefold temporal succession takes place, no one of which is present in the multiplication of light, for this reason there is a great difference between light and sound. However, the multiplication of both as regards itself is successive and requires time.

Likewise, in the case of odor the transmission is quite different from that of light, and yet the species of both will require time for transmission, for in odor there is a minute evaporation of vapor, which is, in fact, a body diffused in the air to the sense besides the species, which is similarly produced. There is also a strong attraction of the nostrils for this kind of vapor and of species, so that sensation may be produced, as Avicenna shows in the third book on the Soul and as we know by experience. This results in the removal of the covering that is over the organ of smell, according to Aristotle in the second book on the Soul. Therefore in the sense of smell there is a twofold local motion, one from the resolution of the vapor, and the other from its attraction, besides a succession in the multiplication of the species. But in vision nothing is found except a succession of the multiplication. The fact that there is a difference in the transmission of light, sound, and odor can be set forth in another way, for light travels far more quickly in the air than the other two. We note in the case of one at a distance striking with a hammer or a staff that we see the stroke delivered before we hear the sound produced. For we perceive with our vision a second stroke, before the sound of the first stroke reaches the hearing. The same is true of a flash of lightning, which we see before we hear the sound of the thunder, although the sound is produced in the cloud before the flash, because the flash is produced in the cloud from the bursting of the cloud by the kindled vapor. Therefore his statement that there is a difference in the transmission of light and of the other sensory impressions can be understood, because this difference is not one of instantaneousness and time, but of less time and more time. For all authors, whether sacred or others, who state that light is multiplied instantaneously, are to be understood in regard to a divisible instant, which is imperceptible time, and not in regard to a real instant, which is the indivisible terminus of time, just as the point is of the line. If, therefore, the vision of the species and the visible multiplication take place in imperceptible time, how was it said above that vision will take place in a perceptible time? It is evident that besides the multiplication there is a judgment of vision in regard to the object seen, and this judgment must be known to the sense; wherefore the judgment must be made in a perceptible time.

The eighth condition required for vision is a healthy state of the eye together with its natural arrangement; for an eye that is torn out, or blind, or much injured, or clouded from some flowing humor, or from a resolution of vapors confusing the pupil cannot judge regarding objects, as is evident, and therefore need not be considered here. For if anything need be said further on this point, it will be explained in what follows. Concerning position, which is the final condition in vision, an explanation cannot be given here, because it coincides with other matters of which mention must be made later.

TENTH DISTINCTION

*In three chapters. The first shows with greater precision than
above what things are perceived* per se *and
what* per accidens.

CHAPTER I

HAVING stated these eight conditions without which
vision cannot function, we must consider of what
things vision takes cognizance, and in what ways they
are perceived and certified to, and how and why vision errs in
taking cognizance of visible objects, although vision has been
produced by direct rays. We must note, then, that when these
nine conditions are present in just degree, that is, they neither
exceed nor fall below what is required, a reliable vision is assured. When, therefore, they differ from the due measure either
by excess or deficiency, error is present in vision. Moreover, the
twenty-two qualities enumerated above, as light, color, remoteness, etc., are determined by vision ; and besides this, vision perceives man and horse and the other things of this world. For
by light and color these twenty things are recognized. Then
through the medium of light and color and those twenty qualities other things are known, as is possible for the sense, for the
particular senses are not able to certify regarding all things; but
those twenty-two the particular sense and the common sense
and imagination are able to comprehend without error, provided the eight conditions previously mentioned are present
in proper measure. Those qualities, moreover, are called the
sensibles *per se,* certainty in regard to which can be secured
from the senses; but the sensibles *per accidens* are those that
cannot be apprehended in this way.

Although we previously touched upon these sensibles *per se*
and *per accidens,* yet in order that no mistake may be made they
must be explained more fully. I say, then, that the sensibles *per
accidens* are twofold: certain can be determined by other faculties of the sensitive soul, as, for example, by the estimative
and memorative faculties, as previously stated; certain, however, are called sensibles *per accidens* with respect to particular
senses and the common sense and imagination, since such senses

do not perceive things of this kind independently, but because they are found in the same things together with their own sensibles *per se*. As, for example, since enmity with respect to a lamb is present at the same time with the form and color of a wolf, the lamb in looking at a wolf saw something hostile and colored, but the eye *per se* forms no judgment concerning the hostile object, but judges it such, because it is found in connection with the colored object. Moreover, since a particular sense and the common sense are commonly called senses, for this reason the sensibles in regard to which they certify are called sensibles *per se,* and those concerning which they do not certify are called sensibles *per accidens,* although some of them can be recognized by other inner faculties of the soul. For the estimative, cogitative, and memorative faculties are not called senses in the ordinary meaning of the term, although they are parts of the sensitive soul, and therefore the sensibles determined by them are called sensibles *per accidens,* because the sensibles are referred to the particular senses and the common sense.

But there are other sensibles besides those that are recognized by the faculties of the sensitive soul. As, for example, when I see a strange man I cannot perceive by the sense whose son he is, nor at what hour or in what place he was born, or what name he bears, Peter or Robert; and there are countless things of this kind that are accidental to each person, in regard to which no faculty of the sensitive soul can inform us, nor can one know the truth except through information given. And yet on looking at that man vision falls upon all his qualities. For if he be the son of Robert, and a Frenchman, and born in Paris during the first hour of the night, in looking at him the eye sees Peter, a Parisian, born in the first hour of the night, son of Robert, because these things are coincident with his color, and form, and other visible characteristics. In like manner the natural substances of things, both in things animate and inanimate, are not perceptible by some faculty of the sensitive soul except *per accidens*. Those things are excepted that are harmful or useful, which the estimative faculty grasps, and sense, however, falls upon this *per accidens*. Hence when I see a man I see substance and an animated object, and therefore vision falls in a measure on his natural substance, and on his soul also, which is a spiritual thing; but this is surely *per accidens*. Moreover, the sensi-

LOUIS IX

From the Seurre Statue at Versailles

bles belonging to one sense are sensibles *per accidens* of other senses, whence hot and cold, moist and dry, odor, sound, savor, are sensibles *per accidens* with respect to vision, and thus the sensibles belonging to each sense are sensibles *per accidens* with respect to other senses. Sensibles, then, *per se,* as has been said, are twofold: certain are proper, namely, nine, and certain are common, namely, twenty, because they can be perceived in common by several senses, especially by sight and touch. For as Ptolemy says in the second book all things that vision perceives touch discerns, except light and color; and all things of which touch certifies can be certified to by vision, except four proper sensibles, namely, hot, cold, moist, and dry.

CHAPTER II

Concerning those things that produce species in vision.

MOREOVER, that we may know how sensibles of this kind are recognized *per se,* we must know in the first place whether all things propagate their species to the sense. The determination of this is difficult, but Ptolemy in the second book of the Optics settles this question with the statement that only light and color propagate their species to the eye. This view Alhazen maintains in the fourth book; whence other things are not active upon the sense or upon the medium. The reason why they are not active is that they are all magnitudes or properties of magnitudes, as is evident, and magnitude is not active, because it is a quality of matter which is not active but passive, as Aristotle states in the first book on Generation, and Avicenna agrees with him in the second book on the Soul. For the medium or instrument that takes up the sound is soundless, and the instrument that takes up color is colorless, as he states. Therefore his opinion is that the medium and the senses do not have to have the natures of the sensibles whose species they must take up, in order that they may judge concerning the sensibles perceived by means of these species. Whence the humor glacialis does not possess some nature of light or color to the degree possessed by objects outside it. For although the eye has light, this is in respect to the perception of color, not in respect to light, because the object acted upon does not possess in actuality but in potentiality the ability to become like the agent. Nor does the anterior glacialis possess some degree of color, by which it may be made really like colored objects outside itself, of which it has to form judgments, although the eye has in its humors and coats some weak substance of color, by means of which imaginary colors sometimes appear, as will be explained when we consider the iris. But the eye does possess form and magnitude and corporeality, and other common sensibles that are appropriate to it, and therefore it is not fitted naturally to receive the species of these things, nor are they themselves active. And although Aristotle says in the second book on the Soul that the final perfection of every sense consists in its organ being the medium of sensibles, yet that degree of mediumship does not exist in things pertaining to the senses; since if it did exist and its species were produced on the sense, the sense would not judge concerning that mediumship, and therefore vision would not be able to receive the species of things so as to judge by means of these species concerning things whose natures are similar in vision. When, therefore, the objection is made that these are sensibles *per se,* that they therefore act on the sense, just like proper ones; we must reply that they are not called sensibles *per se* because of their action on the sense, but because the sense is able to certify concerning them. And if the objection should be made that vision will not certify concerning them, since they do not propagate their species to vision, we must reply that such is the case; for its own species is not required in all things, but the species of vision is sufficient along with the species of light and color and with certain other considerations. When these have all been combined certainty can be secured, as will be explained later. If it be said that authors on perspective state frequently that shape and quality and the like of the thing seen are arranged on the surface of the sentient member, and that they cannot reach there except through their species, we must reply that the statement is not their own, or has not been correctly translated; for they do not mean to say more than that from the whole magnitude and form the species of light and color come which are arranged on the surface of the sentient member, and this suffices.

When it was stated above that we see the air or the heavens at a distance, and that it is certain that in the water of a river or in some other body of water that has great width the heavens are seen by reflection, just like an object in a mirror; and an object in a mirror is seen by this means, because its species is reflected from the mirror to the vision; some one might then say that the celestial transparency of air at a distance produces a species by means of which it may be seen in water. But we must state that no species of the thing seen exists there, but the species of vision, which in the air without water is multiplied along a straight line to the celestial transparency at a distance, and apprehends that transparency with the aid of the species of light illuminating that transparency; and when it is seen by means of water reflexively, the species of vision is reflected from the water to the air seen at a distance, and the species of the thing is not reflected. Hence not everything that is seen by reflection is seen by means of its own species. But this happens as in the case of several familiar visible objects, but this must not be understood generally, because I can see water by means of a mirror, but the species of water is not propagated there, but the species of vision is, and this is the case here.

CHAPTER III

Distinguishing three universal modes of perception through vision.

IN the next place, we should know that besides the particular modes of perceiving the sensibles *per se,* there are three universal modes, according to the authors of Perspective. But in particular Alhazen explains these modes and he does so adequately, except that sometimes an inept translation of words occurs. There is, then, first an impression by the sense alone without any faculty of the soul, and it is thus that light and color in general are perceived. For vision is able to decide that there is color or light without error when it beholds an object, provided the eight aforesaid qualities are in their proper proportion; and therefore these two are perceived by the intuition alone of the sense. But the species and modes of color and of light cannot be so easily recognized; for if a strange color appears which we have not seen before, we will not know what species of color it is. Likewise if we see some bright object in the air, which has a light different from other objects with which we are familiar, as, for example, a star with a train or some other object, and we have not seen it before, we cannot decide by the vision what that light is. Likewise if we have seen some color before, and later have forgotten it, then when it again appears to the sight we can judge it a color, but we will not perceive what color it is. Likewise when in infancy we saw the full moon we did not perceive whether it was the light of the sun or of the moon until we became accustomed to it and the fact became fixed in our minds that such a light belongs to the moon, not to the sun. This is also true of the stars, because many men at some time or other see Jupiter, or Venus, or Mercury, and because of the beauty of these stars they look at them with pleasure, and they are then told by astronomers that the light of one particular star is of this kind, and the light of still another is of that kind, and they are made sensible of the difference. But after time has passed, when on another occasion they see one of those stars, they do not distinguish whether the light is that of Mercury or of Venus or of some other star, because they have forgotten the impression of the particular light of each of those stars seen formerly, but they recognize the lights of these stars by means of a second perception which is by similitude, according to Alhazen. This mode of cognition concerns not only color and light, but all things in which we distinguish the universal from the particular, and particulars from one another. For example, when I see a man whom I have seen before, if I have the impression that I have seen him before, I recognize then not only a man in general, but that particular individual whom I distinguish from others by means of this kind of cognition. If, however, I have forgotten, I see a man, but I do not know who he is.

We must bear in mind, however, that when the statement was made that vision perceives color or light as a universal by the sense alone, and not as a particular, the particular is excluded which is lower in the line of predication, as, for example, the species of color. Again, particulars designated by the species of something are excluded, as the light of the sun, and the light of the moon, because perchance light does not have species but modes, because all lights of stars have their origin in the rising sun. But the indefinite particular is not excluded, for it is as general as its own universal and is convertible with it, as some color, some light, some man, some ox. Therefore the recognition of universals from one another and from particulars, and particulars from one another by a comparison of a thing seen with the same thing seen before, by recollecting that it was seen before and known to the beholder, produces here a second mode of comprehension through vision.

But there is still a third perception, which cannot take place by the sense alone, and does not depend on a comparison with previous vision, but without limitation considers the thing present. For its perception several things are required, and the process is like a kind of reasoning. As, for example, when one holds in his hand a transparent stone, and does not perceive its transparency, but if he exposes it to the air, and if there is some opaque body behind it at the required distance and if the light is sufficient, he will see the light and the opaque body beyond the stone; and then, since he is not able through the medium of the stone to see the object that is behind it, unless the stone be transparent, he reasons that it is clear and transparent. But in ordinary things we employ this perception instantaneously, and we do not perceive that we are reasoning, although we are doing so. For a man reasons naturally without difficulty and labor; as, for example, when a boy is offered two apples, one of which is finer in appearance than the other, he chooses the finer one, but for no other reason than because it looks finer to him, and for this reason should be chosen rather than the other. Whence he follows this reasoning; that which is finer in appearance in so far is better, and what is better is rather to be chosen, therefore the finer in appearance should be chosen; and yet he does not perceive that he is reasoning, because of the swiftness of the reasoning process innate in man, as Alhazen teaches.

And now in metaphysical and logical terms I have established the view of Alhazen, and I have proved that our knowledge of the science of reasoning, which is logic, is derived from nature, but we are ignorant of the proper terms at the beginning, and these through their zeal for discovery the first authors on logic have found, but we learn them by study. Because of these terms the formal subject of logic exists, not because of the potency of the science itself, because this is innate in every one, as Alhazen here maintains and I have proved elsewhere. Thus are comprehended the twenty common sensibles, with their species, for they could not be determined except through this perception, and it is evident that the sense alone is not able to determine in these two modes; and this is called the sense alone when vision is in the pupil and in the common nerve reaching to the common sense. For unless imagination and the memory of the previous sight of an object be present, there will be no comprehension in the second mode. But imagination and memory are beyond the common sense. The third mode is still further removed from the sense pure and simple, because in this mode more things are taken into consideration than in the second mode, and there is more recourse to reason because of the process of ratiocination. But these modes do not have names properly translated. The first Alhazen calls perception by the sense pure and simple. The second he chiefly calls perception by science. The third he calls perception by syllogism, because of the mode of reasoning. But these names are not proper, because the faculties of the sensitive soul have these cognitions, for which neither science nor syllogism is needed as they are generally accepted. But concerning this we shall learn more definitely when we inquire what are the faculties of the soul which form these judgments through the mediumship of vision. This cannot be accomplished before it becomes more apparent, in the case of examples from different kinds of visibles, how they are determined.

Second Part of Perspective

FIRST DISTINCTION

Here begins the second part of this treatise, which is on the particular modes and causes of vision along a straight line in the main. It has three distinctions. The first is on vision as determined by the structure of the eye and is in three chapters. The first chapter is on those things that men see at a distance and on what they see near at hand.

Chapter I

SINCE, moreover, the knowledge of opposites is the same, as Aristotle says in the Topics, and in the first book on the Soul asserts that that which is straight is the test of itself and of that which is not straight, because by the privation of health sickness is perceived, therefore I shall designate particular modes of determining visibles at the same time with the defects of vision and with its errors, so that at once the defect itself and the error may be apparent by the determination of the contrary truth. In the first place, then, we must give an explanation of vision in relation to those things that relate to the structure of the eye. Those whose eyes are deep-set for this reason must see further than those whose eyes are prominent. The first reason for this is the greater strength that a deep-seated eye has owing to its greater proximity to the common nerve in which is located the visual force, as in a fountain. The second reason is because a deep-set eye is more protected from ills and is more remote from injuries than a prominent eye, and therefore is stronger. The third reason is because the visual force is more concentrated and unified, while it is more covered within the concavity of the bone, so that it thus takes a narrower and straighter path to the object seen, and is less scattered and dilated, so that it thus falls into the position of the visual pyramid. For this reason when a man wishes to view something at a distance with care, he applies the hollow of his hand to the bone of the eye, in order that the visual force may be more concentrated and less dispersed. A proof of this is the fact that the eyes of animals, as in the case of fish, which do not have the pro-

[501]

tection of eyelashes, do not see well at a distance, since the visual force is dispersed and dilated too much, since the eye does not have anything surrounding and confining it. Aristotle takes this view in the nineteenth book on Animals, and it is supported by experience. For a man in a well or in some other deep place will be able to see stars by day which he will not see at the surface of the well, as Pliny states in the second book of the Natural Philosophy, and experience teaches this. One cause of this is owing to the narrowness of the path, because the visual force is compressed for a long time, so that it proceeds more directly to the place of the stars that are above the well, and this is because of the covering that it has in the depth of the well. Thus the eye deep-set in the head in the same way is able to see better for this reason, which will be touched upon below. Ptolemy expressly states this in the second book of the Optics in these words, "Those who have deep-set eyes see further"; the reason for this is the visual force which is produced because of the compression, that is, the concentration and unification, and because of the narrowness of the place. For when it issues from narrow places, the vision is extended and elongated, because the force of the eye of necessity is more concentrated and compressed into a smaller place, and for this reason is stronger; because every united force is of stronger action. Its compression is evident in the figure. If bc is the opening of the uvea, and a is the pupil of some eye deeper-set, it is evident that its force falls between the lines e and f; but if it were at d, the force would pass through the gh lines, which are more divergent. Some with considerable grasp of this science of perspective reject the reason which Ptolemy and Aristotle assign and which experience teaches, alleging certain conclusions which are rightly shattered by so weighty an authority and by the force of experience. I make this statement, because it is not necessary in this place to dissolve all doubts that can be urged against the truth, for an infinite number can be adduced against any truth whatever.

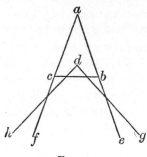

FIG. 37.

But besides this explanation from concavity, another can be given regarding the humors of the eye and depends on the small amount of the albugineous humor; for when this is plentiful it has the same effect on the glacialis as upon one who looks into a large, deep body of water, the large amount of which so shortens vision that it cannot see farther. Avicenna is of this opinion in the nineteenth book on Animals; and Averroës in his book on Sense and the Sensible cites as a reason for far vision the protection of the eyelashes, saying that the eyelashes preserve and guard the eyes from heat and cold and from many impediments, and that for this reason there is greater strength in eyes possessing eyelashes, which have far vision. He cites the case of many animals that see farther than man, because they have thicker eyelashes.

We must next consider why many old people, when they wish to see things distinctly, as in reading letters, see better at a distance than when the object is near. For they hold objects that they wish to examine further from them. The reason for this Ptolemy explains in the second book of the Perspective, for their eyes abound in moisture; for old people have much superfluous accidental moisture. When therefore the moisture is scanty the vision passing through it is immediately set free from it, and is thus able quickly to see distinctly an object appearing close at hand; but when there is an abundance of accidental moisture the eye is confused, and is not so quickly freed on account of the quantity of the moisture. For this reason an object must be further removed from the eyes before it is seen distinctly; for this moisture, which flows in the eye and on the surface of the cornea and the eyelashes, not only occupies the body of the eye, but renders moist the air near the eye; and therefore from a point close at hand such eyes cannot see, but the vision must be freed from that moisture and must pass through a longer distance. The first explanation touched upon the cause of vision at a distance through the natural moisture of the eye; here we are talking about the accidental superfluous moisture. But we are speaking here of vision at a distance in a different sense from that in the former case; for what we here term near and far is contained there under one of those terms, namely, under the term near, because remoteness is there taken as great distance, and here we are speaking of distance and a discriminated perception which always takes place near at hand. But there can be greater proximity or remoteness, which are degrees in proximity opposed to the remoteness of which we were speaking in what precedes.

CHAPTER II

In this chapter the causes are given for clear or distinct vision in darkness and in light.

SINCE mention has been made of the discrimination of vision, because it is one thing to see a long distance, another thing to discern, we must consider what are required for discrimination and distinctness of vision as regards the structure of the eye. Without doubt the humor glacialis must be of good size, so that on it the parts of the object can be clearly and sensibly distinguished. For if it is small, the species of the parts of the object seen will occupy positions too close and greater confusion will be caused. Moreover, it must be pure, and likewise the humor albugineus; for impressions and spots are quickly detected in a clean thing, as is evident in the case of spots on a clean rag, and therefore the species of things impressed on the eye will appear better and more clearly if the humors are pure and cleansed. But the humor albugineus must be of proper size; for otherwise it will be like deep water with respect to the humor glacialis, as has been said, and the vision will be obscured. Moreover, the weblike structure and the cornea are thin and fine and quite pervious, in order that they may not cause a shadow on the glacialis. Moreover, they must not be wrinkled, but they must have a smooth and expanded surface, since if they have wrinkles they cause a shadow; and this is the reason why old people are deprived of a distinct and discriminated vision, since the weblike structure and the cornea have wrinkles in aged people, just like the skin of their whole body.

Not only must we consider keenness of vision in seeing for a greater distance, and discrimination in vision through the nature of the structure of the eyes; but we must take up this question why some eyes see in the dark and in the twilight and in little light better than in the full light, and other eyes the reverse. Without doubt those that have a great deal of the humor albugineus need much light before it becomes clear; particularly if it is thick, and especially impure; and therefore such eyes do not see well at night with insufficient light. There is the same result if the humor glacialis is large and thick and impure, and if the weblike structure and the cornea are thick and wrinkled: for the action of light must be full and vigorous in order that these may be rendered clear, and in the day and in full light such eyes see well, and not otherwise. But those that have a scanty but clear and pure moisture in the humors, and have the web and the cornea quite transparent and without wrinkle, are not able to see in the strong light; because a strong light confuses such an eye from its excessive clarity, and to such a degree takes possession of the vision with the glare of light, that as regards external visible things the eye is unable to make distinction in them. As, for example, a man that has stood in a strong light, on turning to dark places is unable to discern objects in these places owing to the strong species of light that acts to excess in his eyes; for a more vigorous excitation of the mind always obscures weaker ones. Therefore men with eyes of this kind see well in the twilight and by the light of a candle at night and by the light of the stars. For all that has been said in regard to distinctness of vision and vision in the dark and in the light we have the authority of Aristotle and of Avicenna in their books noted above.

Concerning vision, however, in the dark and in the light another reason can be given, namely, when the eye has a great deal of light of its own; for the eye in man, in the horse, in the cat, and in many other animals shines of itself, as is apparent when a man in the dark moves the eye from its position by the finger. But some people have more light, some less; and those having much are able to see in dim light and in the dark, if the other causes affecting the humors and the web and the cornea are present which I have mentioned. But those having a small amount of light do not possess this power; especially if the other causes affecting the humors and the web and the cornea are not present.

Opus Majus

Chapter III

Concerning various errors of vision owing to the structure and complexion of the eye.

THE fact that the object seen appears single results from excellence in the structure of the eye; when, namely, the pupils have the same position with respect to the common nerve; since in that case the species come from the two eyes to the same place in the common nerve, and a single judgment is formed. When, however, nature is at fault, as happens in the case of one who squints, since the glacialis of one eye does not have a position similar to the glacialis in the other, the species naturally come to different places in the common nerve, and for this reason the man who squints must spend much effort in reducing the eyes to a similar position, so as to avoid error and grasp the unity of the object. Moreover, although the eye is correct in structure, nevertheless manifold difficulties arise from excessive heat or cold, as men frequently stand in hot places, for example, smiths, bakers, cooks, and the like; for the eye is resolved and destroyed by intense heat and loses its natural arrangement, and the judgment of sight is hindered. Likewise, as Averroës says in his book on Sense and the Sensible, hindrance to vision is caused when the organ is cooled by things in which intense cooling is inherent. For the eye is weakened and obscured in places where there is much snow or much water, and for this reason the shores of the sea appear confused and lacking in light, and so likewise the regions of snow.

So likewise the eye loses its natural formation in those suffering from strong drink, infirmity, and anger. For this reason an object appears double to the intoxicated and the infirm, and the thing seen seems to vacillate and be moved, because excessive moisture of the vapors ascending to the eyes of those enervated by the power of wine or of the warm humor dominant in the condition of disease, disturbs the eyes and causes them to be displaced from their natural position, as in the case of an angered man. For the heat ascends around the heart, and inflames the blood, and resolves the vapors, which easily rise to the eyes and penetrate owing to their channels, and displace the eyes from their natural position, so that the species cannot be formed in one place on the common nerve, nor in one place on the glacialis of the same eye, according to Averroës in the passage mentioned. For because of the movement and ebullition of the vapors the species is formed in different parts, like the species of the sun and of the moon in agitated water, and while it is being formed in one part it is not yet obliterated from another, and for this reason two species appear, just as the species of the sun and of the moon in agitated water appears double to us.

Likewise from suffering in the head a resolution of vapors to the eye sometimes happens, by which the vision is deranged, as in dimness of vision and in vertigo, and then the object seen is thought to be displaced, as Ptolemy explains in the second book of his Optics. This aids in understanding the cause of scintillation, and in this way one thing appears two and the object seen appears to move. Avicenna says in the third book on the Soul that, when some one of the causes is present that have been described in the books on Physics, which deranges circularly the spirit that is in the anterior ventricle of the brain; and when the visual force has given to it the impression received, the species does not remain fixed in one place, but is displaced circularly in accordance with the motion of the resolved spirit, and in this way the object will seem to be moved circularly. Moreover, Avicenna in the third book on the Soul gives three causes affecting the structure of the common nerve and of the eye that result in an object appearing double. For the vitreous humor, which extends from the eye to the common nerve, and the visual force, which flows from the common sense to the common nerve and to the eye, are thin bodies and very mobile, and for this reason easily changed from their position, and this displacement can take place either to the right and left, or before and behind. But if they waver to the right and left, in that case the two species coming from the two eyes cannot be formed in the same place on the common nerve, but one falls to the right, and the other to the left, and thus two appear, and of necessity one thing appears two. Likewise if they waver forward and backward, one species will be formed more in the front and the other more behind, and therefore two separate species will appear. When both motions occur, there will be a movement of the species, like a vertigo, and the object will appear to waver in accordance with the two positions.

The third cause he assigns to the uvea, which easily receives motion. For by the movement of the nervous spirits and by much intense heat it can be disturbed within, and by the effort of the eye is dilated, and by its own nerve of which it is composed it can be dilated or contracted as that nerve is contracted or distended. It can also be disturbed externally from many causes, as, for example, when the finger compresses the uvea or the same thing happens in other ways, and by these disturbances the opening is sometimes changed in a straight line, sometimes obliquely, and this variation can take place in one eye and will not happen in the other, or will take place in both eyes at the same time, but in different ways. Therefore the species itself will be diversified in both eyes and consequently in the common nerve, so that the object and the species appears larger or smaller, and thus one species will have a larger place in the common nerve than the other, and therefore an object that is single will appear double.

Besides all that has been said regarding the fact that one object appears as two, there are still several natural cases with their causes. It sometimes happens, then, that extraneous humor coagulates below the uvea between the glacialis and the opening; and sometimes this happens from above downward as regards length, sometimes crosswise as regards width, sometimes circularly; and in this way a division of the glacialis is made, so that it views the same object through its two different parts, and therefore one object appears to it as two. Physicians touch upon this cause in their books and teach the cure, as is shown by Avicenna in the care of the eye. But if this cause did not exist it is thought that deception in this regard can take place. It is believed, in fact, that the appearance of two objects can be produced otherwise from the fact that vision is produced by external transmission, and because species can be seen in some manner. For there are many men to whom a single object when seen appears double, and this is not owing to a difference in their eyes, since it occurs if they look at the same thing with one eye. Therefore with one eye they see two objects when all the causes already mentioned have been excluded. Wherefore this cannot take place except for the reason that the species of the object, while it is near the object, is stronger and has more of the nature of the object, and therefore is more sensible than when multiplied at a greater distance. When, therefore, a man has weak eyes, the faculty of vision not only is weak as regards itself, but more weakened from distance will stop at the species of the object near the object, and the species will take the place of the object, so that the weakened faculty is terminated at the species, just as the vision weakened from distance is terminated at vapor. But a strong eye penetrates the air in which the species is near the object, and the species is hidden because of the strength of vision, just as vapor in the air near the eye is hidden and penetrated because of the vigor of the eye. This will frequently happen to people with weak eyes, particularly when they look carelessly. Sometimes also people with good eyes in some way or other have this experience, namely, when they are very careless in looking and half close the eye, and both they themselves and the object seen are in dark places and at times of mists, as at twilight.

This must be the reason, or it is because one eye has two pupils. Although this is possible, I have not met with such a case. For Solinus in his book on the Wonders of the World makes mention regarding a certain region in which women usually had two pupils. Pliny, also, in the sixth book shows that throughout different parts of the world there are people with double pupils in their eyes. When this happens one object can appear double.

SECOND DISTINCTION

Concerning the method of direct vision as regards the species of sight and of the object seen; in four chapters.

Chapter I

THE causes of vision as regards the species of vision and of the objects visible must be considered next. It is now easy to give the reason why the eye sees from the outside air charged with vapor and cloud, and when the eye is in such air does not see or perceive the vapors and clouds. For this point has been touched upon incidentally above, but must now be considered in relation to its principal cause. For the strength and weakness of the visual ray must be the cause of this; for when it is near such air and in it the visual force is strong from its proximity to the eye, because of its strength it can penetrate the denser air, and nothing is seen or perceived by the vision, except that which can terminate the vision, as has been stated before. Therefore the air charged with vapor is not perceived in this case. But when the eye is at a distance from air so charged, the species of the eye weakened finds resistance and is terminated, and therefore is able to see a cloud at a distance. From this experiment it is evident that vision is the result of external transmission. For if the species of the object seen were alone responsible, no explanation of this vision could be given.

We must consider species not only as regards itself, but as regards position, without which the species cannot be formed or formed distinctly, unless position be carefully noted. We must state, then, that one eye produces its species to the object seen, and the object seen produces its species to the eye in the same place, whence they have a common axis, which is perpendicular to all parts of the eye, because it passes through the center of all the parts. Therefore since the perpendicular approach is strong and potent, the eye judges most vigorously by means of the species of the part that comes along this line, and grasps this part with final certitude, as far as one eye can grasp it. Therefore it is said in the book on Vision that no visible object is seen at the same moment in its entirety, and this must be understood of final certitude, but one part only on which the axis mentioned falls. Nevertheless with the same look the whole

Optical Science

object is seen which is the base of the visual pyramid, and more as has been stated, and therefore several things are seen at the same time. But except for complete certitude both the parts on both sides nearer the end of the axis are seen more clearly, and those more remote are seen less clearly. When, however, the eye is moved, so that it may make sure of the separate parts seen, the axis passes over these parts, and certifies them successively one after another.

Since naturally the two eyes have a similar position with respect to the common nerve, the axes of the eyes will have a uniform position for every point on which they fall, and they will fall necessarily on the same point of the object, and then that point will be seen better and with more certainty by the two eyes than by one. We are to understand, moreover, that from the common nerve an imaginary straight line is directed between the two eyes to the object seen, meeting the

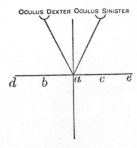

FIG. 38.

axes of the eyes in the same part of the object seen, and this line is the common axis, and that point on which these three axes fall is seen with final certitude, as is shown in the figure, and other parts of the object are seen with more or less distinctness according to the different positions they occupy with respect to this axis. For point *a* is seen most distinctly, because the three axes are concurrent at it, and *b* and *c* are seen more distinctly than *e* and *d*.

But that part is most distinctly seen to which, when the axes terminate, its own species is perpendicular, for then the strength of the impression is double. For this reason *a* is seen more distinctly by means of the axes than *c* and *b,* for the species of vision of *a* itself is perpendicu-

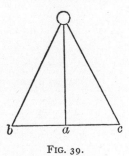

FIG. 39.

lar to it, as is clear. The species on *b* and *c* is not a perpendicular species in this way, for *b* and *c* are perpendicular to the eye but not perpendicular at the points *b* and *c*. But the species of *a* itself is perpendicular to itself and to the eye.

[511]

Opus Majus

CHAPTER II

*In which is shown by two different experiments and by different
figures how one object is seen as two.*

BUT not only for the reasons mentioned in the preceding distinction is one object seen as two, but for many other reasons. This experience happens more frequently and clearly when one or both eyes are moved from their position, as, for example, when a man without definite purpose revolves one of his eyes from its natural position, or when he places his finger on the eye and displaces it. For then the two species come to different places on the common nerve and one object appears to be two. It happens also that an object appears double at a great distance from the axes because of the sensible difference of angle, which

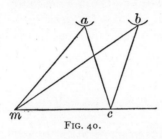

FIG. 40.

the species forms in the eyes, as is shown in the figure. For let *mc* be the object seen, and *a* and *b* the eyes, and *ac* and *bc* the axes fixed on the point *c,* which is seen by them with final certitude; then some part can be so far removed from the axes, as the point *m,* that it will be seen double because of the sensible difference in the angle that it forms in the eyes, since *mac* is far larger in the eye *a* than *mbc* in the eye *b;* and therefore both species, because of this difference, cannot come to the same part of the common nerve, but the larger angle must occupy a larger part of the common nerve, and for this reason *m* appears double to the sight. Not only does this happen when the point seen falls to the right and to the left of the axes, as represented in the figure, but when it is at some distance to the right with respect to one of the axes and to the left with respect to the other, namely, when it falls between the intersection of the axes or beyond it, as is shown in the figure. For if the axes of the eyes *a* and *b* are fixed attentively on the part *o* of the visible object *mon,* then the visible object *k* below the intersection of the axes will appear double, and *h* visible beyond the intersection will likewise appear double necessarily. For an experimenter can prove this by taking a stick the width of a palm, and the length of four, five, or six, with a smooth surface. Let him also take three different visible objects, formed out of either wax or wood as large as the last joint of the little finger in the shape of a pyramid, and let them be of different colors for greater distinctness, and be arranged in the order *hok,* so that there be a sensible distance between them. The middle one of these should be in the middle of the board and one of the others at the remoter end of the board, and the third one midway between the middle object to be viewed and the eye. The board at the end toward the eye should be somewhat concave, in order that it may be applied easily to the eyes, and that the board may be applied easily at the end of the nose toward the eyes. The eyes must then fix their axes on the middle object, which will be seen as one, and both of the other two will appear double, for *k* and *h* will appear as four and *o* will be seen as one.

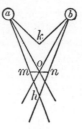

FIG. 41.

CHAPTER III

In which a figure is arranged for these two errors by means of one experiment together with a consideration of several disappearing images.

BY means of the same board, if it has sufficient width, an experiment can be made in regard to the first of these errors. Let, then, one figure suffice for both errors and let it be similar to the figure here given. For *a, c,* and *b* will be seen as they are, provided the eyes are focused rightly, so that the extremities of the visual pyramids may fall on *c* and *b,* and the axes on *a.* But if other objects, or those same objects, namely, *a, b, c,* are arranged on the longer diameter *hd,* so that *c* is placed in the position *m,* and *b* in the position *n, m* and *n* will be seen as four; and just as *c* will be seen as one, when it is on the shorter and transverse diameter, so also will *l,* which is not too far distant from it and from the axes; but *f,* which is quite a distance out of line, will be seen as two, as was noted in the first error. For it will be seen by the eye *p* under the angle *fpk,* which is less than a right angle, and it is seen by the eye k under the angle *fkp,* which is a right angle, and therefore it must appear as two owing to the difference in angle. An experimenter can make

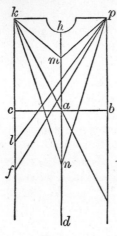

FIG. 42.

many experiments in this matter without the board. For he can at night raise a finger between himself and a candle. If then he fixes the axes on the candle, the one finger will appear as two. In these cases we must bear in mind that if the right eye be closed, the left image will disappear, and when the left eye is closed the right image will vanish. The blessed Augustine expressed wonder at this, and writes in the eleventh book on the Trinity, second chapter, that it would be a lengthy matter to give the reason for this phenomenon. It is, in fact, a lengthy matter for one ignorant of perspective, since he must first learn this science. Likewise it is a lengthy matter to reach the reason for this thing, since the teacher must give careful consideration to those things that have been written in this fifth part of this plea, and especially to those things that are said and written in this chapter on the causes of vision as regards the species. It is certain, then, that when the axes of the eye are fixed on the visible object a, the visual force nevertheless tends to the visible

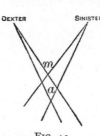

FIG. 43.

object m, but the species coming from the right eye tends to the left, if it proceeds further, and likewise the species of the left eye tends to the right, for these species intersect at the point m, and separate in such a way that the right species passes to the left side, and the left one to the right side, as is clear to the sense. Since, then, m appears double, the image corresponding to the right eye must be beyond m to the left, because the species of the right eye tends in that direction. Therefore when the right eye is closed, the left image must vanish; and the reasoning is similar with regard to the left eye and the right image, as the figure shows.

Optical Science

And yet the right image will not always disappear when the left eye is closed, nor the left image on closing the right eye; but it easily happens that when the right eye is closed the right image disappears, and when the left eye is closed the left image disappears, as any one can prove in the case of the fixed stars in summer at twilight before the darkness of night, and the same experiment could be made on far distant fires.

Chapter IV

Concerning the fact that an object appears double owing to the elongation of all particular axes from the common axis, with an exposition of all the ways in which an object can be placed and a statement of the cause of good or bad vision in all those positions.

NOT only is there a difference in false vision, because there is a difference of position of the object seen with respect to the axes, as has been said, but the axes themselves can diverge too far from the common axis, as is shown in the figure. For the angle *abd* in eye *b* is far greater than angle *acd* in eye *c,* and for this reason there will be an error, and *a* will appear double, at which the axes *ba* and *ca* terminate, and this happens because they diverge from the common axis *ed*. This takes place when the eyes turn their axes from the common axis in

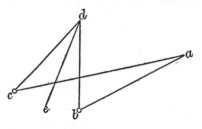

FIG. 44.

the direction of one eye, and the other eye follows as far as it can turn, and therefore the axes are not terminated at *d,* nor are *bd* and *cd* the axes, but *ba* and *ca,* for the axes are thus turned and bent from their natural position. They can terminate also at the same point of the object of vision, but in a different position with respect to the common nerve; and in this case that point appears double, as is evident by elevating one eye from its right position or both eyes. From these oblique positions it is clearly evident that, whether the axes deviate too far from the common axis, or the object of vision or part of the object of vision is too far from the axes of the eyes, the object will be seen imperfectly, and this happens either in one eye or in both, or there may also be a displacement of the ends of the object from the position in front of the face. The object directly opposite the face, on which object the special axis and the common axis are concurrent, will be seen with final certainty. If, in fact, the object is near the axes, it will be sufficiently visible in the same direction; and in this way the vision of the same thing will be lessened up to a position of such great obliquity that one object will appear as two, just as we have stated before. The reason for all these things, according to Alhazen in the third book, and according to Ptolemy likewise in the third book, is that when the object is seen in front of the face, or near it, the species of the object comes to the surface of the glacialis under a large angle and occupies a large part of the pupil, in which the parts can sensibly be distinguished; but when the obliquity is great the species comes under a small angle to the organ of sense and occupies a small part of it, so that the species of the parts of the object of vision are crowded together without affecting the sense, and are collected in a confused manner, and therefore no definite judgment is formed concerning them. All these matters are evident, which must be known in regard to position with respect to the eye. For any one can easily distinguish now the differences of position. For there is the position in front of the face when the object is placed before the eye or the eyes, and one end is not raised nor does the other deviate. There is also the oblique position through the raising of one end and the depression of the other; and this is called the oblique position. Moreover, in the position in front of the face there is the position of one part with respect to the axes, and the other parts deviate more; and likewise in the oblique position certain parts are more remote from the axis, certain parts nearer to it. We have stated how comprehension and error occur in all similar cases. A position, however, that is outside not only the visual, but the whole pyramid, excludes vision entirely.

THIRD DISTINCTION

In which consideration is given to the triple mode of vision in reference to the eight conditions of vision mentioned previously. The distinction contains eight chapters, in the first of which examples are given in regard to perception through sense alone.

CHAPTER I

HAVING determined these matters in regard to the eye and the position of the species, we must now consider further concerning the triple mode of vision in reference to the eight necessary conditions without which vision is not possible. Light, then, and color are perceived through sense only, and no error is made in regard to them when these eight conditions are fulfilled without excess or defect; under these conditions light is seen as it is and color is seen as it is. When, however, these conditions are in excess or defect, error or defect in vision occurs. For the light of the stars is not seen by day, when the solar light in full strength comes to the eye, because that light is in excess with respect to the eye and the light of the stars; as, for example, when a man is at the surface of a well the principal solar light comes to his eyes excelling the principal light of the stars. But if he descended to the bottom of the well he would see the stars that were over his head, not only for the reason touched upon previously, but because the solar light would be tempered, since only the accidental light of the sun would come to the eye and no principal ray, and therefore the stars would be seen by means of their principal rays and would not be hidden.

But in regard to the Galaxy it is strange that it cannot be visible in the celestial sphere, or in the sphere of air, but only in the sphere of fire. Now the Galaxy is in one sense a circle in the celestial sphere, which is called the Milky Way, consisting of many small stars clustered, and this part of the heavens produces, according to Aristotle in the first book of the Meteorologics, the impression of continuous light through the meeting of the solar light with the lights of small stars of this kind, and this impression is called likewise galaxy. Hence the term is used in two senses, for cause and effect: and the light appears as continuous and lengthened out, although the stars are distinct. But distance causes this, as would be the case if one looked from a distance at a pot perforated in many adjacent parts, in which fire is contained. For owing to the distance the fire would appear continuous to him because of the proximity of the holes, a proximity that vision would not discern because of the great distance. This impression, however, the eye would not perceive in the celestial sphere, although this light passes through this sphere, nor in the air, although it passes through the air likewise. But in fire it is perceptible, because the celestial sphere is of such excessive rarity that light cannot be incorporated in it so as to be visible. But air is of greater density than is here required. For since this impression is weak owing to the weakness of the lights of the small stars, it can quickly be lost in the darkness of the place, nor does it suffice to clear away the shadows of the denser air. But in the highest part of the sphere of fire the Galaxy can be visible to the eye, because it is properly proportioned for visibility because of its mean between the excessive rarity of the transparent heaven and the greater density in the air than visibility of this kind requires. Therefore in fire it can be visible, as Aristotle states, although he does offer too little explanation regarding the cause. But the light of the other larger fixed stars and likewise of the planets has so much strength that it is not dimmed in the air, nor in the sphere of fire, nor in the celestial sphere, and therefore uniformly lights up the whole medium, namely, the spheres of the heavens and of fire and of air; and therefore vision does not perceive in some part a difference in the incorporation of their light. For this reason there is not some distinct impression of visibility by means of the lights falling from other stars than that received from the stars of the Galaxy, wherefore philosophers make no mention of some other impression, which is pure light, differing from that which is called Galaxy. Thus it is manifest that Galaxy cannot be visible in the sphere of air nor of the heaven, owing to the medium's lack of the proper density. In the air because of the lack of sufficient rarity, in the heaven because of its excess. We must note, however, that a consideration of refractions in the sphere of fire is important for our conception of the Galaxy; for all rays that fall at oblique angles on the surface of fire are refracted. But of this the explanation is to be sought elsewhere.

It is likewise strange that the light of dawn appears to us at that time and not earlier; for the whole heaven is illumined except in the shadow of the earth. I am here calling the whole world heaven from which outside the shadow of the earth the air is illumined, and the sphere of fire and the celestial spheres. We see clearly the stars at night in every part of the horizon; therefore it seems that we should likewise see the spheres of the heavens and of fire and of air illumined outside the shadow. For between us and the stars the air is of necessity illumined, also the sphere of fire and the spheres of the heavens, not only by the light of the stars, but also by that of the sun, which crosses in the air through the sides of the shadow, and therefore just as at dawn we see the air illumined, so is it probable that the illumined air should be seen earlier. But excessive distance together with excessive rarity solves this problem. For the stars are dense bodies and have much fixed light of their own, and from both these causes can be seen by means of their species diffused in the shadow to the eye. But the illumined parts of the spheres, and the sphere of fire and the air outside the shadow are bodies of too great rarity, and do not have any fixed light, but merely light passing through them, and for this reason the light is weak and they are far distant. For these reasons they cannot be seen by night, because the species coming from them into the shadow is too weak and cannot affect the eye. But when the sun approaches its rising, and this is when it is in the eighteenth degree of the circle of its depression below the horizon, as Ptolemy shows in the Almagest, its rays fall in the air nearer to us and enter the top of the shadow and its sides, and in this way the nearer illumined air can cause a stronger species to reach the eye, and it begins to be visible and becomes more so as the nearer air is illumined. There is the added reason, moreover, that the nearer air is denser, and especially so when the light comes to air full of vapor, the greatest altitude of which is fifty-one miles and some fraction of a mile, as is shown in the book on Twilights. Owing to this density more light is retained in such dense air, just as in the case of the stars, and therefore a stronger species reaches the eye. These facts show us that the dawn is not caused by the refraction or reflection of light in the clouds, as those who are informed know, but it is caused by the accidental species of the sun, which comes to us from its rays passing through air filled with vapor and cloud, just as the accidental species from a ray of the sun falling through a window comes through the whole house.

It happens also that a small light or a luminous body of small size appears sometimes to be of great extent in the case of certain things because of their sensible distance and because of the rapidity of motion in shooting stars, as Ptolemy states in the second book of the Perspective. For fiery impressions in the air from ignited vapors like stars, which are called in Arabic *Assub,* ascending and descending, are bodies of small size. But on account of distance and rapidity of motion they appear to possess a long light. A similar phenomenon is found in the case of sparks ascending rapidly from a fire; for the rapidity of their motion frequently causes them to appear extended at great length, when they are, however, of small size.

Color, like light, is perceived by the sense only: and if those nine conditions, concerning which we have stated that they are necessary for vision, are fulfilled without excess or defect, vision will perceive color correctly. If, however, these conditions are in excess or defect, vision will not perceive it correctly. As, for example, if a colored body is sufficiently dense to terminate vision, the color seen will be judged to belong to that body. But if it is not sufficiently dense, as in the case of a crystal, behind which a colored body when placed will appear as the color of the crystal, although it is not. Moreover, when the eye has looked at strong colors and then turns to light places, the species of the strong color will remain in the eye for a time, and at first the color will appear to it red, then purple, and afterwards black, and so vanishes, as Aristotle states in the second book on Sleep and Waking. The error is due to an excess of light changing in this way the judgment of color. Ptolemy, moreover, in the second book of the Perspective shows that different colors appear as one for two reasons. The first reason is because in an object of different colors one appears, owing to excessive distance, so that the angle containing the whole object has not the suitable size. When the separate angles, which contain the different colors, are not perceived, from the compression of the parts that are not discerned, it results that the color of the whole object is one differing from those of the separate parts. The second reason is found in the motion of a swift body, as in that of a hoop with several colors, in which one and the same ray does not pause on one and the same color, since the color recedes from it because of the speed of its motion; and so the same ray falling on all the colors is not able to distinguish between the first and the last, nor between those that are in the whole hoop, but they appear as one, and it seems that that color is as it were a mixture of them all. Moreover, concerning these matters there are an infinite number of examples, and some have been placed at the beginning and in different places; and therefore I pass them by.

CHAPTER II

Concerning perception through knowledge.

THE things that are perceived through knowledge are distinctions of one universal from another, of one particular from another, or of a universal from a particular, as we have stated; whence the difference and discrimination of visible objects are considered in this perception, and this perception in the first place and *per se* applies to light and color, since they are especially objects of sense. When, therefore, the moon is outside the shadow of the earth it has a clear and white light; when it is in the upper part of the shadow it has a reddish light; but when it is in the lower part the light is not visible; when, moreover, it is in conjunction with the sun at new moon its light does not appear. Therefore vision perceives these differences, but the sense alone is not able to make certain of this matter, but after it has seen these differences many times and has viewed the moon, it can recognize that which appears at such a time or under such and such circumstances and what is not visible under others. The explanation of this matter is, however, difficult, yet it is certain that the light of the moon is caused by the sun, in the same way as the light of all the stars, as has been stated above. But as Ptolemy says in the second book of the Optics, when the moon is in conjunction with the sun that which prevents the illumination of the moon toward us is its proximity, since almost half of the lunar body is opposite to us, because the other part is illumined. Therefore the solar rays cannot reach the part toward us; nor can the principal rays reach this part, as is evident; but they are far divergent and separated. Therefore the accidental rays are not sufficient to light up the moon. But when it is in the shadow, the earth, which hides the moon from the sun, is far removed from the moon, and for this reason the principal solar rays are much more convergent owing to the narrowness of the shadow in its upper part; and for this reason the accidental rays are able to come from near at hand in great force to the body of the moon, and therefore light it up. But since accidental rays are weaker in their action than principal rays they do not clearly nor fully illumine the moon, and therefore it is somewhat reddish or pale, shading to red, and it is redder when it falls less into the thick part of the shadow, and paler the more it falls into the shadow. And yet the moon can enter the thick part of the shadow and descend in its own eccentric toward the earth, because the accidental rays are not able to light it up, owing to the great divergence of the principal rays of the sun itself, and the whole moon remains in shadow, just as at conjunction, because the moon does not have light of itself, but is a dense body.

Similarly an example can be cited in regard to color. For if the eye views a body of a single color through the medium of a very thin parti-colored cloth, if the apertures of the cloth are large it will see the color of the body as it is; but if they are small and fine, the color of the object placed behind it will appear mixed, and therefore from the differences in the rarity of the medium through which it is viewed the color will appear different, and in this way there will be an error in knowledge. The reason for this is in doubt. For it is evident that the colors of the parts of the body do not come to the vision except through the apertures of the cloth between the threads, and the colors of the threads come according to their lines and peculiar twists to points different from those to which the species of the colors of the parts of the body placed behind the cloth come. Wherefore the colors of the parts of this body are formed at points on the eye different from those at which the colors of the threads are formed. For this reason it does not seem that the color will be mixed. But we must state that such is the case. For when the apertures are minute, the colors passing through them are very near to the threads, and for this reason the colors of the threads and the colors passing through them are very close and touch at points at an insensible distance apart. Since this is the case, the difference of these colors will not be perceived, and hence a mixed color will appear to the eye.

CHAPTER III

OF those things that are perceived through reasoning likewise notable examples can be given. First among these is distance or remoteness. In regard to this the first consideration is that excessive distance hinders vision, because the same object at a distance makes a small angle, which when near would make a large one, as is evident in the figure. Since from the small size of the angle it results that a small part of the pupil is occupied, the object cannot sensibly be distinguished as it should in the eye, and for this reason the object is imperfectly perceived because of excessive distance. Distance is perceived and determined, if it is moderate by a continuous series of sensible objects lying between the eye and the remote object. As, for example, when a person is near a wall and sees another wall beyond the first more elevated than it and quite a distance from it, he cannot judge of the distance between them because there are no bodies in a continuous series between them, or he cannot perceive these bodies because of the interposition of the first wall beneath which he is standing.

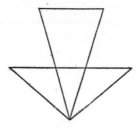

FIG. 45.

Hence it happens that when we are not near high mountains, but are in level country, we cannot judge of the height of clouds; nay, we reckon that they are more remote from us than they are, because there are not sensible bodies lying between us and them, but the air only, which is not sensible to us, and for this reason we cannot judge of the height of the clouds under these circumstances. But when we are near high mountains, although mountains are not very high with a maximum height of about eight miles, we shall see clouds on the tops of the mountains and the summits higher than the clouds. From this fact Alhazen concludes in the second book that the clouds are not of great height, although vapors easily rise fifty-one miles, as is shown in the book on Twilights. But not all vapors form clouds, for only aqueous vapors do so; and not all vapors are the substance of clouds, but terrestrial vapors rise higher although they are heavier, because dryness brings out the full effect of heat and a dry substance retains heat well after it has been received, as, for example, stone retains heat better than wood. Hence it happens that a stronger and more abundant heat of the sun is retained in terrestrial vapors than in aqueous, and for this reason they rise higher. Now, moreover, that no objection might be raised in regard to the height of clouds by means of the contrary statement in the book on Twilights, I have made mention of this book.

Distance, then, is judged when there is a series of objects between the eye and the object of vision, and this is true in the case of moderate distance, and when the eye has viewed those objects and has made certain of their measurements. But if any one of these conditions is not fulfilled, distance will not be determined. Moreover, a moderate distance with respect to vision, that is, one whose extent is determined by vision, is a distance at the end of which no part with an extent sensible with respect to the whole distance is hidden from vision. A moderate distance with respect to the object of vision, in which vision perceives one part of the object of vision, is a distance at the end of which no part of that object of vision bearing a sensible proportional relationship to the size of the object of vision is hidden from vision. But a distance which is excessive with respect to vision is that at the end of which an extent bearing a sensible proportional relationship to that whole distance is hidden from vision. And a distance excessive with reference to the object of vision is one that hides from vision parts in proportional relationship sensible with reference to the whole. Therefore an error is made in the determination of distance owing to excessive remoteness of objects from the eye. For in this way trees at a great distance, although they are quite far apart, appear continuous or to be near one another. For this reason also the planets will be judged to be in the same surface as fixed stars because of the immense distance of the stars from the eye, although the planets are a very great distance from the fixed stars. Moreover, a figure of many equal sides placed directly opposite the eye looks like a circular figure, and the circle looks like a straight line, and a sphere will be judged to be a plane figure. For owing to excessive distance the angles of the figure, although they are sensible with respect to the whole at the required distance, yet when they are at an excessive distance will be hidden from vision with respect to the whole, and therefore an angular object will be judged to be round, because when such an angle is hidden, the figure appears round. Likewise when the gibbosity of the arc of a circle is presented to the sight, although the middle of the gibbosity of the circle is nearer the sight than the ends of the arc at the diameter, yet this nearness is not apparent to the sight because of the excessive distance; and for this reason the approach of the part nearer the sight is hidden, and the gibbosity itself is removed in the judgment of vision; wherefore the curved line will appear straight. This is the reason why, when the moon is in its first or third quarter, the line of the circular base of the luminous solar pyramid enveloping the body of the moon appears to be a straight line, when at other times it appears to be curved. A sphere will appear as a plane surface for the same reason. The nearness of its convex surface exceeds imperceptibly the nearness of the limits of that convex surface because of the excessive distance. Therefore both sun and moon appear to be plane surfaces although they are spheres.

Chapter IV

Concerning the shape of the moon as regards its different phases; also some additional matters at the end.

By what has already been said the reason can be shown for the difference in the form of the lunar light as it fills and wanes. For sometimes the base of the pyramid of solar light enveloping the body of the moon appears to be a curved line, as, for example, before the seventh day and after it, but on the seventh it appears to be a straight line. The reason for this Aristotle in the second book of the Heavens and the World and Averroës hide by imperfect and cursory statements; and the book of the Problems of Aristotle in Latin by the obscurity of its translation leaves us in doubt. For it is quite strange why the same curved line appears sometimes straight, sometimes curved, from the same distance. For if in accordance with the reason given in regard to excessive distance the curved line should appear straight, how then can it many times, nay, through almost the whole lunar month, appear curved, and only twice be judged straight?

Let us then withdraw from the realm of sense and deal with the real fact that the moon is a spherical body, and in the first place let us suppose that it is situated near us at a moderate distance, and the sun likewise, yet so situated that they have the same relation to each other, and that they have their motions as in the heavens, and that they bear the same relation to our vision as when they are in the heavens, except that the distance is not excessive. Then here we shall see two pyramids; one is the visual, whose base is the portion of the moon's surface exposed to us, and the other is the luminous solar pyramid, whose principal base is the surface of the sun. Since this pyramid is cut off, because the surface of the moon meets it before it can reach its own vertex, it must have there a secondary base, although much smaller than the first, and the greater portion of the moon is presented to the sun. But before the part of the moon presented to our sight begins to be illuminated at any point, namely, while the sun and moon are in conjunction, the base of the pyramid of solar light does not include any part of the base of the visual pyramid. But as soon as the moon is free from its conjunction, so that some part of its illuminated portion is exposed to us, the base of the solar pyramid occupies that part of the base of the visual pyramid, and therefore their circles at once intersect at two points, and include within themselves the illuminated part. And as the portion of the base of the solar pyramid cuts more of the base of the visual pyramid, so does the light increase in the portion exposed to us. The circle, therefore, of the base of the solar pyramid at a moderate distance will always appear as a curved line and never as a straight one; because excessive distance alone causes it sometimes to appear as a straight line. But at an excessive distance, just as is now the case, it must frequently appear curved. For the circles on a sphere are to be understood in two senses, namely, parallel circles like the equator on the celestial sphere and the tropics and other circles parallel to the equator on both sides of it; and there are other circles intersecting one another and equidistant circles of this kind, as, for example, those passing through the poles of the sphere like the colures on the celestial sphere, and all are great circles on the sphere. Of the former one alone is a great circle, namely, the largest of the parallel circles, as, for example, the equator in the heavens; for those circles alone are great circles on a sphere that pass through the center of the sphere and divide the sphere into two equal parts.

Let us, then, consider the sphere of the body of the moon, restricting ourselves to that portion exposed to us in such a way that we have a clear notion of the largest of the parallel circles, which divides the body of the moon into two equal parts, also after it the other parallels, as many as we desire, whose pole is the lunar pole toward us. Let us also have a clear notion of the great circles intersecting one another at the poles of the lunar sphere. This one of these circles, however, is sufficient for our purpose, whose gibbosity is directly exposed to our sight, and which cuts the moon into two parts east and west and passes through the pole nearer us and through the other pole on the opposite side. Let us call this the colure. It is certain, then, that excessive distance hides the gibbosity of this colure, as stated above. Hence of necessity this curved line appears to be straight. But no distance can hide the gibbosities of the parallels, since the whole circumference of each of these has the same position with reference to the eye, and one part of the circumference is not nearer the sight than any other part, so that it is visible to the sight at every distance, and therefore no part of these circles can be hidden. For this reason they are always visible in their circumference and revolution, just as we see in the case of the circular line which is the circumference of the base of the visual pyramid. For that circle is one of these parallels and the largest of those that can be exposed to our vision, and it is evident that the vision of each one judges this to be a perfect circle; and it would do so in regard to all the parallels that might be marked in the portion exposed to us, but no one of these has been marked so far as the moon in itself is considered. The visual pyramid, however, marks one parallel,

which is the circumference of its base, and the solar pyramid
marks another parallel, which similarly is the circumference of
its base. When, moreover, this circumference of the base of
the solar pyramid touches the portion of the moon exposed to
us, its gibbosity of necessity is directed toward the sun, as we
see by the eye. The reason for this is found in the fact that it is
a portion of a circle which is almost a great circle on the sphere;
for it is a part of one of the parallels described around the portion of the lunar sphere exposed to us, and this parallel is
greater than any other that can be described there. But it is not
a large circle cutting the lunar sphere into equal parts, because
half of the lunar sphere is not visible to us, but a portion slightly
less than half, as we are now assuming, and as what follows will
explain in the proper place. Since, however, the arc of the solar
pyramid is almost a portion of a great circle, its concavity in the
portion of the moon visible to us cannot lie toward the sun. For
if it were the arc of a very small circle, its concavity could lie
toward the sun, as is evident. The gibbosity of that arc will lie
toward the sun at new moon; and when it first touches the circumference of the base of the visual pyramid, the arc of the
visual pyramid and the arc of the solar pyramid are equal, and
lie together and terminate at the ends of the chord of the visible
portion of the moon itself. But when the solar pyramid occupies
some part of the portion of the moon exposed to us, the arc of
the solar pyramid leaves the arc of the base of the visual pyramid, always, however, conterminal with it, and they separate,
each containing the illuminated portion, and they intersect at
the ends of the chord of the portion of the moon exposed to us;
and then the arc of the solar pyramid is like the arc of a parallel
almost the size of a great circle. Moreover, we must imagine
that it was at first on the circumference of the base of the visual
pyramid, and afterwards was continuously moved from it
toward the colure of which mention was made before, which
passes through the poles of the moon, namely, through that
pole exposed to us and through the one opposite to it, dividing
the moon into two halves, as if it were moved through a quarter
of the moon from the circumference of the base of the visual
pyramid, until it becomes the colure. When, therefore, it becomes the colure, its gibbosity is of necessity concealed from
us because of the excessive distance, and the circle will appear

as a straight line. But not before; since it was always previously the arc of a parallel, and parts of the circumference of parallels have the same position with respect to the eye. For no part comes nearer to the eye than any other part, as has been noted before.

Wherefore, from the first illumination of the moon until the portion of the base of the pyramid comes to the position of the colure, it will always be in the form of an arc, both actually and according to the judgment of the sight. But when on the seventh day it reaches the position of the colure, it appears to the sight of necessity in a straight line, the diameter, as it were, of the surface of the moon which appears to us plane. Then when it is in the other half of the moon, it again becomes curved, because it is now assuming the nature of a parallel. Since, moreover, it is the arc of a parallel almost a great circle, its concavity must be toward the sun. For in that half of the moon so large a parallel could not be drawn, whose gibbosity is toward the sun, for it might easily be possible in the case of a small parallel, as is evident to one considering the matter. If, then, that arc of the pyramid be moved until it lies on the arc of the base of the visual pyramid, and the whole circumference of that parallel lie on the whole base of the visual pyramid, the whole surface of the moon exposed to us will of necessity be illuminated and the same will be the base of both pyramids, and the moon will then be full. Then, owing to the varied position of the sun with respect to the moon, the arc of the base of the solar pyramid begins to recede from the base of the visual pyramid, and the moon begins to wane in light, just as in the period of new moon it increased, so that the base of the solar pyramid always appears as a curved line because of the explanation in regard to the parallel, until the base of the solar pyramid arrives at the position of the colure on the twenty-first day, and then it again appears as a straight line, just as it did on the seventh day. Thus, therefore, can the form of the lunar light through its varied phases be understood by means of an excessive distance of this kind and by means of the explanations of the circles.

Therefore it is evidently impossible that the heaven is a plane figure, although the vision so judges it, or at least judges that it approaches closely to a plane figure. For just as we have here said, the angles of a polygonal figure of equal sides appear in consequence of excessive distance to have rotundity. For little by little the angles disappear, because they have no relationship to excessive distance, nor does the access of the angle to the eye exceed sensibly the part of a circle inscribed in such a figure, or of an inscribed sphere, because the size of the angle is small or not sensible at all in respect to such great remoteness. Not only is this statement made by Alhazen in his third book, but the same author maintains this in his book on Vision, when he says, in the tenth proposition, "Rectangular magnitudes seen from a distance appear circumferences." But since rectangular figures of this kind must also be equilateral, another translation substitutes for the above, "Squares because of distance appear round," and not only squares, but every equilateral figure, because the same explanation applies to them all. But in regard to other polygons, in which circles and spheres cannot be inscribed, the statement is not true, because there can be a sensible access of the angle to the eye although the distance be great. I have added this for the understanding of this occultation. If, then, the angles of an equilateral body little by little disappear, until the body appears round, so that such a body does not disappear at one and the same time owing to the flattening of its angles, a round body, because it does not have angles, will at once wholly disappear, and at a great distance will appear to be a plane figure. Therefore if the heaven were extended to the east and west in a plane figure, the stars would disappear all together at the same moment at their setting, since they are of spherical figure. But we see the reverse, because part after part sets and disappears, and in like manner rises. Wherefore this cannot happen in a plane distance and therefore the heaven is not a plane extension but a curved one.

Chapter V

Concerning the comprehension of magnitudes.

As the comprehension of distance has been explained as a reasoning process, so too with magnitude. Both the author of the book on Vision and many others thought that magnitude was appreciated by the size of the angle at the eye, whence at the beginning of that book it is assumed that objects seen under a larger angle appear larger, and under a smaller angle smaller, and things seen under equal angles appear equal. But this does not suffice, as Alhazen shows by examples; since if in a circle different diameters are marked, as *ab, cd,* it is evident to the sense that *ab* is seen under a much smaller angle, and yet the diameters are equal. Similarly in regard to the sides of a square, for the side *ab* makes a much smaller angle at the eye than *dc,* and yet the sides are equal, and the vision perceives that sides of this kind are equal; and in like measure the vision judges that the diameters of the same circle or of equal circles are equal at a moderate distance. Therefore comprehension of the size of the angle does not suffice. Moreover, if an object is seen at a

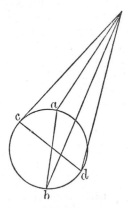

FIG. 46.

lesser distance and at a greater, provided that the excess is moderate, the angle will vary sensibly. But the vision will not judge that the object seen is greater and smaller; so that if the eye be placed at the vertex of a shorter pyramid, the angle in it will be greater than at the vertex of a longer pyramid, by the twenty-first proposition of the first book of Euclid. And if the distance be trebled, namely, so that the first distance is one cubit, the second two, and the third three, there will be an extraneous difference of angle, and yet it will be judged to be of the same size. Since, then, this is a fact, there can be no determination of the magnitude of an object in accordance with the size of the angle. But it is necessary that the angle be considered and the length of the pyramid, and that the base of the pyra-

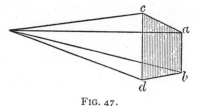

FIG. 47.

mid, which is the object of vision, be compared with these. The length of the pyramid is apprehended by the perception of the size of intermediate bodies, as was stated previously in regard to distance. This is done in the case of objects familiar to the eye and at a moderate distance by comparison and sudden reference to some definite measure ready to the memory, like the size of the man measuring as regards himself as a whole or a part, and all these things are determined by the visual axis passing over visible objects.

But error occurs in apprehension of magnitude when the distance is excessive, since it will appear much less than it really is. The reason for this is found in the excessive distance, which hides from the vision parts proportional to the whole in a sensible relationship; and when the occultation of parts perceptible to the sense shall have taken place, the angles in which they fall are not perceived, although they are proportional to the total angle. Hence when the axis passes over the object of vision, the lines from it and many parts are hidden, whence the total appearance is rendered smaller. And also owing to the smallness of the angle, perceived with difficulty, the species will not be well arranged on the sensible part of the perceptive member, and therefore the size will not be clearly judged.

CHAPTER VI

IN regard to spherical bodies, like stars and other objects, it is not possible for the eye to see one half, but the eye of necessity sees a smaller portion. For the rays of the extremities of the object meet at the eye; but rays that would come from the perimeter of half of a sphere would touch the ends of a diameter, by the nineteenth proposition of the third book of the Elements, and would make right angles with the ends of the diameter, as is shown in that proposition. Therefore it remains that they will not meet by being produced.

That stars for a constant reason seem larger at rising and setting than when at the meridian, is stated by Ptolemy in the third and in the fifth book, and by Alhazen in the seventh. It can be explained owing to the fact that the vision judges the sky as though it were a plane figure extended above the head to the east and to the west, when the eye looks toward either of these. But what is seen near the head seems nearer, and therefore a star when it is at the meridian seems to be nearer, and therefore when on the horizon it seems to be more distant. But what seems to be more distant seems to be larger, since it is seen under the same angle, just as a matter of fact what is more distant is larger since it is seen under the same angle with a smaller object. As, for example, *ab* is more distant from the eye, and is larger than *cd,* and *cd* than *ef.* Therefore it remains that stars appear of larger size on the horizon than at the meridian. And this is manifest in another way. The remoteness of these stars when they are on the horizon is apprehended by the interposition of the earth; but they cannot be so apprehended when they are at the meridian, because of the imperceptibility of the air. Therefore since the remoteness of these is more perceptible when they are on the horizon than when at the meridian, it follows

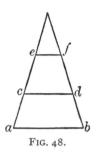

FIG. 48.

that they seem at that time more distant than when they are at the meridian. Therefore as before they will appear larger.

The perception of motion and rest, which is said to be the result of reasoning, can also be explained. Motion is apprehended by a comparison of the object moved with another object in respect to which it changes its position. Hence vision does not apprehend motion except when it perceives a thing in two places and in different positions; and the position of the object of vision is not changed without involving time. Wherefore motion is not apprehended except in a perceptible lapse of time. Rest likewise is apprehended by vision from the perception of the object of vision in the same place and in the same position in a perceptible lapse of time. Vision errs frequently in the perception of motion and rest. For sometimes when the clouds are in motion the motion is thought to be that of the moon, and this error results from excessive distance; for it does not occur when the distance is moderate. Hence we see that a pole fastened in water is continuously at rest, and we perceive the motion of the water passing by. The error mentioned above in the motion of the moon occurs when the clouds are numerous and continuous, since motion is not perceived except by the approach of one thing to another or the recession. When, however, the clouds are few and divided, we can discern their motion by their successive approach to a star and their recession from it. Therefore, on the other hand, when the heaven is covered by clouds, because of their continuousness and multitude we do not discern motion in them; and yet we see that the moon is moving very rapidly, because it is passing swiftly through the different parts of the cloud, not only owing to its own proper motion, but also owing to the motion of the clouds. When an observer walks in the direction in which the moon lies or other stars, it seems to him that the stars move before him in the direction in which he is going; since at the end of his motion he judges the star to be as far off and to hold the same relative position as at the beginning of his walk. Owing to these impressions the faculty, distinctive through the medium of vision, concludes that the star moves before the face of the observer in the direction in which the observer is walking; and likewise if he flees in the opposite direction it will seem to him that the star is following him. Just as if he should see a man ahead of him, who always keeps the same relative position, they of necessity must be advancing with an equal motion in the same direction, and therefore the observer reasons that the stars are moving in his direction, either preceding or following. For his position with respect to the star is the same as far as the judgment of vision is concerned.

The reason for this is the excessive distance between him and the star, because of which he does not perceive that by his motion he is departing from the star or approaching it, and therefore he judges that he always keeps the same relative position. In the same way it happens that when the sun is in the south and a man is going to the east, it always seems that the sun is in line with him; and if many men stand in the same east and west line, although they be far apart, yet the sun appears directly in front of each one of them. This effect is caused by the excessive distance and the magnitude of the sun. Moreover, the shadows of these men seem to be parallel; and likewise the rays of the sun coming to them seem to be parallel, although they meet at the center of the sun; but owing to the excessive distance their meeting is not perceived, and therefore the rays seem to be parallel and the shadows likewise. When, moreover, one views the planets, although they are moving swiftly in the heavens westward, he judges that they are at rest and does not perceive their motion. The cause of this is found in the fact that, owing to the excessive distance, the vision does not perceive their approach or recession with respect to some fixed object, nor does it perceive a difference in position. Therefore the visual ray is judged to be unmoved, retaining the same position with respect to the object, and therefore the vision judges that the object is at rest.

Moreover, when one turns frequently in a circle, on coming to rest he thinks that vision and other objects are moving in a circle, since after the observer has been set in motion the visual faculty is moved within. And although the observer comes to rest, the visual faculty will not immediately do so, but its motion will continue in the observer after he has come to rest; because the humors of the eye are easily moved, and when motion has been imparted to them they readily retain it, just like water and the visual rays also, which are bodies of fine texture, easily moved and capable of continuing an imparted motion. For they belong to the class of evaporations and resolutions, and therefore the vision continues its motion within after the observer himself has come to rest. Since his vision is in motion, he thinks that the objects of vision are in motion, as Aristotle states in the second book of the Heavens and the World, and Averroës and Ptolemy in the second book and Alhazen in the third book of the Perspective. Moreover, when a man is on a moving ship, trees and other objects on the bank seem to him to be moving, and this is owing to the motion of the visual faculty. Those objects in particular seem to move that are far from the axes; for if the axes are carefully directed to an object near the water, it does not seem to move.

CHAPTER VII

Concerning scintillation.

CONNECTED with these matters is a difficulty very philosophic in character, but more insoluble than any other except the rainbow. Every night we can view objects in which a doubt of this kind is present. Hence we see nothing so frequently of whose cause we know less: it is the scintillation of the stars. The fixed stars sometimes manifestly scintillate, and sometimes they do not. The planets, however, according to Aristotle do not scintillate. Scintillation is a certain tremor of the star and an apparent motion, and this occurs particularly when the stars are in the east or in the west, as Aristotle maintains in his second book on the Heavens and the World, because they then seem most remote, as we have stated, and therefore the vision is less certain in regard to them. For Aristotle in the first book of the Posteriores and in the second of the Heavens and the World says that the reason for this is owing to the distance of the fixed stars. Hence, since the planets are near, they do not scintillate, as he states. He says, moreover, that this is not a phenomenon in the stars, but is seen only because of the revolution and tremor of the vision, because, as he states, the planets are near, and for this reason the vision has power over them. But the vision, when directed to the fixed stars, quivers because of the distance: because the tremor of vision causes an apparent motion of the star itself, for it makes no difference whether the vision is moved or the object of vision. This is the opinion of Aristotle, as we clearly infer from several translations and especially from that purer one that has been made directly from the Greek.

But although he says without reservation that the planets do not scintillate, he, however, maintains in the second book of the Heavens and the World that the sun in a manner has a tremor, and especially so when it is at rising and near it. The reason for this is found in the fact that this tremor is not the motion of scintillation but a weaker motion than that. For a stronger tremor is necessary for scintillation, nor does it occur except on the horizon or near it; but scintillating stars have a tremor everywhere. Venus and Mercury near the point of their rising and setting seem to have a slight tremor, as experience shows, but it is not reckoned a scintillation, because it is slight and does not occur except in those places. Hence this tremor in the sun and in these planets contains no proof with regard to the scintillation in the fixed stars, nor does it occur everywhere in the heavens as it does in the case of the fixed stars; and therefore those tremors are not reckoned among scintillations. But since the longer orbit of Saturn is of equal remoteness with the fixed stars, Saturn, when he is at his longer distance, will scintillate, owing to the distance, just like the fixed stars: this, however, we do not see. It can be stated, moreover, that since the diameter of Saturn is 29,250 miles, as is evident from the previous statements in those matters touched upon regarding arithmetic, he is nearer to us by this number of miles than the fixed stars, and therefore his distance is not so great.

Moreover, a light intense and quite perceptible is required in the object of vision to the end that it may scintillate, because it seems to project darts of light. Hence Averroës says that the sun has that motion of which mention was made above, more than other planets, owing to the brilliancy of its light. If it be said that not all the fixed stars scintillate, although they are more distant than the planets, we must answer that those stars that are larger and have more light scintillate more than other stars. Hence for scintillation a sufficient brilliancy is required, because a manifest and sensible image is present in scintillation. If, then, the objection be raised that the light of the sun and of the stars is stronger and more brilliant when they are at the meridian than when they are on the horizon, because then the rays of the stars fall more at right angles, why at that time is the tremor more apparent in them, if brilliancy of this kind is required and is conducive to scintillation? We must reply that as a lessened brilliancy is not sufficient for scintillation, so an excessive brilliancy confuses and absorbs the eye to such an extent that the tremor is not perceived.

The fact that stars appear to be more distant on the horizon than at the meridian causes the vision to err in its perception of the visible object; for since it erroneously judges the star to be more distant when it is on the horizon, it makes a greater effort to see the star, and from the effort there results a stronger movement and straining of the eye. For in consequence of the great effort the eye is compressed, and the coats and humors recede from their natural position, and yet they immediately return to the same position, and therefore straining and tremor occur. Nature, moreover, always returns to the place that is injured or in need, and sends more abundantly spirits and supplies of heat, and therefore in an effort of this kind on the part of the eye spirit and natural heat are released from the common nerve, and an excess of this kind stirs up the humors and causes them to recede from their natural position, to which they immediately return again. Thus a tremor of the eye occurs and consequently a tremor apparently in the object of vision. Ptolemy assigns this cause in the second book of the Perspective. Also since the vision estimates the sun and stars to be more distant when they are on the horizon, it therefore makes more effort and is strained. And according to this the precise reason can be found why the brilliant planets, especially the sun and moon, Venus, Mercury, and Jupiter, do not scintillate; because the vision easily determines them and reckons consequently that they are nearer, according to the statement of Ptolemy in the second book of the Optics, because brilliant objects, like the sun and moon, are reckoned near; those, however, that are less luminous are not reckoned so. Alhazen, moreover, says in the third book that a strong color, although it be more remote, yet appears nearer, because it easily affects the sight; and since this is a fact, the vision does not make an effort in regard to planets of this kind, and therefore is not strained. Moreover, as a matter of fact they are nearer than the fixed stars, and therefore a weaker species comes to the sight from the fixed stars, and the species of vision is weakened in consequence of the distance, and for this reason makes more effort in regard to the fixed stars.

But if it be said that the eye puts forth more effort in beholding small stars than larger ones, and that therefore strain will occur more quickly; we must reply that another cause, which relates to brilliancy, is lacking in them. And if it be said that this effort depends upon a man's choice, and therefore depends upon his will, for which reason this effort is under his control; that he can therefore make an equal effort on a large star as on a small one, on a planet as on a fixed star, and on a star on the horizon as on one at the meridian, wherefore an effort of this kind does not have any bearing in this matter, we must reply that it does. For it is the habit of vision to put forth more or less effort according to the distance of the visible object, and according to the weakness of vision itself, and according to the lack of visibility in the object. Moreover, in this matter vision is trained and practiced, and habit is a second nature, as Aristotle says, and especially so in vision, as the authors on Perspective teach. Hence one does not perceive that he sees by reflection and refraction, but thinks that he sees by means of straight lines only, because he has been accustomed to see by straight lines, as will be stated below. Therefore the effort of vision is not under the control of the rational soul, just as the other judgments of habit are not so controlled, although here some strive by a sophistry of this kind to disprove this effort of vision and certain other natural phenomena habitual and similar to vision. If it be objected that vision does not judge concerning the distance of the planets and the stars, for by reasoning alone do we comprehend the distances of the stars, and that therefore vision will judge equally concerning the fixed stars and the planets as far as concerns the phenomena of visible things that rest upon distance; we must reply that such is not the case. For although vision cannot determine the distance of the stars, because bodies do not exist in continued succession between the stars, yet owing to the greater impression made by the more brilliant planets, as has been said, they appear nearer, although vision cannot state how much nearer they are. And again because it receives a weaker species from the fixed stars than from the planets, since species is weakened by distance, vision puts forth more effort in regard to the species of the fixed stars than in regard to the species of the planets, and similarly the species of vision is weakened by distance, and therefore it is not so active when it comes to a very distant object of vision, and for this reason puts forth more effort and a strain takes place in it and greater movement.

If it be objected that just as vision is weakened by distance, and fails and strains and relaxes again, so it fails in consequence of the density of the medium to secure a true comprehension of the object of vision. Therefore if we assume a density of medium proportional to the distance of scintillating stars they would scintillate. This is not believed to be true. Averroës replies to this in the second book of the Heavens and the World;* for he well maintains that density of medium would tend to produce scintillation and tremor, saying that if the sun quivers only at setting and rising, it is because of the density of the medium. If, however, the sun does so everywhere, then it is because of the strength of the light, which is stronger than in the other planets. He maintains, therefore, that density of the medium tends to produce tremor. Therefore although this is generally denied, yet this is not improbable; and therefore stars scintillate more at rising and setting, not only for the reason stated above, but because of the thickness of the medium

* Bacon evidently intends this to be the conclusion of the condition stated at the beginning of this paragraph.

charged with vapor, since a multitude of vapors abounds in the medium around those hours, because the sun raises at that time the vapors, and does not consume them as at midday; because the solar rays are weak at sunrise and sunset, since the rays fall at oblique angles to the horizon, as has been explained in what precedes.

But if the thickness of the medium does not do this, yet the motion of the medium can have this effect, as Averroës shows in the same passage. For the medium is in continuous motion, and therefore the species of an object while it falls in one part remains in this part after it has moved from its position, until a remaining part succeeds to the place of the first part, and therefore each has a species of the visible object, and they produce species similar to themselves in the same eye, and in different parts of it, and in the common nerve; as Averroës likewise shows in his book on Sense and the Sensible by an example in regard to the species of the sun falling on moving water. For the species does not disappear immediately from the part moved, but remains in it for a time, until a remaining part comes into its place, and then both produce a species in parts of the same eye and optic nerve, and in this way the same object seems to have a change of position continuously, and therefore to tremble. Moreover, Ptolemy approves of this view in the second book of the Optics, giving this example in regard to moving water and a moving medium.

Averroës, moreover, offers a third reason because of intermittent vision, giving the example of a man who looks at an object in one place, and if he moves his eye by pressing it with his finger, he will see the object in another place because of the motion of the eye, since the species of the object is not fixed in one definite place, but is in several places. And likewise if a man looks at an object under a condition of frequent change, namely, now with one eye now with the other, or with one eye frequently closed, provided it be opened and closed continuously, the object seems as though it were in different places; and so subject to a tremor, as it were, and to a change from place to place. The eye, moreover, does this when the distance between it and the object is great; for one frequently closes his eyes and opens them. Although the eyelids may be open, the visual faculty in the pupil and nerve is fatigued from the strain, and the act of seeing at all or at least distinctly is interrupted; and therefore the species of a distant object is not fixed on the sight, because the object is thought to move to and fro.

If it be said that when the air is set in vigorous motion by the wind there would be greater and more violent scintillation, our reply must be that, just as the necessary brilliancy, neither too much nor too little, is required for scintillation, as was stated above (and just as a certain distance likewise is required: for stars might be so far distant that they would not scintillate, and just as some have so little light that they do not scintillate); so may we speak concerning the motion of the medium. For the motion of the air, which is caused by the motion of the heaven and of the vapors, a motion that is continuously found in it, is sufficient for scintillation; and this is fixed for the scintillation of the stars, so that a greater motion is not required, nor does a lesser one suffice. If it be said also that species multiplies itself in straight lines in the same medium, nor does it depart from a straight direction because of the motion of the medium, because its path does not vary except by refraction and reflection, which do not occur in the motion of the same medium, and therefore the species will not be produced in different places but only in one place, and thus it will not have a different position in the eye; we must reply that it is true that species always keeps the same direction in the same medium, and multiplies itself directly in one path and one place. But, however, since the different parts fall successively in the same place, and the first part having the species retains it after it leaves the direction of the species, and another part comes into the place of propagation of the species before the species disappears from the first part, therefore the two parts having different positions produce species in different parts of the eye and cause the phenomenon that has been mentioned. If, however, it be said that the rays of all stars and planets pass thus through a tremulous medium, we must reply that the other reasons relating to strain of the eye and brilliancy of the object of vision are missing, as is manifest from the solutions of the objections offered.

From all these statements the reason for scintillation can be gathered, although with difficulty, owing to the various objections occurring. For on the part of the eye there must be effort owing to which the eye is strained. For because of this effort an excessive freeing takes place of spirits and forms of heat, which compel the humors of the eye to leave their natural position, and nevertheless from its effort there result a compression and constriction of the eye, in consequence of which the parts of the eye do not retain their position. Again in the third place there arises from this an interruption of vision, because of which the visible object appears to change its position, as has been explained by Averroës. These three things, then, result from eyestrain, which is caused not only by the weakness of the visual power and of the species, owing to the actual distance, but because of the judgment of the apparent distance; and therefore vision makes a greater effort on the fixed stars than on the brilliant planets, which it judges to be near because of their excessive brilliancy. But not only is this effort required, but also sufficient brilliancy on the part of the scintillating body, because a scintillating body seems to scatter darts of light, and for this reason Saturn and small stars do not scintillate. There must likewise be a tremor of the medium, as has been stated, and all these conditions are required for scintillation, owing to the distance of the object of vision, because an object placed at the required distance does not scintillate; and for this reason Aristotle ascribes the phenomenon chiefly to distance, although many attendant conditions must be considered. In this way scintillation in the heavenly bodies is to be understood, of which Aristotle speaks, although there is a special kind of scintillation in these things here below, of which mention will be made later on.

Chapter VIII

And now at the conclusion of this discussion in regard to the way in which we see in straight lines owing to the three methods of vision, by the sense alone, by recollection [*scientia*], and by a syllogistic process, there is rightly a doubt, which faculty of the soul it is, that in recollection and the syllogistic process acts in regard to things made visible through the medium of the visual sense. If we accept the terms recollection and the syllogistic process in the sense in which they are used in matters pertaining to logic, nature, and metaphysics, in accordance with the general practice of philosophers, this faculty must be the rational soul; because the syllogistic process and recollection pertain to it alone, as these terms are accepted in the sciences mentioned. Alhazen calls this part of the soul the distinctive faculty, which according to him reasons and understands; for sometimes these terms and ones like them are found, so that it would seem according to their literal meaning that the faculty is the discerning and rational soul.

But it is well known that a dog recognizes a man seen previously when it sees him again. Moreover, the ape and many other animals act in this way, and distinguish between the objects of vision of which they have a recollection, and they recognize one universal from another, as a man from a dog or a tree, and they distinguish individuals of the same species; and therefore the perception which writers on perspective call perception through recollection belongs to animals as well as to men. Therefore this faculty must be a function of sensitive life. But likewise it is manifest that the same holds true for the perception that is termed perception through the syllogistic process; for motion is recognized through it; as, for example, a dog, when someone raises a stick to strike it, flees; which it would not do if it did not perceive that the stick is changing its position with respect to itself and is approaching it. Similarly when an animal, for example, a dog, cat, wolf, or some other animal, holds an animal on which it feeds, while the prey is still, the plunderer stands motionless; but when the captured animal flees, the plunderer follows until it seizes its victim if it can. It would not do this except for the reason that it perceives that the position of the prey has changed with reference to itself, and therefore it perceives motion and rest and distance. We must grant that animals have some perceptions of this kind by a certain natural purpose and instinct without deliberation, and the faculty that acts is cogitative, which is mistress of the faculties and employs the other faculties of the soul. For there is here required a recollection of this kind of objects of vision for the distinction of the universals and particulars, and this recollection belongs to the imagination itself, as was previously stated, if it is exercised with respect to light and color and the twenty common sensibles, since imagination is the storehouse of the species coming from them. If, however, it deals with the things pertaining to the estimative faculty and the memory, that particular kind of memory serves here in recalling them. For although the lamb flees from the wolf that it has not seen, yet if it has seen the wolf it flees more quickly and carefully when it sees him a second time. And thus a distinction is made through the cogitative faculty by means of memory, which is the storehouse of intentions apart from the senses with regard to sensible matter, as was explained before. Therefore the perception by which things seen previously are distinguished from other things is present in animals. Wherefore there is here a double use of the term; or rather there is a fault in the translation, which does not have a proper word for this kind of perception. Likewise there is ambiguity, because the term syllogism should be limited to its ordinary use. For without doubt in no way can the fact be hidden that animals perceive the distance of objects, and motion, and rest, although in regard to other common sensibles such is not the case.

But as regards formal reasoning we must consider that the arrangement of the reasoning in a logical figure and the distinction of the conclusion from the premises pertain only to the rational soul. But a certain gathering together of several facts into one in consequence of a natural purpose and instinct, the several facts resembling premises and the resultant one a conclusion, because it is gathered from them, can be found in animals. For we see angered apes prepare plots against men and coördinate many things, so that they may secure their revenge, and therefore they assemble into one that which they draw from many sources. We see also spiders arrange their web, not haphazard fashion, but in various geometrical forms, so that flies may be caught easily by them. The wolf eats earth, so that he may be heavier when he seizes a horse or bull or stag by the nose, in order that by reason of the weight of the earth he may weigh down the animal and hold it. I have seen, moreover, a mouser that wanted some fish swimming in a large stone vessel; and when it was unable to catch them because of the water, it drew out the stopper and let the water out until the vessel became dry, in order that it might capture the fish in a dry place. It therefore conceived of several acts, in order that it might secure the end it had in view. The bee makes all its houses hexagonal, selecting one of the figures that fill up space, so that no vacant space may be left between the houses; and it does not wish that there should be this space, lest the honey or the young should fall outside of the hives and perish. With this end in view, then, resembling a conclusion it assembles in its mental process many facts which resemble premises. This is true also of a host of facts, in which animals think of many things in their order with respect to an object that they have in mind, just as if they were drawing for themselves a conclusion from the premises. But they do not arrange the course of their reasoning in form and logical figure, nor from their deliberation do they distinguish the last from the first. Nor are they conscious that they are following a course of reasoning of this kind, because their reasoning takes place thus from intuition alone and natural instinct. This course of reasoning is similar to argument and syllogism, and for this reason authors on Perspective call it argument and syllogism. And assuredly they call this kind of reasoning syllogistic more appropriately than they call the distinction of universals and particulars seen previously the cogitative faculty through knowledge.

FIRST DISTINCTION

*In which the author considers reflected and refracted vision, dividing
the subject into three distinctions. The first one is on reflected vision and contains six chapters. The first
chapter is on reflection in general.*

CHAPTER I

AFTER our discussion of vision in straight lines we must
now speak of vision in other ways, namely, in reflected
and refracted lines. Since, moreover, what has been
said concerning the parts of the soul and the structure of the
eye, and the path of the species in the coats and humors of the
eye to the common nerve, and concerning the triple mode of
perceiving sensibles by the sense alone, by syllogistic reasoning, and by recollection [*scientia*], is common to vision effected
by straight lines, by reflected lines, and by refracted lines, less
need be said in regard to these matters. First, then, as regards
the reflection of vision we must recollect that as far as concerns
the judgment of the human vision a dense body can impede
wholly the species, as a wall and dense bodies of this kind; or
in part, as water, glass, and crystal. For every dense body in
so far as it is dense reflects species, not because violence is done
to the species, but because the species takes the opportunity from
a dense body impeding its passage to multiply itself by another
path open to it. A dense body may be rough or smooth. The
parts of a rough body are unsymmetrical, and therefore each
part makes its own proper reflection. For this reason the parts
dissipate the whole species, nor can it as a whole reach the eye,
and therefore there cannot be a sensible reflection or a representation of the object of vision. But owing to the equality and
smoothness of the surface of a polished body, as in mirrors, all
the parts are symmetrically arranged for a single action, and
the species comes back whole and sensible to the eye, and the
image is manifest; not, however, such a perfect one as when
the eye sees by means of a straight line, because reflection

Optical Science

weakens the species, as has been stated in the book on Multiplications.

Since, if the species passed through the medium of the mirror, it would make the angle *a* equal to the angle of incidence, which is *b*, by the fifteenth proposition of the first book of the Elements of Euclid, which states that the opposite angles are equal, the angle of reflection, namely, *d*, must be equal to the angle of incidence, since the ray forms an angle on this side of the mirror like the one formed below it. This, moreover, is proved in a simple manner, as follows: Let *abc* be a plane mirror, *d* the visible object, *e* the eye, and let *ab* and *bc* be equal, *da* and *ec* be perpendicular and equal, let *db* be the radius of incidence, *be* be the radius of reflexion; then since *ce* and *cb* are equal to *ad* and *ab*, and the angles contained within the sides are equal, since they are right angles, it follows by the fourth proposition of the first book of the Elements that the remaining corresponding angles are equal, namely *g* and *f*, which is the proposition. If, therefore, the triangles are equal, the proposition is evident. If, however, one triangle is larger than the other the angles of incidence and reflection are still the same, and are unchanged, and therefore the proposition will always hold. But the author of the book on Mirrors supposes that the triangles are similar, and therefore *ab* will be to *cb* as *da* to *ec*, and therefore the angles *g* and *f* are equal.

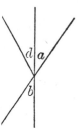

FIG. 49.

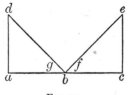

FIG. 50.

By this means also we show that the law holds with regard to convex and concave mirrors. For *a* and *b* make equal angles with a plane mirror, which is *dc*, but the angles of contact [tangency] are equal. Therefore if these angles are taken from those formed with the plane mirror, the angles that are left, namely, *f* and *g*, will be equal, which we wish to prove. In the same way we prove the law in regard to the convex mirror. For *a* and *b* make equal angles with the plane mirror *gf*. Therefore if to these angles are added the angles of contact, which are always equal, the angles *ahd* and *bhc* will be equal, which

[547]

is the proposition. The proof is given in this way in the book on Mirrors, and in the book of Alkindi on Aspects.

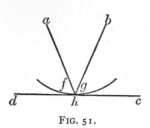

Fig. 51.

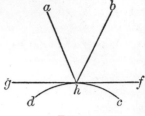

Fig. 52.

Chapter II

In the next place, we must bear in mind carefully that the mirror contains nothing nor is anything seen in it, as is generally thought. But the object opposite it from which the species comes is seen, as Alhazen shows in many ways in the fourth book. For as the end of the straight line *oa,* since vision is effected by means of this line, is a visible object itself, so must the end of the reflected line, namely, *oda,* be *a.* Moreover, the species is not seen except by accident, as has been explained above. We might also assume that the same conditions would hold with regard to the species as with regard to a spot impressed on the mirror or with regard to some part of the mirror that has been marked, on which the species would be impressed, but which would not of necessity have a determined position, in order that one might see the spot on the mirror or some part of the mirror that had been marked. Therefore in vision effected by means of reflection a determined position of the eye is not required. This reasoning, however, is false. For unless the eye is at *o,* it will not see anything by reflection at *o.* For if this reflected species were anywhere else, it would not reach the eye, owing to the equality of the angles of incidence and reflection. This, then, can be shown in many ways, but since all having a knowledge of perspective are in agreement on this point, we need not dwell upon it fur-

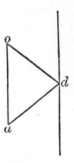

Fig. 53.

ther. Many truths become manifest to the student in consequence of this fact; for, in the first place, it follows that the species is not fixed in the substance of the mirror, nor is it impressed upon the mirror, as is generally supposed, but merely passes by means of the surface of the mirror in the opposite direction in accordance with the equality of the angles of incidence and reflection.

Moreover, since this is the case, if the light coming from the moon and the stars were the light of the sun reflected from their surfaces, as the rank and file of philosophers think, in seeing the moon and a star we should see the sun. This, therefore, is evidently false not only because of the equality of the angles of incidence and reflection, as has been shown in what precedes, according to Averroës in the second book of the Heavens and the World, but for the reason now given. In the same way it follows that a comet is not the reflection of the solar light from the surface of a star, as many have maintained that the tail following the comet is nothing else than the light of the sun reflected from the surface of a star to us, or that the light coming to us from a comet is the light of the sun reflected from the surface of some star. But this is a false notion. For in that case in seeing a comet we should see the sun, which is not true. Moreover, since the rainbow is merely the image of the sun reflected from a moist cloud, as all agree and as the fact is established, in accordance with the proof given below in the section on Experimental Science, then in seeing the cloud we should see the sun and nothing else; but this, however, seems absurd, since our vision judges that it beholds colors and a colored bow. But the sun does not possess such a figure nor such colors. But we shall make sure of this matter later on in a broader discussion.

Moreover, in addition to these facts we must note that the object does not appear to the vision by reflection in its own position, because vision is accustomed to see by means of straight lines at their extremities, and for this reason vision does not perceive the bending of reflection; and therefore it judges that the object is always in the visual ray, and the place of the image, which we call the appearance of the object, is at some point of this ray. This result is due to the fact that vision is caused by external propagation, and for this reason the vision judges that the object is in the direction of the species of the eye. But it is not always, however, in the same place, but as in many instances is at the intersection of the visual ray with the cathetus, which is the perpendicular drawn from the object to the mirror. Sometimes it is not at that intersection, but in the visual ray alone, because it can be equidistant from the cathetus, as in the case of a concave mirror, as we shall explain. When it intersects the cathetus, the intersection takes place in many ways. For sometimes they meet behind the head, sometimes in the eye, sometimes on the surface of the mirror, sometimes beyond the mirror, and this last in several ways. For it happens sometimes that the object appears as much beyond the mirror as it is distant from the mirror, and this diversity happens owing to the difference in mirrors. Therefore we must now take up this question.

CHAPTER III

MIRRORS, then, are of seven kinds, in which, according to authors on Perspective, vision differs; namely, spherical, conical, cylindrical, polished on the outside and on the inside. These make six; the seventh is the plane mirror. For each of the first three classes can be concave, that is, polished on the inside, or convex, that is, polished on the outside, making six in number; the plane mirror has only one structure. In the case of these mirrors, then, I wish, following the views of authors on Perspective and particularly of Ptolemy and Alhazen, to consider as briefly as I can the modes of vision according to the diversity of mirrors.

In plane mirrors, then, very little error occurs, because the objects appear in their proper form and size. For the position alone is altered, since the right appears on the left and the reverse and the top at the bottom, whence towers appear inverted in the water, since the reflection takes place from the plane surface of the water. There is, however, an error in plane mirrors that is common in all mirrors, namely, the object does not appear in its own place, nor is the place of the image there. When, moreover, we speak of the place of the image, we mean the appearance of the object, for this is all that we mean by the term.

Neither the object, then, in these mirrors nor the place of the image appears in the place of the object, but always in the visual ray, for the two reasons given. But in plane mirrors the image is determined at the intersection of the visual ray with the cathetus, namely, as far beyond the mirror as the object of vision is distant from the mirror. This law does not hold in the case of other mirrors. It can be shown by proof. For let *a* be the object of vision, *o* the eye, *ad* the cathetus, *od* the visual ray. I say that *db* is equal to *ab* itself. But *bd* is the distance of the image of the object from the surface of the mirror, and *ab* is the distance of the object from the same surface of the mirror; it appears, how-ever, as far beyond the mirror as it is distant from the mirror. For the angles *e* and *f,* since they are right angles, are equal, and *g* and *h* are equal, by the fifteenth proposition of the first book of the Elements of Euclid, and *h* and *c* are equal, because they are the angles of inci-dence and reflection. Therefore it is evident that *c* and *g* will be equal. Since, then, the angles *e* and *g* of the triangle *egd* are equal to the angles *f* and *c* of the triangle *acf,* and the in-cluded side is common to both triangles, it is

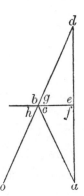

FIG. 54.

evident by the twenty-sixth proposition of the first book of Euclid that these triangles are equal in all their parts. There-fore the sides *ab* and *bd* will be equal. Wherefore vision judges that the object is as far beyond the mirror continuously and in a straight line as it is in front of it in the case of plane mirrors. By this and previous statements the error of many is removed, who believed that the species of the object was there in reality and that it diffused itself through the medium of the mirror and appeared there. But no visual species exists in the mirror, as has been stated, nor does it enter the mirror, so that vision should be effected by means of an entry of this kind, but it merely passes by means of the surface of the mirror to the end of the reflection in the opposite direction, according to the equality of the angles of incidence and reflection. Hence the place of the image does not seem to be at the intersection of the visual ray with the cathetus because of the reality of its existence in that place, but by reason merely of its appearance.

[551]

In spherical mirrors polished on the outside [convex] also according to the judgment of the vision the object appears at the intersection of the visual ray with a line drawn from the object to the center of the sphere. This intersection can be beyond the mirror, or within, or on the surface of the mirror. The same holds true in the cylindrical and conical mirrors. All the errors, moreover, that are in plane mirrors, occur in convex mirrors also, and more, since in these the object of vision frequently appears less than it is; sometimes, however, equal or greater, but very rarely. But the image appears less, because the width of the surface of the mirror is less, from which the rays intersecting at the eye are reflected, than it is in plane mirrors; for the rays reflected from a convex mirror are more dispersed than those from a plane mirror. Therefore that the rays may pass to the sight just as from a plane mirror, the reflection must be from a shorter surface than from a plane mirror. The representation, moreover, of the image follows the condition of the reflecting surface. In these mirrors, therefore, hardly anything appears as it is, the arrangement of the parts excepted, which is the same in the mirror as in the object. In these mirrors that which is straight appears curved; for since the reflection of the outer rays is on a convex surface, the termini are more distant from the center of the eye than the extremities of the median ray, and that which happens in the turning is judged to be present in the object. Very rarely, however, does it happen that what is rectilinear appears so. It does so when the sight is in the surface in which the line seen and the center of the sphere lie. The mathematical proof of this fact is too lengthy to be given here. Again we must note that in convex mirrors the distance of the image from the mirror is less than that of the object of vision, while in plane mirrors it is equal. The reason for this is found in the fact that in convex mirrors the ray intersects more quickly with the cathetus than in plane mirrors, as is evident to the inquirer.

In cylindrical mirrors polished on the outside the same error is present as in convex spherical mirrors, and more in addition. For in these an object seen at a distance appears smaller than in convex spherical mirrors. The reason for this is apparent if one considers the difference between the surfaces of the former and the latter. In these mirrors, then, very large objects appear very small, and rectilinear objects appear much more curved than in convex spherical mirrors. But we must note that in these mirrors the reflection sometimes takes place from the length of the cylinder, as when a line seen is equidistant from the axis of the cylinder, and in this case the reflection is the same as in plane mirrors, with this exception, that, since the line from which the reflection takes place has breadth, it appears somewhat curved. Sometimes the reflection is from the cross direction of the cylinder, and in this case the image is very much distorted and very much shortened. Sometimes the reflection takes place from a midway position, or from one approaching more nearly the length or breadth. Images will be formed in accordance with these several positions.

In conical mirrors polished on the outside, likewise, the same errors occur as in convex spherical mirrors, because the image is smaller than the object of vision, and what is rectilinear appears curved, and the reflection differs in these as in cylindrical mirrors, because the reflection takes place from the length of the cone, or from its width, or from a position between. Moreover, in these the shape appears conical. For in general it is true that the species comprehended by reflection is assimilated to the shape of the surface of the mirror. In these, also, the further an object is distant from the mirror the smaller it looks, and the nearer it approaches the larger it appears.

Chapter IV

Among all mirrors the greatest deception is in the concave spherical ones; for the deception in regard to size occurs in these as in the others, since sometimes it is greater, sometimes less, sometimes equal; and besides this there is a deception in regard to number, since sometimes one object appears to be two, sometimes three, sometimes four, according to different positions, so that this number it is impossible to exceed. Moreover, in these a disarrangement of parts is apparent, since the object appears sometimes erect, sometimes inverted; and thus it is manifest that in these mirrors nothing appears except with deception. In concave mirrors, however, straight lines appear sometimes straight, sometimes convex, sometimes concave; and convex lines appear sometimes convex, sometimes concave; and sometimes concave lines are apprehended as convex, as is proved in the sixth book of Alhazen, seventh chapter; and this happens in accordance with a difference of position with respect to the mirror. In these mirrors, then, sometimes the cathetus is equidistant from the visual ray, and in this case the place of the image is the same as the point of reflection, and this is true because it is a point of divisible reflection, and if we consider one part, the image should appear beyond the mirror, but if we consider the other, it should appear this side of the mirror, as will be evident. But since the figure is one and continuous, the whole appears at a distance midway between the two, namely, at the point itself of reflection. But when the cathetus and the visual ray intersect, the object appears at their intersection, and this occurs in several ways, according to difference of position. For sometimes the place of the image is in the mirror, sometimes beyond it, sometimes this side of it; and this is either between the sight and the mirror, or in the center itself of vision, sometimes behind the eye.

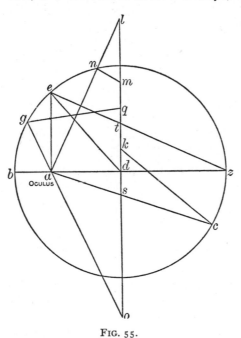

FIG. 55.

All these facts are made evident in the figure given below. For the form t is reflected from e to a by the ray ea, equidistant from the perpendicular td, and appears at e; and m is reflected from n to a, and intersects the perpendicular ml; and k is reflected from the point c to the eye a, and appears at s; and q falls to g, and is reflected to a; it intersects, moreover, the cathetus behind the eye, namely, at o; and z falls to e, and is reflected to the

eye. But the ray *ae* nowhere intersects the cathetus drawn from
the point *z* through *d,* except in the center itself of the eye,
whence *z* appears there. In all these different images nowhere
is any one of them really perceived unless its position is beyond the mirror, or between the sight and the mirror. Hence
those that appear in the center of the eye or behind the head
appear as things not determined by vision. For vision is not
constructed by nature to perceive the position of forms unless
they are in front of the eye. When, moreover, the eye is at the
center of a concave mirror, it is the only thing visible to itself;
for no form is reflected to the center except that which comes
from the center. The perpendicular, in fact, returns upon itself.
If, however, the eye is placed on the periphery or outside it,
the eye is not visible to itself, but the reflection is in the opposite
direction. If, however, the eye is placed below the periphery,
no one of the objects that are in the semidiameter in which it
lies, is visible. If, however, some visible object is placed at the
center, it cannot be seen by reflection, for its species is not reflected except upon itself. In regard to the number of images we
must note that when the eye is so placed that from four parts
of the mirror the reflection of the form of the same object is
made, and there is an intersection in different places of each of
the rays with the cathetus, there will be four images. When the
reflection is from three parts of the mirror there will be three
images; when from two parts, there will be two images; when
from one part, there will be one image, as is very accurately
stated in the fifth book, part second. And note that all proofs
dealing with places of reflection seek to answer the question,
where the angle of incidence can be equal to the angle of reflection, and as many images appear at the same time as there
are points of this kind under the same position and with respect
to the same eye; if, however, the rays in different places intersect the perpendicular at a sensible distance. For when the distance of the point seen is greater from one eye than from the
other, the positions of the images will be different with respect
to either eye, but the difference is imperceptible, and for this
reason the two appear as one.

We must note that distance and proximity are reflected in
different ways from concave mirrors; as is evident from the

thickness, and because of their great proximity, we do not perceive the real colors that are in them. I do not, however, deny that owing to the different incidence of the light at various angles those colors are now more manifest, now more hidden, now brighter and livelier, now obscured and weakened. This is the case also in the colors of the rainbow; for in reality they exist only in appearance, as the incidence of light at fixed angles produces them. The rainbow is caused by reflection not by refraction, since it varies according to the view of the observer, as Experimental Science will show.

Drunken men and those weak in health, according to Aristotle in the third book of the Meteorologics, and according to Seneca in the book on the Rainbow, see themselves, and it seems to them that they see themselves walking in advance. In explanation of this Seneca says that the species coming from them, that is, their visual powers, are weak, and therefore the air, although not dense, is able to resist the species and reflect it back to the sight, and for this reason the species is formed in the air in front of them and returns to the eyes and to the whole body. Hence they see themselves just as they would in a mirror. Here alone is vision effected by the species of the eye, and not by the species of the object of vision, except that the eye together with the whole body is seen, and the species of the eye is reflected to all the anterior parts of the body, and the man is seen in front of himself, because the position of the image is in front of the man at the intersection of the visual ray with the cathetus. But that this vision is effected only by the species of the eye is evident, because the species of other parts of the body and of the clothes are strong, so that they penetrate the air, which reflects the weak species of the eye. It is thus evident that the sight produces from itself its own species. This vision is weak because it is effected through the species of the eye alone; and the species of vision is weaker and grows so more quickly than that of the other part of the eye, because the eye possesses a more tenuous and weaker substance. If it be said, then, that the visual rays could be reflected when they are directed toward the heavens and fail in the profundity of the air or of the transparent sky, as was said before, and similarly in deep water, and that a man would then see himself when he views

that deep water from a distance, which is not true; we must
reply that this does not happen unless the air near these persons be somewhat dense, which can happen in the case of
drunken men, owing to the moisture from the vapors of the
wine that are set free, and in the case of the infirm, owing to
the vapors always released near them from disease. Hence evil
and foul vapors are always near these people in the air, by
which the air near them is tainted and rendered dense, so that
in their vicinity it acts like a mirror, which would not happen
in another more remote part of the air. Likewise the air near
the ground is made dense by vapors arising from the earth and
from the water; and therefore from both causes of density the
air near at hand can have the quality of a mirror. Therefore
owing to this difformity in parts of the air it happens that one
part has the quality of a mirror and another part does not have
it with respect to the eyes of drunken men and of those in weak
health. But the strong eye looking in water finds it of uniform
density. The same is true in the sphere of the heavens at a distance; and vision does not find there a denser part that might
have the quality of a mirror, nay, it always finds it rarer, and
therefore the species is multiplied until it fails without reflection. But if it be said that a strong eye finds vapors in the air
and parts of clouds, so that reflection might take place, we must
reply that it passes through vapors because of its strength and
also through the light and thin clouds; but it does not pass
through thick clouds. One does not, however, see himself because of the distance of the mirror and because of the lack of a
perfect polish; for they do not possess polished and regular
surfaces at all. Distance, however, is the chief obstacle, just as
if a large mirror were placed at a distance of one league or two
or three, however large it might be, a man would not on this
account see himself; and therefore he could not see himself by
means of the clouds, since they are distant from us about fifty
miles, as is shown in the book on Twilights.

The vision of drunken men and of those in weak health can
be explained in another way, namely, by direct vision. For their
species are in the air in front of them, and because the visual
faculty is weak it therefore ends at once and the species in the
air is like an object, just as we stated before in regard to the

weak eye which sees sometimes the species along with the object so that one object appears to be two, errors which do not happen in the case of a strong eye for the reason given there.

When the eye views a candle and lowers the eyelashes, it sees the candle project rays in the form of a radiant pyramid whose vertex is in the candle, and the dispersion of the rays is quite sensible to the eye. The reason for this is found in the fact that the rays of the candle fall on the lids and the lashes are polished, possessing the property of a mirror, and a reflection for this reason takes place from them to the eye, when they are so inclined that the eye is able to receive the rays reflected at angles equal to those of incidence. Therefore this phenomenon does not occur in any position at all of the lashes, but only in one determined.

When a man views something bright and polished, like a metal cross on a campanile or lofty tower, he will see a body of this kind scintillate strongly when the rays of the sun or moon fall on it and are reflected to the sight. The reason of this is the sensible variation of the angle owing to the motion of the star. For although on account of the distance of the star from us we do not perceive its motion, yet owing to the moderateness of the distance of such a scintillating body we are able to judge in regard to the fall of the light at different angles owing to the motion of the star, and therefore it seems to project rays according to the different positions and to scintillate. For if we should imagine a wheel whose center is the center of the world, and the circumference is the revolving heaven, then although the radii extended from the center to the circumference, that is, branches or rods fastened at the center and extended to the circumference, would not seem to move near the circumference owing to distance from the sight, they would, however, be seen to move perceptibly about the center by an eye placed near it. Therefore similarly the rays of the sun falling on an object here below will make a sensible variation in the angle, although the motion in the sun would not be apparent to us. This is the new kind of scintillation, which I promised in what precedes that I would mention.

Optical Science

Chapter VI

It is generally known among students of perspective that when a mirror is placed in a vessel containing water and a double image appears in it, one will be that of the sun, and the other that of some star situated near the sun. But it cannot be a fixed star because the sun hides these, nor is it one of the planets, since the planets are distant sometimes more, sometimes less. But the images always have a uniform distance. Moreover, the phenomenon happens in the light of the moon as well as in that of the sun; likewise in the light of a candle; which they neglect to try. Wherefore it is not a star which appears, but it is the double image of the sun or moon or candle reflected from the double mirror. For the surface of the water is like that of a mirror, and by it one image is formed and the other is formed by the mirror. It is thought that the image formed by the water is larger and more perceptible, since the ray that forms the other image is much weakened because it is first refracted at the surface of the water, then it is reflected from the mirror, and thirdly is refracted at the surface of the air. But reflection and refraction greatly weaken the species, so that it is not able sufficiently to represent the object; and for this reason the former image is weaker and smaller and less perceptible. But this reasoning yields to mine that the greater image is made by reflection from the mirror; because the mirror is dense and has lead as one of its parts, which impedes the passage of the species; and for this reason the mirror has the means of receiving the image and returning it. For water owing to its rarity has less of the quality of a mirror, and therefore gives back a weak image. Now as to the objections raised in regard to the refractions, we must state that the weakening which happens through them does not make the image less than that formed by the water, but less than it would be if the mirror were in a dry place outside the water.

It is generally believed that it is absolutely true that in a broken mirror as many images appear as there are broken parts. But this is not the case except when the broken parts do not keep the same position but have a different one. For if they retain the same position that they had in the unbroken mirror, only one image will appear, because the species coming is made one and remains one whether the mirror be whole or broken, provided the parts retain their same position; because there is one point of reflection, and there is one place on which it falls. When, however, the parts of a broken mirror are placed differently, the species necessarily are counted, because in its changed position the points of reflection are different and in different places, and therefore different images appear.

SECOND DISTINCTION

Of the third part, which is on refracted vision, in four chapters.
The first chapter treats of vision by refraction in general.

CHAPTER I

HAVING showed how vision is effected by straight and reflected lines, we must now show, in the third place, how it is effected by refracted lines. Although this is more difficult than the aforesaid subjects, yet we now are in a position to understand by means of what has been said, because this topic has many points of agreement with the others, as was stated in that part which deals with direct vision. We have seen how all rays must be refracted in the vitreous humor except the axis of the pyramid of rays, which passes through the centers of the coats and humors, and that no ray of the visual pyramid is refracted at the cornea, or at the albugineous humor, or at the anterior of the glacialis, since the whole pyramid falls perpendicularly to those three bodies. And the rays would pass to their center if the vitreous humor were not before that point, and therefore the vertex of the pyramid is of necessity cut off and the pyramid is shortened and truncated. But many objects can be seen besides those from which this pyramid comes; but not by means of rays reflected on the eye, since in that case they would recede from it; and therefore they must be seen by means of refracted rays. For let *ac* be the anterior glacialis and *bd* the cornea, and *feo* the pyramid of rays, then the ray *pn* comes from a visible object outside of the visual pyramid. This ray does not fall perpendicularly on the cornea, nor does it enter the opening of the uvea, or, if it were to enter, it would not pass to the glacialis, but would cross beyond to the side of the eye, to the point *l,* for example. Therefore, since the visual force exists only in the glacialis, *p* will not be seen by means of the ray *pl;* but since the cornea is

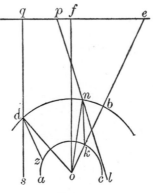

FIG. 57.

denser than the air, and the ray *pn* does not fall perpendicularly on the cornea, although it falls inside of the pyramid before it comes to the cornea, it must be refracted in its progress. Similarly if from a point outside of the pyramid of rays a ray falls on the cornea, and outside of the visual pyramid, as *qd,* it will not pass to *s,* but will be refracted at the point *d* in the surface of the cornea, between the straight path *ds* and the perpendicular *do,* to the point *z* in the glacialis. And so *p* will be seen between the straight path, which is *nl* and the perpendicular *no* to be drawn from the point of refraction, and the refracted ray will go to the point *k* in the glacialis, and in this way *p* will be seen by the refracted ray, namely, *pk.* And for this reason it is less clearly seen than objects that are in the base of the pyramid, since they are seen by straight and perpendicular rays. The same holds true in regard to the visible point *q,* as is evident from the figure.

Similarly whatever is seen by straight and reflected rays, is of necessity seen at the same time by means of refracted rays, and thus it is seen with greater certainty, because it is seen in two ways; and in this manner are the excellence and certainty of vision rendered complete. For point *p* is seen by the perpendicular ray *pg,* which goes to the center *o,* and nevertheless it is seen by means of *pe.* For *pa* does not go to *d,* but is refracted at point *a* of the cornea, between the straight path *ad,* and the perpendicular *ao,* to the point *e* in the surface of the glacialis.

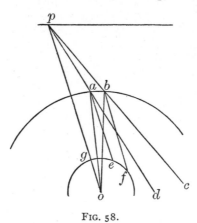

FIG. 58.

Moreover, *p* is seen not only by one refracted ray, but by an infinite number. For from *p* itself an infinite number of oblique rays can be drawn to the surface of the cornea, and each of these will be refracted and will fall into the opening, so that it will come to some point of the glacialis, as is evident in the case of the ray *pb;* for it does not pass to *c,* but is refracted at the point *b* of the cornea between the straight path, which is *bc,* and the perpendicular, which is *bo,* so that it passes to the point *f* of the glacialis; and the same is true of an infinite number of rays. Therefore vision is much improved and perfected by countless refracted rays of this kind, in which every visible object is seen, except that which is seen by the perpendicular ray. Moreover, we understand that anything that is opposite the opening can be seen by refraction and will not be seen by the straight rays, namely, when some obstacle of small breadth is interposed; as, for instance, a small straw, standing opposite the eye between it and some visible object, hinders the passage of the species of some part of it in a straight line. Then oblique rays will fall on the cornea from that object; since besides the one perpendicular which would fall if the obstacle were not there, an infinite number of oblique rays fall, as we have now seen. Therefore the object will be seen by refracted rays only and not by straight rays, as is evident by experience if one holds between his eye and some object a straw or a needle; and particularly can one try this with a candle.

<h2 style="text-align:center">CHAPTER II</h2>

Concerning the differences in the appearance of the position
of the image by refraction in planes.

WE must understand that vision by refraction is at the intersection of the visual ray with the cathetus, as has been stated in regard to reflection. But this can take place in various wonderful ways. To the end that we may understand all the different appearances of this kind, we must consider how differences of this kind occur in plane, concave, or convex bodies. The variation is also dependent on the position of the eye, whether it be in a rarer or denser medium and the object of vision conversely. If the eye is in a transparent rarer medium and between the eye and the object of vision there is a denser medium, like water of a plane

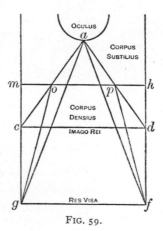

FIG. 59.

surface, or crystal, or glass, and other transparent substances of this kind, then the object appears far larger than it is; for it is seen under a larger angle and appears much nearer than if the medium were uniform. The proof of this fact is evident in this figure. For the visible object *f* will be seen at *d,* where the visual ray *ad* intersects the cathetus *fh;* and similarly *g* will appear at *c,* where the visual ray *ac* intersects the cathetus *gm,* and therefore the whole object *gf* will appear in the position *cd* nearer the eye, and will be seen under a larger angle, than if the body were one. For under the angle *oap* it will be seen through these two bodies, but under the angle *gaf* it would be seen through one medium without re-fraction. If, however, the eye is in a denser medium, and the object of vision is a rarer one, then the converse is true. For the object will appear smaller, not only because it will be seen under a smaller angle, but also because it will appear more remote. For *o* will be seen at *h,* and *f* at *k* beyond the object of vision, so that *of* will appear at *kh;* for the visual ray *ab* intersects at *h* the cathetus *hc,* and the visual ray *ad* intersects at *k* the cathetus *pfk;* and it is seen under a smaller angle than if it were seen through only one medium. For now the whole object is seen under the angle *dab* because of the refraction; and with-out refraction it is seen under the larger angle *fao.*

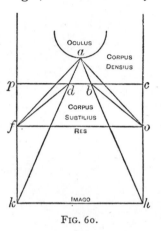

Fig. 60.

Chapter III

Concerning the diversity in the position of the image in the case of spherical surfaces.

If, however, the bodies are not plane by means of which the eye sees but spherical, there is a great diversity. For either the concavity or convexity of the body is toward the eye; if the concavity, then there are four cases. For there are two if the eye is in the rarer medium, and two if it is in the denser medium. If, therefore, the eye is in the rarer medium, and the concavity of the medium is toward the eye, the eye can be between the center of the medium and the object of vision, or the center be-

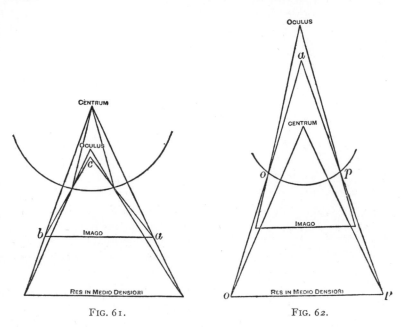

FIG. 61.   FIG. 62.

tween the eye and the object of vision. The force, moreover, would not proceed here from the center of a denser or rarer medium, because the center of both is the same, and the concavity of both is toward the eye, because the center of the containing and of the contained spheres is the same. I shall, therefore, state all these cases first, and then illustrate them in the figures; for it is necessary to do so owing to the brevity of the rules in each case and the large size of the figures. All these facts are made evident in these figures, which are here given in the order of the cases mentioned above.

If, then, the eye is in the rarer medium and the concavity is toward the eye, and the eye is between the center and the object of vision, the object will appear nearer than it is. For the visual angle will thus be greater than if straight lines should be drawn from the eye without refraction to the extremities of the object and under a larger angle, and yet the image is less than the object. If, however, the eye is in the rarer medium and the concavity is toward the eye and the center of the denser body is between the eye and the object, the object will still appear nearer. But the angle will be less and the image smaller. If, however, the eye is in the denser medium, and the concavity toward the

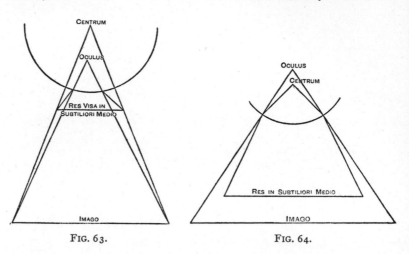

FIG. 63.   FIG. 64.

eye and the eye is between the center of the concave body and the object, then the object will appear more remote beyond its actual position, and under a smaller angle, and the image will be larger. But if the center of the concave body is between the

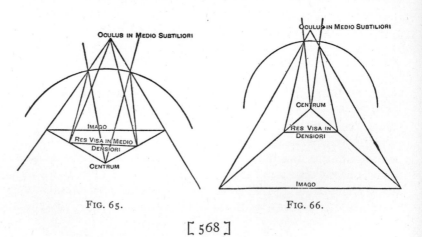

FIG. 65.   FIG. 66.

eye and the object of vision, the other conditions remaining the same, the object of vision will still appear more remote and under a larger angle, and the image will be greater.

If, however, the convexity of the body is toward the eye, there will similarly be four cases; for there are two if the eye is in the rarer medium, and two if the eye is in the denser medium. If, then, the eye is in the rarer medium and the convexity of the medium in which the object of vision is situated is toward the eye, then the object of vision can be between the center and the eye, or the center between the eye and the object of vision. If the object is between the eye and the center, the image will be nearer and larger and the angle greater. But the

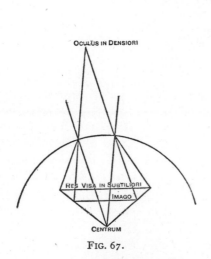

FIG. 67.

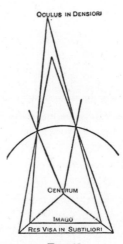

FIG. 68.

position of the image will be more remote. If, however, the eye is in the denser medium, and the object of vision is between the eye and the center, the image will be remoter and smaller, and will be seen under a smaller angle. But if the eye is in the denser medium, and the center is between the eye and the object, the image will be nearer and smaller and will be seen under a smaller angle, and the size of the angle under which the object is seen is perceived to be smaller than it would be if there were only one medium. And this is also the case when it contains that angle which the lines of the straight path make, and which end outside of it at another point; but it is shown to be greater, as is evident in the first figure, when the angle converges to another point within it, but then the angle which the lines of the straight path make is less than the angle under which the object is seen, and therefore the angle under which the object is seen is greater than if there were only one medium. For then is it seen under the angle *bca,* included by straight lines. And in the following figure it would be seen under the angle *oap,* included by straight lines, if there were only one medium, and thus under a greater angle than is the angle included by the broken lines under which the object is seen through the two media. We are to understand the matter in this way in all the other following figures.

Chapter IV

Concerning examples regarding refractions of this kind.

SINCE these figures in regard to the mode of vision by refraction have been described, examples can be given in objects of vision. First, in regard to a rod, which seems broken when one part is in the air and the other part in the water and the eye is in the air. For on this point contention is common among philosophers, when they dispute on any matter, nor is the question ever solved by them, since they are ignorant of this third part of Perspective. Now since the eye is in the same medium as the upper part of the rod, the eye will see it by direct vision, just as it is. But since the eye is in a rarer medium with respect to the lower part of the rod, which is in the water, the first rule given above in regard to a plane medium, or the fifth in regard to the denser medium in which the object is situated, whose convex surface is toward the eye, is applicable here. Nor is the force of which we may speak present in the waters to which we are accustomed, namely, of rivers and ditches, since although water has naturally a convex surface, wherever it is, owing to its constant tendency to flow to a lower position, as has been stated above, waters familiar to us in streams and fountains and other hollows have as far as regards our sense the upper surface plane. And however we may speak, the object of vision in the water must appear nearer the eye than is its true position,

and larger, as is shown in both figures. Therefore the part of
the rod which is in the water will not appear to the sight as
continuous and in a straight line with the other part, but nearer
the eye, and therefore the rod of necessity must appear of a
curved and angular shape, as if it had been broken on entering
the water, as shown in the figure. For let *fb* be the rod, *a* the
eye, and *hm* the surface of the water; *b* will send its species to
c, but will not pass to *o* by
a straight path, but will be
refracted in the rarer medium to *a,* so that the
straight path is between
the refracted ray and the
perpendicular drawn from
the point of refraction,
namely, *gc.* But the object
appears at the intersection
of the visual ray with the
cathetus. The cathetus is
bdp, and the visual ray *ac*
intersects at the point *d* of
the cathetus. Therefore *b,*
the extremity of the rod
will be seen at *d,* and in

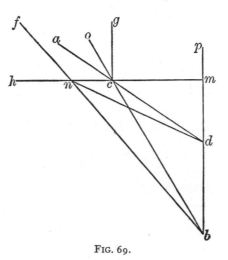

Fig. 69.

the same way each particle of the section that is in the water will
be seen in the straight line in which *d* itself lies. Therefore the
whole portion that is in the water will appear in the line *nd.*
Wherefore the whole rod will be seen in the line *fnd,* and therefore in the curved line with an angle at *n,* and thus the rod will
appear to be broken. Moreover, since a man can see in the water,
if he had the required skill to stay under the water, he could
see the rod broken at the surface of the air, just as he now sees
it in the water because of the second rule with its figure regarding a plane body, or because of the third rule with its
figure, where the eye is in the denser medium whose concavity
is toward the eye.

There is a similar occurrence if an object is placed in a vessel
and the observer steps backward until it is no longer seen; the
immersed object will be visible again at the same distance between it and the observer, if water is poured in, as is stated at

the beginning of the book on Mirrors. Any one can try this, although it seems wonderful or rather not true to those unacquainted with the fact. The reason for this is evident from the rules given, namely, the first on plane surfaces and the fifth on concave surfaces. For since the eye is in the rarer medium and the object in the denser, the object must appear nearer and more elevated toward the eye where the intersection of the visual ray with the cathetus occurs, and the image will appear larger. Wherefore it will seem to the sight that the object placed in the vessel is raised from the bottom of the vessel to the surface of the water. Nor is another drawing required here than the one made in the places mentioned above, and therefore that one suffices.

If, then, we view the sun or moon and stars at their rising and setting through aqueous vapors, as we often do in summer and in autumn, we see those luminaries of unusual size, as any one experiences. But the reason of such a phenomenon is found in the first rule with its figure, where the eye is in the rarer medium and the object is in the denser, whose concavity is toward the eye, and the eye is between the center and the object of vision. For vapors of this kind are spherical and concentric with the world, because they recede equally from the center; and therefore their concavity will be toward the eye, and the eye will be between them and their center, which is the center of the world. Therefore, as we have shown from that drawing, the image of the object is nearer and is seen under a larger angle, and therefore the object appears larger and nearer.

If the objection is raised that the image is smaller than the object, for which reason it should appear smaller; we must reply that the larger size of the angle together with the apparent nearness is the prevailing factor in this matter. For a nearer object, other things being equal, appears more clearly in respect to its size, and particularly so when it is seen under a larger angle. If again it be said that the rays of the stars find vapors and clouds not only at the horizon and near it, but also toward the meridian and at the meridian, but the sun when it is near the meridian or at the meridian does not appear of unusual size; therefore it should not near its rising and setting.* Probably some trained in the science of perspective have judged that

* This sentence is incomplete in the text.

vapors are not the cause of this phenomenon, owing to this objection. But they have been deceived, because they cannot give another reason; for that reason which was given above in regard to the size of the stars at the horizon is applicable at all times, but this appearance of size is temporary, not constant, and therefore has a temporary cause. Moreover, we see, when the air is serene and dry in the east or west lacking vapors, that the stars have their accustomed magnitudes; but when the air is charged with vapors the appearance of unusual size occurs at this time. It is therefore evident that vapors are the cause. But the objection is removed by the fact that the rays of the stars near their rising and setting fall entirely at oblique angles and therefore are refracted at the surface of the air according to the tenor of the rule mentioned. But when the star approaches the meridian the rays approach right angles in their direction, for which reason they are not so much refracted as when the star is at its rising. If it be objected that all rays of planets are refracted about the tropic of Cancer, as has been previously explained, because they do not fall to the center of the world, but toward the horizon, the fact must be conceded. But, however, they are far less refracted and they approach nearer to the perpendicular when the star is near the meridian; and therefore, although at that time it appears of larger size owing to vapors, it is not, however, of the unusual size of which we are here speaking. But the larger size of the angle of refraction and the wider divergence from the direct path cause the object to appear larger and nearer.

If, however, we consider the stars and the media according to their natural arrangement, apart from vapors and the remaining reason of constant application, concerning which mention was made above, the third rule in regard to spherical bodies applies, whose convexity is toward the eye and the eye is in the denser medium, since it is in an elemental medium, and the object is in a rarer medium, namely, in a celestial medium, and the eye is between the center and the object of vision. The stars will appear smaller than they are and than they would appear if there were only one medium, since they are seen under a smaller angle, and thus there will be an error of vision in regard to the stars. If it be said that the image is far larger than the object, and therefore it will appear larger: again if it be said that the position of the image is far beyond the object, and therefore it will appear to be more distant, and therefore objects will appear to be larger, for we have shown above that things which seem to be more distant appear larger; we must reply to the first objection that the size of the angle is the prevailing factor in these appearances. Therefore since the star is seen under a smaller angle, the magnitude of the image offers no difficulty. To the second objection we reply that because of the transparency of the clear media, intervening bodies are not perceived, and therefore the distance of the image is not perceived, because from too remote a point, as has been explained previously, distance is not judged by the sight unless intervening objects are perceived. Therefore although the position of the image is more remote, and would appear here to the vision through an error, yet as a matter of fact the vision does not perceive this remoteness, and therefore the object should not appear large on this account.

If a man looks at letters or other small objects through the medium of a crystal or of glass or of some other transparent body placed above the letters, and it is the smaller part of a sphere whose convexity is toward the eye, and the eye is in the air, he will see the letters much better and they will appear larger to him. For in accordance with the truth of the fifth rule regarding a spherical medium beneath which is the object or on this side is its center, and whose convexity is toward the eye, all conditions are favorable for magnification, since the angle is larger under which the object is seen, and the image is larger, and the position of the image is nearer, since the object is between the eye and the center. Therefore this instrument is useful to the aged and to those with weak eyes. For they can see a letter, no matter how small, sufficiently enlarged. If, however, the larger portion of a sphere or the half of it is used, then according to the sixth rule the angle is larger, and the image is larger, but it is more remote, because the position of the image is beyond the object, since the center of the sphere is between the eye and the object of vision. Therefore this instrument is not so powerful as it would be if it were the smaller portion of a sphere. Moreover, instruments of crystalline bodies of plane surface, according to the first rule on plane surfaces, and instruments of concave spherical bodies, according to the first and

Optical Science

second rules on spherical surfaces, can produce this same effect. But among all these instruments the smaller portion of a sphere whose convexity is toward the eye is the best magnifier, for the three reasons effective at the same time, as I have stated.

That a candle appears larger at a distance than near at hand, provided that the distance is not too great, is due to the fact that it is seen not only by direct, but also by refracted rays, and the vision does not perceive the refraction, and for this reason it judges that it sees by means of straight lines where the visual ray intersects the cathetus drawn from the object. Hence the object of vision seems for this reason to be dilated to *gr*, because the points at its extremities are seen not only by means of the ray *au*, and by another ray *cp*, but also by the ray *ao* refracted at the point *b* on the surface of the eye and by the ray *cd* refracted at the point *m*, and *ob*, the visual ray, intersects at the point *g* the cathetus *ca*, and the refracted ray *dm* intersects at the point *r* the cathetus *ac*, and therefore the diameter of the object of vision appears to be *rg*, and considerably larger than *ac*. Another reason, particularly in the case of weak and careless vision, might

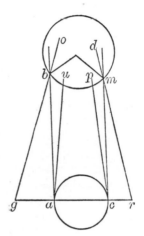

FIG. 70.

be the fact that the species near the object is strong, and therefore naturally fitted to terminate weak and careless vision, and for this reason the size of the object seems greater in accordance with the extent of space in which the species appears sensible. For this frequently happens to weak eyes, to infirm people, to those intoxicated, and to those who look at the object of vision in a negligent and indifferent manner. Other examples can be given, in which much scientific knowledge is displayed just as in these; but since the present discussion is more in the nature of a plea than of a formal treatise, those now given must suffice.

LAST DISTINCTION

Concerning the relation of perspective to theology and to practical applications, in four chapters.

CHAPTER I

WE have now spoken of the principles of perspective as far as they are necessary for scientific knowledge and for the understanding of their practical applications. I wish now in conclusion to intimate how this science possesses an ineffable usefulness in regard to divine truth. First we must bear in mind that, since this science attests natural phenomena, as is evident by what has been said, and consequently it is clear that it elucidates and explains the other sciences, this science must be serviceable to divine truth, because it requires a knowledge of the sciences and of temporal matters. Moreover, since divine truth unrestrictedly considered must be understood and expounded, and since it is ordained for the direction of this world, this science of perspective is necessary in both ways. For in God's Scripture nothing is so much enlarged upon as those things that pertain to the eye and to vision, as is evident to one who reads the Scripture through; and therefore nothing is more necessary for the natural and spiritual meaning than definite knowledge of this science. This fact I wish merely to intimate in passing, since it is not necessary to delay at this point on many examples of this kind, because when the truth of the matters set forth in Scripture is known it is very easy for every theologian to draw from them profitably their spiritual meaning. For when it is said, "Guard us, Lord, as the pupil of thine eye," it is impossible to know God's meaning in this prayer unless one first considers how the guarding of the eye is effected, so that God deems it right to guard us according to this similitude. For when something is stated as an example and similitude, that which is exemplified cannot be understood unless the meaning of the example is also understood. As, for example, when the Lord says, "Be wise as serpents," the Lord intended that his disciples should consider the qualities of the serpent in which its wisdom consists, and the nature of the dove in which the sweetness of simplicity is found.

[576]

Optical Science

But we shall not understand the guarding of the pupil except through the science of perspective. For the pupil is the anterior glacialis, which is supported by two humors in front of it and behind it; and is contained in one web and three coats, and receives moreover a constant and unrestricted influx of spirits and forces from the plenteous source of supply in the optic commissure; and thus it requires seven things for its protection. This, then, is the literal exposition, to which the Psalmist wishes the spiritual to be likened when he prays for the guarding of the spiritual pupil, that is, of the soul; for the perfect guardianship of which seven things are necessary, namely, virtue, gift, beatitude, spiritual sense, fruits, and revelation according to the states of rapture, and in addition the continual influx of the gifts of grace from the plenitude of the Crucified. But the principal virtues are seven, namely, three theological, charity, faith, and hope, and four cardinal, justice, fortitude, temperance, and wisdom; by means of which our spiritual pupil must be guarded. Moreover, the gifts of the Holy Spirit are seven, and the petitions of the Lord's prayer are confined to seven. But the beatitudes are eight, as is evident from the fifth chapter of Matthew, and therefore we shall add to the seven guardians of the bodily pupil as an eighth that of the eyelashes, so that as many bodily defenders may correspond to the eight spiritual ones. Now the spiritual senses are five, and those things that are directly allotted to the protection of the pupil are five, namely, the web, the albugineous humor, and the three coats. For the vitreous humor can in this view of the subject be understood with the pupil, because it is continuous with the anterior glacialis in the weblike structure. And without question the whole is called the pupil, although more particularly the anterior glacialis. Or the five may be designated thus, cross, humor, web, coat, and eyelash. For these five are the essential guardians, although they are divided in some manner into branches, as are the humor and the coat. But there are twelve fruits, as the Apostle enumerates in the fifth chapter of the Epistle to the Galatians, and therefore if we take the pupil strictly as the anterior glacialis, and consider all things remote as well as near it that can be found for its protection, we shall find twelve, namely, the eight mentioned above, and the eyelids and the eyebrows, which have special function in the protection of the eye, as was noted above. And since the visual nerves descend from the anterior part of the brain, in which are located the common sense and the imagination, from which the forces and spirit flow to the vision, nor is the act of vision completed until the visual species reaches these two, as was explained above, there will be in general twelve things allotted to the protection of the bodily pupil, just as there are twelve fruits in the protection of the spiritual eye. And we have said that there are required for vision not only internal reception, but external transmission, and coöperation by its own force and species: similarly the spiritual vision requires not only that the soul should receive from without, namely, from God, graces and virtues, but that it should coöperate through its own virtue. For the exercise and agreement of our free will are required together with the grace of God to the end that we may see and secure the state of salvation.

CHAPTER II

EIGHT conditions are also required for vision; namely, light, distance, and the others already noted, and this is paralleled exactly in the spiritual vision by the eight beatitudes. But this is also evident in another way; for conditions similar to these eight are required for spiritual vision. For just as we see nothing corporeally without corporeal light, so is it impossible for us to see anything spiritually without the spiritual light of the divine grace. And just as a moderate distance is required for vision, so that a body is not visible if it is too far off or too near, the same condition is required for spiritual vision. For remoteness from God through unbelief and a multitude of sins takes away spiritual sight, and so also do an excessive presumption of intimacy with God and scrutiny of his majesty. But those who with moderation approach his feet exclaiming with the apostle, "O depth of the riches of God's wisdom and knowledge, how incomprehensible are his judgments, and how unsearchable are his ways," will learn from his teaching according to the prophet, and "will go gradually from strength to strength, until the God of Gods appears in Sion." And so in regard to the other six conditions it is easily evident to one considering the subject how their similitudes coöperate in the spiritual vision; and therefore I need not dwell upon them individually.

Moreover, since vision is threefold, namely, by sense alone, by memory [*scientia*], and by reasoning, similarly it is necessary for man to have threefold vision. For by sense alone we perceive few things and imperfectly, as, for example, light and color, and we have this perception weakly, namely, whether these objects of vision exist or which they are; but by memory we perceive of what kind and quality they are, whether the light is that of the sun or of the moon, whether the color is white or black. But by reasoning we perceive all that pertains to light and color in accordance with all of the twenty common sensibles. Therefore the first kind of perception is weak, the second is more perfect, and the third is the most perfect. The conditions are similar in spiritual vision; for what a man knows by his own sense alone is little, because he lacks the double perception in addition to this, namely, that acquired through teachers from youth to old age. For we can always learn through those wiser than we are. And therefore we lack the third kind of perception, which comes through divine illumination.

But in another fashion is vision threefold; namely, direct, refracted, and reflected. The first is more perfect than the others, the second is less certain, and the third the least certain. For this reason we have shown above that action along the straight line is the most potent, and that refraction is less weak than reflection. These laws hold in vision as well as in other things; and they must be effective in spiritual vision as well as in our physical vision. A comparison can be drawn here in many ways; for directness of vision belongs to God; deviation from the straight line through refraction, which is weaker, befits the angelic nature; reflected vision, which is weaker, may be assigned to man. For just as a mirror because of its suitability aids vision, and gives to the species an opportunity of multiplying itself to the eye, so that vision may be effected, so does the body animated by the sensitive soul by its own nature and fitness aid the intellectual soul in its perception, and give it perception in those matters in which the intellect is dependent on the corporeal sense. Therefore the perception of man, however perfect it may be, is weaker than the angelic perception for this reason, and rightly may be called a mirrored perception because of the similitude stated. I am speaking of the natural man with the exception of the Blessed Virgin, and in accordance with the common state of man and of angel. Man has a threefold vision; one perfect, which will come in a state of glory after the resurrection; the second in the soul separated from the body in heaven until the resurrection, which is weaker; the third in this life, which is the weakest, and this is correctly said to be by reflection. As the apostle says, "We now see by means of a glass darkly, but in glory face to face," and after the resurrection in perfect directness, and before it in a deviation from that directness of vision in our soul. For this reason the soul will not enjoy perfect vision until it is united to its own body, just as it will not possess other blessings in full measure before that time, as theologians are well aware, and because there is a certain natural desire in the soul for its own body, which cannot be realized except by the resurrection. Moreover, in our present state is vision threefold, namely, direct in those that are perfect; refracted in those that are imperfect; and in the evil and in those who neglect the commandments of God by reflection, according to the Apostle James; for it is compared to a man beholding his natural face in a glass.

CHAPTER III

As the wisdom of God is ordained for the direction of the universe, so is this science of vision evidently and beneficially ordained for its beauty. I shall give some examples both of refraction and reflection. For by reflection one thing appears to be many and infinite in number; for in this way sometimes many suns and moons are seen in the sky, as Pliny states in the Natural History. This does not happen except when the vapor has been arranged like a mirror and is complex and in a different position. And what nature can do, art perfecting nature can accomplish in greater measure. Hence mirrors can be so made and placed in such a position and arranged, that a single object of vision can be multiplied at will. Therefore one man will appear many, and a single army will appear to be several. The principles relating to this phenomenon have already been touched upon, one of which concerns the broken mirror, whose parts are placed in different positions and produce different images according to their number. The other principle concerns the case of the water and the mirror, from both of which a different image is reflected. If, therefore, as many mirrors as we wish should be arranged in both these ways it is evident that a single object will appear in as many images as we wish, and thus to the advantage of the state images of this kind might profitably be produced. They might also be used against unbelievers to inspire terror. Moreover, if one knew that the air is dense, so that reflection could be obtained from it, he might produce many unusual appearances of this kind. In this way we believe that demons show camps and armies and many wonders to men; and by reflected vision all things hidden in secret places in cities, armies, and the like can be brought to light. For the dragon, which poisons both animals and men and corrupts them with its breath, was detected in its lair by the philosopher Socrates, as the histories bear witness.

Similarly mirrors might be erected on an elevation opposite hostile cities and armies, so that all that was being done by the enemy might be visible. This can be done at any distance we desire, since, according to the book on Mirrors, one and the same object can be seen by means of as many mirrors as we wish, if they are placed in the manner required. Therefore they can be placed more closely and more remotely, so that we might see an object as far off as we pleased. For in this way Julius Caesar, when he wished to subdue England, is said to have erected very large mirrors, in order that he might see in advance from the shore of Gaul the arrangement of the cities and camps of England. Mirrors, moreover, can be so arranged that as many objects as we desire may be visible and all that is in the house or in the street; and any one looking at these objects will see them as they really are, and when he hastens to the places where they appear, he will find nothing. For the mirrors will be concealed in such a manner with respect to the objects, that the positions of the images are in view, and the images appear in the air at the intersection of the visual rays with the catheti, and therefore those looking at them would run up to the places where they appear, and would judge that the objects are there when there is in reality nothing except an image. And thus in accordance with such principles as have now been touched upon in regard to reflection and in accordance with similar ones, not only could results be attained advantageous to our friends and terrible for our enemies, but very great comforts can come to us from philosophy, so that every deceit of jesters may be dimmed by the beauty of the wonders of science, and men may rejoice in the truth, banishing far from them the tricks of the magicians.

Chapter IV

THE wonders of refracted vision are still greater; for it is easily shown by the rules stated above that very large objects can be made to appear very small, and the reverse, and very distant objects will seem very close at hand, and conversely. For we can so shape transparent bodies, and arrange them in such a way with respect to our sight and objects of vision, that the rays will be refracted and bent in any direction we desire, and under any angle we wish we shall see the object near or at a distance. Thus from an incredible distance we might read the smallest letters and number grains of dust and sand owing to the magnitude of the angle under which we viewed them, and very large bodies close to us we might scarcely see because of the smallness of the angle under which we saw them, for distance in such vision is not a factor except by accident, but the size of the angle is. In this way a child might appear a giant, and a man a mountain. He might appear of any size whatever, as we might see a man under as large an angle as we see a mountain, and close as we wish. Thus a small army might appear very large, and situated at a distance might appear close at hand, and the reverse. So also we might cause the sun, moon, and stars in appearance to descend here below, and similarly to appear above the heads of our enemies, and we might cause many similar phenomena, so that the mind of a man ignorant of the truth could not endure them.

PART SIX OF THIS PLEA

It is also the sixth part of the Opus Majus, on Experimental Science.

CHAPTER I

HAVING laid down fundamental principles of the wisdom of the Latins so far as they are found in language, mathematics, and optics, I now wish to unfold the principles of experimental science, since without experience nothing can be sufficiently known. For there are two modes of acquiring knowledge, namely, by reasoning and experience. Reasoning draws a conclusion and makes us grant the conclusion, but does not make the conclusion certain, nor does it remove doubt so that the mind may rest on the intuition of truth, unless the mind discovers it by the path of experience; since many have the arguments relating to what can be known, but because they lack experience they neglect the arguments, and neither avoid what is harmful nor follow what is good. For if a man who has never seen fire should prove by adequate reasoning that fire burns and injures things and destroys them, his mind would not be satisfied thereby, nor would he avoid fire, until he placed his hand or some combustible substance in the fire, so that he might prove by experience that which reasoning taught. But when he has had actual experience of combustion his mind is made certain and rests in the full light of truth. Therefore reasoning does not suffice, but experience does.

This is also evident in mathematics, where proof is most convincing. But the mind of one who has the most convincing proof in regard to the equilateral triangle will never cleave to the conclusion without experience, nor will he heed it, but will disregard it until experience is offered him by the intersection of two circles, from either intersection of which two lines may be drawn to the extremities of the given line; but then the man accepts the conclusion without any question. Aristotle's statement, then, that proof is reasoning that causes us to know is to be understood with the proviso that the proof is accompanied by its appropriate experience, and is not to be understood of the bare proof. His statement also in the first book of the Metaphysics that those who understand the reason and the cause are wiser than those who have empiric knowledge of a fact, is spoken of such as know only the bare truth without the cause. But I am here speaking of the man who knows the reason and the cause through experience. These men are perfect in their wisdom, as Aristotle maintains in the sixth book of the Ethics, whose simple statements must be accepted as if they offered proof, as he states in the same place.

He therefore who wishes to rejoice without doubt in regard to the truths underlying phenomena must know how to devote himself to experiment. For authors write many statements, and people believe them through reasoning which they formulate without experience. Their reasoning is wholly false. For it is generally believed that the diamond cannot be broken except by goat's blood, and philosophers and theologians misuse this idea. But fracture by means of blood of this kind has never been verified, although the effort has been made; and without that blood it can be broken easily. For I have seen this with my own eyes, and this is necessary, because gems cannot be carved except by fragments of this stone. Similarly it is generally believed that the castors employed by physicians are the testicles of the male animal. But this is not true, because the beaver has these under its breast, and both the male and female produce testicles of this kind. Besides these castors the male beaver has its testicles in their natural place; and therefore what is subjoined is a dreadful lie, namely, that when the hunters pursue the beaver, he himself knowing what they are seeking cuts out with his teeth these glands. Moreover, it is generally believed that hot water freezes more quickly than cold water in vessels, and the argument in support of this is advanced that contrary is excited by contrary, just like enemies meeting each other. But it is certain that cold water freezes more quickly for any one who makes the experiment. People attribute this to Aristotle in the second book of the Meteorologics; but he certainly does not make this statement, but he does make one like it, by which they have been deceived, namely, that if cold water and hot water are poured on a cold place, as upon ice, the hot water freezes more quickly, and this is true. But if hot water and cold are placed in two vessels, the cold will freeze more quickly. Therefore all things must be verified by experience.

Experimental Science

But experience is of two kinds; one is gained through our external senses, and in this way we gain our experience of those things that are in the heavens by instruments made for this purpose, and of those things here below by means attested by our vision. Things that do not belong in our part of the world we know through other scientists who have had experience of them. As, for example, Aristotle on the authority of Alexander sent two thousand men through different parts of the world to gain experimental knowledge of all things that are on the surface of the earth, as Pliny bears witness in his Natural History. This experience is both human and philosophical, as far as man can act in accordance with the grace given him; but this experience does not suffice him, because it does not give full attestation in regard to things corporeal owing to its difficulty, and does not touch at all on things spiritual. It is necessary, therefore, that the intellect of man should be otherwise aided, and for this reason the holy patriarchs and prophets, who first gave sciences to the world, received illumination within and were not dependent on sense alone. The same is true of many believers since the time of Christ. For the grace of faith illuminates greatly, as also do divine inspirations, not only in things spiritual, but in things corporeal and in the sciences of philosophy; as Ptolemy states in the Centilogium, namely, that there are two roads by which we arrive at the knowledge of facts, one through the experience of philosophy, the other through divine inspiration, which is far the better way, as he says.

Moreover, there are seven stages of this internal knowledge, the first of which is reached through illuminations relating purely to the sciences. The second consists in the virtues. For the evil man is ignorant, as Aristotle says in the second book of the Ethics. Moreover, Algazel says in his Logic that the soul disfigured by sins is like a rusty mirror, in which the species of objects cannot be seen clearly; but the soul adorned with virtues is like a well-polished mirror, in which the forms of objects are clearly seen. For this reason true philosophers have labored more in morals for the honor of virtue, concluding in their own case that they cannot perceive the causes of things unless they have souls free from sins. Such is the statement of Augustine in regard to Socrates in the eighth book of the City of God, chapter III. Wherefore the Scripture says, "in a malevolent soul, etc." For it is not possible that the soul should rest in the light of truth while it is stained with sins, but like a parrot or magpie it will repeat the words of another which it has learned by long practice. The proof of this is that the beauty of truth known in its splendor attracts men to the love of it, but the proof of love is the display of a work of love. Therefore he who acts contrary to the truth must necessarily be ignorant of it, although he may know how to compose very elegant phrases, and quote the opinions of other people, like an animal that imitates the words of human beings, and like an ape that relies on the aid of men to perform its part, although it does not understand their reason. Virtue, therefore, clarifies the mind, so that a man comprehends more easily not only moral but scientific truths. I have proved this carefully in the case of many pure young men, who because of innocency of soul have attained greater proficiency than can be stated, when they have had sane advice in regard to their study. Of this number is the bearer of this present treatise, whose fundamental knowledge very few of the Latins have acquired. For since he is quite young, about twenty years of age, and very poor, nor has he been able to have teachers, nor has he spent one year in learning his great store of knowledge, nor is he a man of great genius nor of a very retentive memory, there can be no other cause except the grace of God, which owing to the purity of his soul has granted to him those things that it has as a rule refused to show to all other students. For as a spotless virgin he has departed from me, nor have I found in him any kind of mortal sin, although I have examined him carefully, and he has, therefore, a soul so bright and clear that with very little instruction he has learned more than can be estimated. And I have striven to aid in bringing it about that these two young men should be useful vessels in God's Church, to the end that they may reform by the grace of God the whole course of study of the Latins.

The third stage consists in the seven gifts of the Holy Spirit, which Isaiah enumerates. The fourth consists in the beatitudes, which the Lord defines in the Gospels. The fifth consists in the spiritual senses. The sixth consists in fruits, of which is the peace of God which passes all understanding. The seventh consists in raptures and their states according to the different ways in which people are caught up to see many things of which it is not lawful for a man to speak. And he who has had diligent training in these experiences or in several of them is able to assure himself and others not only in regard to things spiritual, but also in regard to all human sciences. Therefore since all the divisions of speculative philosophy proceed by arguments, which are either based on a point from authority or on the other points of argumentation except this division which I am now examining, we find necessary the science that is called experimental. I wish to explain it, as it is useful not only to philosophy, but to the knowledge of God, and for the direction of the whole world; just as in the preceding divisions I showed the relationship of the languages and sciences to their end, which is the divine wisdom by which all things are disposed.

Chapter II

Since this Experimental Science is wholly unknown to the rank and file of students, I am therefore unable to convince people of its utility unless at the same time I disclose its excellence and its proper signification. This science alone, therefore, knows how to test perfectly what can be done by nature, what by the effort of art, what by trickery, what the incantations, conjurations, invocations, deprecations, sacrifices, that belong to magic, mean and dream of, and what is in them, so that all falsity may be removed and the truth alone of art and nature may be retained. This science alone teaches us how to view the mad acts of magicians, that they may be not ratified but shunned, just as logic considers sophistical reasoning.

This science has three leading characteristics with respect to other sciences. The first is that it investigates by experiment the notable conclusions of all those sciences. For the other sciences know how to discover their principles by experiments, but their conclusions are reached by reasoning drawn from the principles discovered. But if they should have a particular and complete experience of their own conclusions, they must have it with the aid of this noble science. For it is true that mathematics has general experiments as regards its conclusions in its figures and calculations, which also are applied to all sciences and to this kind of experiment, because no science can be known without mathematics. But if we give our attention to particular and complete experiments and such as are attested wholly by the proper method, we must employ the principles of this science which is called experimental. I give as an example the rainbow and phenomena connected with it, of which nature are the circle around the sun and the stars, the streak [*virga*] also lying at the side of the sun or of a star, which is apparent to the eye in a straight line, and is called by Aristotle in the third book of the Meteorologics a perpendicular, but by Seneca a streak, and the circle is called a corona, phenomena which frequently have the colors of the rainbow. The natural philosopher discusses these phenomena, and the writer on Perspective has much to add pertaining to the mode of vision that is necessary in this case. But neither Aristotle nor Avicenna in their Natural Histories has given us a knowledge of phenomena of this kind, nor has Seneca, who composed a special book on them. But Experimental Science attests them.

Let the experimenter first, then, examine visible objects, in order that he may find colors arranged as in the phenomena mentioned above and also the same figure. For let him take hexagonal stones from Ireland or from India, which are called rainbows in Solinus on the Wonders of the World, and let him hold these in a solar ray falling through the window, so that he may find all the colors of the rainbow, arranged as in it, in the shadow near the ray. And further let the same experimenter turn to a somewhat dark place and apply the stone to one of his eyes which is almost closed, and he will see the colors of the rainbow clearly arranged just as in the bow. And since many employing these stones think that the phenomenon is due to the special virtue of those stones and to their hexagonal shape, therefore let the experimenter proceed further, and he will find this same peculiarity in crystalline stones correctly shaped, and in other transparent stones. Moreover, he will find this not only in white stones like the Irish crystals, but also in black ones, as is evident in the dark crystal and in all stones of similar transparency. He will find it besides in crystals of a shape differing from the hexagonal, provided they have a roughened surface, like the Irish crystals, neither altogether smooth, nor rougher than they are. Nature produces some that have surfaces like the

ROGER BACON

From a Fifteenth Century Manuscript in the Bodleian Library

Irish crystals. For a difference in the corrugations causes a difference in the colors. And further let him observe rowers, and in the drops falling from the raised oars he finds the same colors when the solar rays penetrate drops of this kind. The same phenomenon is seen in water falling from the wheels of a mill; and likewise when one sees on a summer's morning the drops of dew on the grass in meadow or field, he will observe the colors. Likewise when it is raining, if he stands in a dark place and the rays beyond it pass through the falling rain, the colors will appear in the shadow near by; and frequently at night colors appear around a candle. Moreover, if a man in summer, when he rises from sleep and has his eyes only partly open, suddenly looks at a hole through which a ray of the sun enters, he will see colors. Moreover, if seated beyond the sun he draws his cap beyond his eyes, he will see colors; and similarly if he closes an eye the same thing happens under the shade of the eyebrows; and again the same phenomenon appears through a glass vessel filled with water and placed in the sun's rays. Or similarly if one having water in his mouth sprinkles it vigorously into the rays and stands at the side of the rays. So, too, if rays in the required position pass through an oil lamp hanging in the air so that the light falls on the surface of the oil, colors will be produced. Thus in an infinite number of ways colors of this kind appear, which the diligent experimenter knows how to discover.

Chapter III

In a similar way also he will be able to test the shape in which the colors are disposed. For by means of the crystalline stone and substances of this kind he will find the shape straight. By means of the eyelids and eyebrows and by many other means, and also by means of holes in rags, he will discover whole circles colored. Similarly in a place where the dewfall is plentiful and sufficient to take the whole circle, and if the place where the circle of the rainbow should be is dark proportionally, because the bow does not appear in the light part, then the circle will be complete. Similarly whole circles appear frequently around candles, as Aristotle states and we ourselves experience.

server. But the altitude commonly taken of an object is said to be the arc of the circle of the altitude intercepted between the elevated object and the horizon, yet, strictly speaking, if the altitude of an object is taken, it is the arc of the circle of the altitude between the object and the visual ray; because the eye is not at the center of the horizon, but is above the center in the axis of the horizon; and therefore objects that are in the air and in the moon are considered according to an altitude of this kind. For they have a difference in aspect because they are near the earth, but the sun and the other remoter bodies are not affected in this way, owing to their great distance. For the amount of elevation of the observer has no sensible difference in regard to the remoteness of those bodies, but it bears a considerable relationship to those that are visible in the air, like comets and rainbows. From these statements, then, it is evident that the altitude of the rainbow, taken strictly, is the arc of its circle of altitude intercepted between the summit of the bow and the visual ray parallel to the horizon, which must be known because of what follows.

The experimenter, therefore, taking the altitude of the sun and of the rainbow above the horizon will find that the final altitude at which the rainbow can appear above the horizon is 42 degrees, and this is the maximum elevation of the rainbow. This elevation contains the arc between the summit of the bow and the visual ray, and this is its altitude, strictly speaking, although besides this there is the arc, which is between the ray and the limit of the horizon, or the limits of the circle concentric with the horizon, through which the circle of the altitude of the bow passes. And the rainbow reaches this maximum elevation when the sun is on the horizon, namely, at sunrise or sunset; and also when it is near sunrise and sunset below the horizon, not up to the end of the evening twilight, nor up to the beginning of the morning twilight, but near sunrise and sunset, as has been said. Then if moisture is ready in advance higher in the clouds, the gibbosity of the rainbow will appear, although the sun is too far below the horizon, since his rays can reach vapors high in the air, although they cannot reach vapors near the horizon. The experimenter, moreover, knows how to make the test, because when the sun is at an altitude of 42 degrees the rainbow does not appear in the sky, except that a small portion of its blue gibbosity can appear near the horizon, if moisture is already present there. When the sun rises higher, the rainbow can nowhere appear. Therefore Aristotle and Seneca state that in summer in the heat of the day the rainbow does not appear. The reason for this is because at the latitude of Paris the altitude of the sun at noon of the equinox is 41 degrees and 12 minutes, the sun at that time being at almost such an altitude that the rainbow cannot appear, and therefore a little later it must be elevated so much higher that at noon it is more than 42 degrees on the circle of altitude above the horizon, and therefore in the heat of summer the rainbow does not occur at noon until the sun descends to an altitude less than 42 degrees.

CHAPTER V

AFTER, therefore, the experimenter discovers this, he must then by his experiments learn the size and shape of the rainbow, and for this purpose he conceives a cone of which the apex is at the eye and the base is the circle of the bow, the portion of which appears colored. The axis of the cone is the line mentioned above, which passes through the center of the eye and the center of the sun and the center of the bow to the nadir of the sun. The base of this cone is elevated and depressed according to the elevation and depression of the sun, as we have stated in regard to that line, and as it is depressed it sinks sometimes to the earth, cutting it and cut by it. This cone can be conceived of as not cutting the earth but as wholly elevated above the horizon and its whole base above the horizon, and this diversity occurs in accordance with the shortness and length of the cones. For it can be of such short length that its base is above the horizon, and then the whole circle can appear colored, as is the case in sprays of the required kind if they are near, just as I have explained in falling rain and dew, when water is sprinkled by anybody in the required manner, and when the water falls from a high place. When, however, the cones are extended so far that they touch the earth, the limit is reached for the appearance of the circle as a whole.

If, however, they are lengthened to such an extent that the base is cut by the earth, then according to the size of the section of the base a portion of the colored circle will appear. And in the first place a larger portion can appear when less of the base of the cone is cut; and then if half of the circle is cut, the other half will appear; and a smaller portion, if more is cut. Thus as more or less is cut, and the cone lengthened, a larger or smaller portion will appear. Moreover, the cone can be so extended that nothing appears; and thus according to the length and shortness of the cones are the bases larger or smaller, and the colored circles larger or smaller, and larger or smaller portions cut off, and the portions belong to larger or smaller circles, as is now evident to any one considering the subject. This appearance of circles and of portions of them is considered with reference to the shortness and the length of the cone, as I have said, although we do not consider the elevation and depression of the sun. But, however, the whole circle of the rainbow never appears in the clouds, but as in many cases a smaller portion, and sometimes a semicircle and a larger portion. For the base of the cone always cuts the earth in the formation of the rainbow in the clouds because of its distance from the eye, and therefore the complete circle is never visible. But when the sun is at its rising and the rainbow is elevated above the horizon about 42 degrees, and the moisture in an infinite number of falling drops is already present, the larger portion of the circle appears through the space of the arc between the visual ray and the horizon; and when the sun is at the altitude of that line* the rainbow is then a semicircle; and when the sun rises above that line the bow is a smaller portion of the circle. Thus as the sun rises higher, the rainbow becomes less and less, because more is cut off from its circle by the earth.

We must consider here, however, that according to Aristotle, particularly in the new translation, the smaller portion of the circle apparent is the portion of a larger circle, and the larger portion is the portion of a smaller circle. Hence when the sun is rising, although more than a semicircle appears colored, yet it is the portion of a smaller circle than when the sun is at a great elevation, nay, at its maximum elevation above the visual ray, at which least of the rainbow can appear. Hence when its gibbosity alone is visible near the earth, while the sun is at the maximum altitude fixed for the formation of the rainbow, that

* *I.e.*, the visual ray.

small portion is part of the base of a larger circle. For we must not think that the cone remains the same and the base the same at the elevation and depression of the sun, but we are to understand that they must be constantly renewed in the conception we should have regarding the rainbow, so that the circle is judged to be larger when the bow is lower, and smaller when the bow is higher. But since a larger portion of the circle of the rainbow appears when the sun is rising, according to the amount of elevation of the observer, if he should be on a high mountain or on a lofty tower he would see a far larger portion according to the amount of his total elevation.

We must also consider that when the sun is just below the horizon the rainbow can appear. But it is the smaller portion, not the larger nor the semicircular. This result is caused solely by the lack of material, for at that time the solar rays do not touch the vapors near the earth, but do reach those situated on high, and therefore the colored semicircle cannot be completed nor a greater portion, but only the crown of the arch, although the greater portion of the circle is above the horizon.

We must understand also that the visual cone and the cone of the iris are not the same, although they are equal, and lie frequently in the same place. For they say, when the eye is unmoved, these cones coincide. When, however, the eye turns to the right or left, turns upward or downward, the head remaining fixed, the visual cone falls in part or in whole outside the position of the cone of the rainbow. This is possible because the center of the eye during this motion is immovable, through which the axis of the cone of the rainbow passes, and therefore this cone of the rainbow remains fixed in its position, although the visual cone moves and changes as the eye looks lower or higher or to the side. And then nothing of the rainbow will be visible except as much as contains the base of the visual cone, since nothing is seen except that which falls below the visual cone; I mean nothing is seen by means of the species coming at right angles. The object thus seen is the principal object of vision, as in this case is the rainbow (or a part of it as contained by the visual cone from its position). In accordance with this will the arc of the bow appear larger or smaller. This point must be carefully considered, in order that the true explanation of the rainbow may be known, and of this I shall speak below.

Since we have now explained that, when the altitude of the sun is 42 degrees or greater, the rainbow cannot appear, it can easily be shown at what time of year and in what localities the rainbow can appear at noon.

Chapter VI

SINCE we have now explained the altitude, magnitude, and diversity in shape of the bow, we can easily show the time and place of its formation. For the reason why the bow cannot appear in summer in the heat of the day has been given by calculating the altitude reckoned suitable for its formation. But then before noon or after it, while the sun is below 42 degrees, the bow can appear. But this can occur in the known climates that are called the seven; but it does not necessarily occur in all regions from the equator to the pole. We must consider, therefore, that the greater altitude of the sun above the horizon is at noon, and the lesser altitude of the sun in all climates in which the sun shines above the horizon, both in winter and in summer, is in Capricorn, namely, at the winter solstice; and for this reason the days are then shorter. But the rainbow cannot be formed in all of these localities when the sun is at the meridian. For in the region whose latitude, that is, the distance of the zenith overhead from the equator or middle of the world, is 24 degrees and 25 minutes or less, and this is for dwellers near the boundary of the second climate, approximately under the tropic of Cancer beyond Jerusalem, a rainbow can never occur when the sun is at the meridian. For if it could occur, it would take place when the sun is at a less altitude above the horizon, and this would be when the sun is at the winter solstice, namely, in the first degree of Capricorn. But this cannot be, since at that time the altitude of the sun is 42 degrees above the horizon, and it has been stated that the rainbow cannot appear when the sun is 42 degrees above the horizon. Moreover, that the altitude of the sun in that region near the winter solstice is 42 degrees is evident, because it is a fourth part of the heavens from the horizon to the zenith overhead, and the zenith overhead is distant from the equator 24 degrees and 25 minutes, as has been stated; for let this be subtracted from a quarter of the heavens, namely,

from 90 degrees, and again let the total declination of the sun
be subtracted, which is 23 degrees and 35 minutes, which added
together make 48 degrees, and this being subtracted from 90
there will remain 42 degrees, the altitude of the head of Capricorn. Therefore when the sun is at this point it will be at noon
42 degrees above the horizon; wherefore the rainbow cannot
be formed on that noon. Therefore no rainbow can be formed
at any noon of the entire year, because both before and after
the solstice the noon will be of greater altitude.

But if we travel from that locality northward to a point
where the latitude of the region is 66 degrees and 25 minutes,
that is, beyond Scotland, where at the winter solstice there is no
day, except that suddenly half of the solar body appears above
the earth, the rainbow can occur in all these regions when the
sun is at the meridian, and in Capricorn, because the altitude
of the head of Capricorn is less, and therefore the altitude of
the sun at noon is less. The bow can appear larger and larger,
not only on that day at the hour of noon in all regions, but on
the days near the solstice and as we travel farther and farther
northward and the latitude of the region becomes greater. But
the bow can appear while the sun is at the meridian, not only
while the sun is near Capricorn, but at many other times. Accordingly the bow can appear in the seventh climate, where the
latitude is 48 degrees and 42 minutes, from the autumnal to
the vernal equinox when the sun is at the meridian. For the
sun at that time on the meridian does not have in the seventh
climate an altitude of 42 degrees, not even on the days of the
equinoxes, since the altitude of the head of Aries and of Libra
above the horizon is only 42 degrees and 10 minutes, as before
stated, and this is made evident by subtracting the latitude of
the region from 90. For if 48 degrees and 48 minutes, which
is the latitude of the region, be subtracted from 90, there remain only 41 degrees and 12 minutes, and this is less than 42
degrees, which is the altitude of the sun at which the bow cannot appear.

If we travel beyond this climate to the north, the bow will
still be able to appear in the heat of summer, when the sun is
at the meridian. For the altitude of the head of Aries is small,
and similarly the altitude of the head of Cancer when the latitude of the region is 54 degrees or 60, and especially when the

latitude is 66 degrees and 25 minutes. For then Capricorn has
no altitude, because the horizon passes through it, and at the
solstices for a moment the horizon lies beneath the zodiac, without declination from it. And since the zodiac moves with the
heavens, it is suddenly separated from the horizon, and the
head of Capricorn revolves beneath the horizon through the
natural day, except that half of the sun appears above the earth.
Hence it has no altitude above the horizon at the winter solstice. And at that time the bow can appear when the sun is at
the meridian, while the half appears above the earth, and the
bow can be larger than a semicircle. And since the half of the
sun suddenly sets, the bow for this reason disappears at once.
Similarly on other days of almost the entire year in that region
the bow can appear, because the greatest elevation of the sun
occurs when the sun is in Cancer, but the sun is not elevated at
that time above the horizon except through its two greatest
declinations, one of which is 23 degrees and 35 minutes, and
the other the same, the sum of which is 47 degrees and 10
minutes. This does not exceed the maximum altitude of the sun
at which the bow can appear except by 5 degrees and 10 minutes. Therefore on a few days as compared with the whole year
the formation of the bow is prevented when the sun is at the
meridian.

But if we advance beyond these localities, the sun will never
be in the south,* but in the north and east and west only, because
to dwellers beyond these localities the sun appears in front of
them toward the pole of the world. This happens sometimes for
a month without night, sometimes for two months, sometimes
for more, until the sun is visible for six months to dwellers near
the pole. Therefore that region whose latitude is 66 degrees
and 25 minutes is the farthest point at which the bow can appear when the sun is at the meridian; just as the first point at
which it can appear when the sun is at the meridian was found
to be the locality whose latitude begins to be in excess of 24
degrees and 25 minutes.

Thus, then, we must consider at what time, and particularly
when the sun is at the meridian, and in what climates the bow
can appear. In these regions the phenomenon can occur in the
true north, namely, when the sun is at the meridian, and in

* See Bridges' note on this passage, Vol. II, page 184.

other parts between the east and the north, and between the west and the north. In summer, moreover, it can occur in the evening between the east and the south, and in the morning in the southwest, because at the summer solstice the sun in the morning has a considerable declination to the north, and then in the locality opposite in the southwest the bow can appear; and in the evening the sun has a declination to the north, and therefore the bow can appear in the southeast. But the bow can never appear in the true south in these climates from the equator as far as latitude 66 degrees and 25 minutes. It can, however, very easily occur at noon in localities beyond this latitude, and this is true up to the pole, since the sun in those regions is always in the north or in the east or in the west; and the bow appears opposite the sun, and it can then appear at every hour of the day. For the sun is never elevated above the horizon except by its maximum declination of 23 degrees and 35 minutes. For this reason the bow can always be visible to these people during the day, when the material is prepared.

From these statements, therefore, it is evident that the bow follows the motion of the sun in two ways; in one according to the elevation and depression of the sun in its circle of altitude, as has been already stated; and in the other according to the motion of the sun above the horizon in its daily motion, because the bow always follows the nadir of the sun, and the nadir moves continuously in an opposite direction to the sun.

CHAPTER VII

THE experimenter further tries to find out whether the bow is caused by incident rays or by reflection or by refraction, and whether it is an image of the sun, as was assumed in the statements made on Perspective, and whether there are real colors in the cloud itself. He must also inquire regarding the variety and cause of its shape; since a statement was made above merely in regard to the size of its form, namely, that sometimes it is a complete circle, and sometimes the larger portion, and sometimes the smaller. But to understand these matters we must employ definite experiments. These are of the following kind, namely, if the observer of the bow moves in a direction parallel to the bow, it follows him at the side; if, however, he moves toward the bow, it recedes; but if he withdraws, the bow follows him, and not only with a slow motion, but with the same speed with which the observer is moving. Hence if a man runs or rides, the bow will seem to travel with an equal speed, as one can clearly perceive if houses or woods or other objects are in front of him in the vicinity of the bow. For he will see that the bow approaches these quite rapidly if they are behind it, or withdraws if they are in front of it.

Likewise by experiment we know that the sun, because of its very great distance from us, of which we cannot judge, seems always to be at the same distance when one recedes before it; and for this reason the sun seems to follow him who recedes, because otherwise the distance would not be judged to be the same. Similarly when one approaches the sun the sun seems to flee before him, because it always appears at the same distance. This appearance cannot be preserved unless the eye judges that the sun is moving in front of it. Moreover, we see clearly an apparent motion of this kind when the sun passes over woods or other elevated objects in the air, from which it recedes or to which it approaches. Moreover, we know that the sun seems to be in the direction of the observer and appears to be moving parallel to him because of its excessive distance. For this reason the sun always appears opposite the observer of the bow, wherever he may move in a direction parallel to the bow. As, for example, if the sun is in the south and the bow in the north, the observer noting their motions eastward sees the sun on one side opposite him and the bow on the other, so that a line passes from the center of the sun through the center of his eye and of the bow; and the motion of the bow varies because the sun seems to move in a direction parallel to the observer and to the bow. For if the sun were stationary according to the judgment of the sight, the bow would move in accordance with the motion of the observer, but would pass through more space than the observer and would pass the observer.

For thus in general it is true that, the visible object being at rest, if the observer moves, the image will move if the mirror is continuous; but if the object of vision moves at the same time in the direction of the observer, the motion of the image will pass through a space equal only to the motion of the observer.

If, however, the visible object is at rest, the image will pass through a greater space. For let *a* be the immovable center of the sun, *c* the center of the bow in the line *abc,* and let *b* and *c* move, so that *b* passes to *d,* and *c* to *f;* it is then evident that the space *cf* is greater than *bd,* and the line *ac* and the line *af* are not parallel but meet in the direction of *a,* and diverge in the other direction, as is apparent in the figure. But if *a* moves toward *g* in the direction of *d,* then *c* will be at *h,* and the lines *bd, ch,* and *ag* will be equal, and the lines *ac* and *gh* will be parallel. But the center of the bow is always in a straight line with the center of the eye in front of it. Wherefore we must assume that the sun seems to move in the direction of the observer, so that in this way the bow may seem to move in a direction parallel to the beholder. Moreover, we know that the

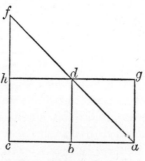

FIG. 72.

sun is visible to the eye of every one. If a thousand men are arranged in a line from east to west their shadows will be sensibly parallel, and also the solar rays falling on them. This is because we do not perceive the convergence of the solar rays to the center of the sun because of its excessive distance. Moreover, owing to this same distance we do not perceive the daily motion of the sun in a short time, but the sun seems to us to be stationary in the sky.

From these facts we learn by experiment that there are as many bows as there are observers. For if two observers at the same time stand and look at the bow in the north, and one of them goes westward, the bow will move in a direction parallel to him, and if the other goes to the east, the bow will move in a direction parallel to him, or if he stands still in the original position, the bow will be stationary. It is evident, therefore, that there are as many bows as there are observers; and for this reason it is impossible for two observers to see one and the same bow, although an ignorant person does not grasp this fact. For the shadow of each observer divides the arc of the rainbow into two equal parts, and therefore, although the shadows are sensibly parallel, they do not meet at the middle of the same bow, and therefore each observer must see his own bow. This is evident, because if the two bows move in different and opposite directions, they will move in accordance with the motions of the observers, and therefore there are as many bows as there are observers.

From these arguments it follows, then, that the bow is seen only by reflected rays of the sun, because if it were seen by incident rays, the bow would be an object fixed in one place in the cloud, which would not vary according to the motion of the observers nor according to the number of the observers. For when the solar rays pass through a rare cloud, the cloud appears to be colored white, and if they pass through a very thick cloud, the cloud appears black, and if they pass through one of moderate density, it appears to be of some intermediate color. But the color of the cloud appears the same to different observers, nor does it follow the motion of the observer, because it is not seen by reflected rays, but by incident or refracted rays. Similarly when a color is produced by incident rays through a crystalline stone, refraction takes place in it, but the same color in the same position is seen by different observers. It is evident, therefore, that the bow is not caused by rays falling directly or by refracted rays. Therefore it must be formed by reflected rays, because there are only the three kinds of principal rays. Nor will the bow be seen by means of accidental rays, since they do not change position unless caused by reflection. Hence from the property of reflection the same thing is evident; for the place of reflection and of the image changes according to a change in the observer. But this is the case here; therefore the bow is caused by reflection.

Nor can it be said that the substance of the bow remains and the position of the image varies in the refraction of the rays, since the change of position in the bow will be in accordance with a very sensible distance, namely, with a speed equal to that of a man running or riding as fast as possible. But the position of the image of an object at rest, although it may vary, does not vary with the same speed as the bow, because the whole change of image is in one common place, and it is therefore called a passage of space. Moreover, the image of an object seen by refraction does not follow the observer if he recedes, nor does it recede if he approaches, nor does it move in a direction parallel to him; which is evident when we look at a fish at rest in water, or a stick fixed in it, or the sun or moon through the medium of vapors, or letters through a crystal or glass. But the objection may be raised that only the place of the image is moved, and the bow can therefore be caused by refraction as well as by reflection. But that the only change is in the place of the image is evident, because the mirror, namely, the matter suitable for the bow, is immovable. But since such is the case, although the observer approaches the mirror there is no change on this account except in the place of the image, so that the visual ray more quickly intercepts the cathetus, and the place of reflection will not escape change, especially since the mirror is not on the surface, but in the depth of the cloud, since all the raindrops have the nature of a mirror, and therefore the place of reflection changes position sensibly in accordance with the judgment of the sight.

But on the other hand, since the sun as a matter of fact is at the same distance with respect to the mirror, there is no difference in the hour of the appearance of the rainbow which we need notice, whether the sun be moving from Cancer toward the south or from Capricorn toward the north, because in a natural day it does not move through one degree. And therefore in the hour of the appearance of the bow there is not a difference of distance of the sun from the cloud that we should take into account. Wherefore the sun's ray will reach the same moisture or part of the moisture, namely, the first part or the second; and therefore some definite part, or the whole moisture itself, becomes an immovable mirror. And it is not sufficient to say that the bow flees before the observer as fast as the sun seems to pursue him, although this is true, so that in this way the place of the reflection and of the bow would seem to vary, because the rays of the sun penetrate the whole of the moist matter, and reflection takes place from every raindrop. And on this account, unless there were another reason, one bow would appear immovable and fixed through the whole of the moisture, having a thickness in accordance with the whole of the moisture.

Wherefore we must state that the bow does not appear except in a definite arrangement of the air as regards a greater and lesser lucidity, so that there may be the required illumination in the direction of the eye, and the determined obscurity in the locality of the bow, because the object is weak and does not appear except in a dark place. When, therefore, the air between the eye and the bow is arranged in the required manner, the cone extends from the eye, whose base is the circle of the rainbow, and terminates in the moist cloud at the place of the required darkness, and the bow appears in that place. But when the eye* shifts in the direction of the bow, it now reaches a remoter portion of the air which is brighter, and it approaches an earlier position of the bow, so that owing to the nearness of the observer the same place with the same arrangement of the air is no longer found, but it is brighter than is required for the appearance of the bow. For it cannot appear in every arrangement of position mentioned, since although the moisture reaches to the eye, the bow, however, will not be seen except in a place of relative darkness. Therefore the base of the cone must fall in the cloud farther on in a place of the required obscurity. And thus the whole cone changes its position according to the motion of the observer, just as if the cone should be carried before the face of a man as he walked, whose vertex is fixed in the eye and whose body is extended in the air to the place of the bow, where, because of its distance from the eye, darkness is formed owing to the thickness of the vapors and of the overshadowing cloud. It is like the case of a man beholding a cloudy vapor at a distance which he cannot see near at hand, for owing to the distance the species of the vision is weakened, and can be terminated by the thickness of the vapors, which it can penetrate near at hand. For this reason it is evident that although reflection takes place everywhere in moisture, yet the bow does not appear everywhere, but only in the place determined. Thus that first objection is answered.

The second is cleared away by the same reasoning; for the mirror in this case does not remain the same, nor in the same place, because of the darkness that is required for the appearance of the colors, and for this reason the bow appears now in one part of the moisture, now in another.

If it is said that when the observer moves to the east the sun moves to the west, therefore the point of reflection will be changed according to the motion of the sun, and therefore the

* See Bridges' note on this passage, Vol. II, page 189.

bow will approach the sun more than it will the observer, it is evident by what has already been said that it will not do so; because the motion of the sun to the west in the hour of the appearance of the bow is insensible, and therefore it is considered stationary, that is, not to be moving westward.

CHAPTER VIII

BUT then it is evident that there will be nothing in the locality of the bow except the appearance of colors, and the appearance will not occur except when the bow is visible. For we have stated that the bow changes with a change in the observers. But sight does not produce colors. For the vision cannot cause colors in a cloud, as is evident; wherefore there will be nothing except in appearance. Moreover, vision by reflection has a visible object at the end of the reflected visual ray, as explained above, and therefore not at the point of reflection or elsewhere; because the object of vision is the terminus of reflection and of the reflected line, nothing therefore is seen by reflection in the cloud.

But if it be said that vision is sensibly and actively excited by the bow, and quite lively colors appear in the bow, and for this reason there cannot be merely the appearance of colors; we must reply that just as there is only the appearance of colors, so is there only the appearance of sensation and of lively change of vision; since a change of this kind has no other cause than defect in vision, as we see in the examples. For when in summer one lowers his head to the ground in the morning, in order that he may see the drops of dew on the ends of the blades of grass, if he views them carelessly or languidly and half closes his eyes, he will see in appearance all the colors of the rainbow. And similarly in the colored circle around the candle; and similarly also when one rises from sleep in summer with his eyes scarcely open and full of moisture, and looks at some small hole through which a solar ray is passing, the colors will be visible to him; and especially to those with weak eyes and to those who are nearsighted. Therefore the phenomenon must be owing to defect in vision, and for this reason there is an appearance only and not a reality. Moreover, this phenomenon is intensified, just as though it existed in the locality of the bow, because the visual ray quickly intersects the cathetus, owing to the small size of the raindrops; and therefore near the point of reflection a phenomenon of this kind occurs, and for this reason in the matter itself and in the locality of the bow.

But if it be said that solar rays passing through a crystal produce real and fixed colors, which produce a species and have objective reality, we must reply that the phenomena are different. The observer alone produces the bow, nor is there anything present except reflection. In the case of the crystal, however, there is a natural cause, namely, the ray and the corrugated stone, which has great diversity of surface, so that according to the angle at which the light falls a diversity of colors results. And viewing them does not* cause the colors to be present here, for there is color before it is seen here, and it is seen by different people in the same place. But in the case of the bow the phenomenon is the result of vision, and therefore can have no reality but merely appearance. This is evident, moreover, by the statements above in regard to the visual cone. When this falls as a whole in the position of the cone of the bow, the whole bow appears in the size possible for it with reference to the altitude and depression of the sun and the arrangement of its own matter; so that if the sun is on the horizon and the matter is prepared, a semicircular bow appears or a larger portion of the sphere, provided the whole visual cone falls in the position of the cone of the bow. But if the sun is on the horizon and the matter is prepared, but the visual cone does not fall as a whole in the position of the cone of the bow, only so much of the arc of the rainbow will appear as the base of the cone of vision cuts off from the place of the bow; therefore it is evident that the bow has no existence except in the vision.

Chapter IX

WE must next consider that the bow is the image of the sun, and to grasp this idea we must consider the opinions of Seneca in his book on the Rainbow, since we must imagine a cloud suspended in the air, and rain descending from it. The vertex

* The sense of the passage seems to require the insertion of the negative.

of the cone falls upon the earth, and the circular base touches the concave surface of the cloud. There are, then, raindrops of small size in an infinite number, and reflection takes place in every direction as from a spherical mirror, and since they descend without an interval they seem from a distance to be continuous, and therefore the image of the sun seems continuous and not multiplex in accordance with the multitude of raindrops. There is a similar phenomenon in the circles colored by spray. And thus the objection is removed that might be made in regard to the multitude of images. But in regard to the shape, size, and color there is doubt; and we must state that spherical mirrors, and especially small ones, change the size and shape of the object of vision in many ways, and render shapes monstrous, and destroy all relationship of the parts of an object to one another, as was shown in the section on Perspective. And after destroying shape and size, and consequently the proper arrangement of qualities, which require shape and the requisite size, they are also able to change the color and to cause a color to appear from that which is without color, and conversely. And because light incorporated in matter resembles color, although in reality it is not color, as rare clouds appear white and thick ones appear black when the rays penetrate them, so in this case can the light of the sun falling on mirrors of this kind show what resembles color, especially since there is nothing present except an appearance, as we have stated.

CHAPTER X

IN addition to these matters we must consider the diversity of colors. All authorities say it is caused by varieties in the texture of the moist cloud, and this is stated in the common text of Aristotle. Hence they say that when the substance of the cloud is somewhat dense, it seems to be darker; and when it is less dense, it seems to be blue; and if it is still less dense, it seems to be green; and if less still, it appears wine-colored and red; if it is still less dense, it appears grayish and pink; and if it is rather rare, it appears to be white. Accordingly the example of Aristotle is given in regard to flame, which, owing to the rarity and density of terrestrial smoke, appears bright and reddish and dark, and it happens so in different ways. But that example is not applicable here, as is evident from the experiment with crystalline stone. For in it colors are produced, and there is no difference in the density and rarity of the substance, and yet real colors are produced in it. And again, since there is no real color in the rainbow, but merely the appearance, we need only give the cause of the appearance or the appearance of the cause. Moreover, in the experiment on sprinkling drops of water nothing is caused by these differences in density, nor in the drops of dew on the ends of blades of grass; therefore it is evident that this reason of difference in density is not the true one. And in this we are not opposing Aristotle, since many other false statements are contained in the chapter on the rainbow and elsewhere in the current translations, as is evident throughout the whole philosophy of the Latins, if any one examines the different translations and the Greek original from which the Latin version was taken. But the opinion of Aristotle has not in all cases been translated, but there has been error in the copies of the Greeks and Arabs, or rather fault in the translators, no one of whom has perfect knowledge of the languages or sciences, as was stated before.

It is necessary, moreover, that another false statement that is found in this chapter on the rainbow should be corrected; and therefore we are to have this understanding in regard to the false statement already corrected. And that the mind may not be in suspense, I say that the statement in the current text is false, namely, that the rainbow is caused by the moon only twice in fifty years. For whenever the moon is full and is not veiled by cloud, and there is moist substance opposite it, the bow can appear just as it does through the agency of the sun. The experience of any one can prove this, and it has been proved by definite experiments.

Chapter XI

But with regard to the shape of the bow there is very great difficulty. For some think that it should be formed in the same way as the base of the cone of dropping dew. But this is impossible. For in drops of spray it is evident by experiment that in a mass of spray of irregular shape the form of the rainbow appears. Similarly those are in error who say that the bow is caused by refraction, so that it has the shape of a pyramid conformed to the curve of the surface of a cone expanded opposite the sun, for which reason, according to these thinkers, it is thought to be bow-shaped. And because the vertex of the pyramid mentioned, as they state, is near the earth, and the pyramid expands in a direction opposite the sun, half or more of that figure must fall on the surface of the earth and the remaining half or less must fall opposite the sun on the cloud. But this explanation is not correct, because it has been proved that the bow is not the result of refraction, since in the case of spray we cannot give a reason of this kind for the shape. For they say that the rays are refracted first at the point of contact of the air and the cloud, and afterwards at the point of contact of the cloud and the higher part of the moisture, so that by these refractions rays converge in the lower and denser part of the moisture; for the denser part is lower because it is heavier. For there the rays refracted as from the vertex of a cone spread out not into a cone, as they say, but into a figure conformed to the curve of the surface of a cone.* It is evident, therefore, that by three refractions the rays take this form. But there cannot be three refractions in spray formed in the rays, but only one; and yet the same shape is found as in the sky; wherefore the cause is not a refraction of this kind.

Lastly, why will the rays not form a cone but a figure conformed to the curve of the surface of a cone? For this will not be in accordance with the law of refraction, because refraction must form a regular cone, since the refraction of all rays falling on one circle of a spherical body is at right angles, and therefore the figure will not be curved more in one part than in another, but will be wholly regular and uniform. Nor can this curvature be caused by the moisture, because the moisture is not of such a form, but according to them is a rounded mass of conical form composed of an infinite number of drops, and therefore there is no explanation of that form in this way.

Another explanation therefore must be sought; and it can be stated that the bow must be in the form of a circular arc. For in accordance with differences in the position of an object

* See Bridges' note on this passage, Vol. II, page 194.

with respect to light different colors appear, as on the dove's neck. Since, therefore, the same color in one circle of the bow appears from one end to the other, all parts must have the same position with respect to the solar ray and the eye. But such a position of identity cannot exist except in a circular figure because of the equal declination of the parts. Moreover, on a vapor of spherical shape two kinds of circles can be marked. One kind passes through its poles like colures on a sphere; the other kind consists of parallel circles intersecting these colures transversely. The circular path of the colure is always vanishing owing to distance, because it does not keep the same position at its extremities and in the middle with respect to the eye, but the parallels are quite apparent in their circular path because of the equality of their position with respect to the eye, as has been stated concerning the moon in the section on Perspective. Since therefore the circle of the rainbow is one of the parallel circles it can be seen in its circular path.

But if the objection be raised against this view that then not only the arc of the cone in its gibbosity would be colored but also elsewhere throughout its whole surface, just like the full moon, which is fully illuminated on the side turned to us, and therefore the whole surface of the base, which is above the earth, would be colored. In reply to this objection it can be said that drops are not present everywhere from which rays are reflected to the eyes at angles equal to the angles of incidence. For this occurs only in the position of a circle, as is apparent in the reflections and refractions of the concave mirror and of other mirrors; and therefore since there can be four or five circles of the rainbow in the drops from which reflections to the eye are made at angles equal to the angles of incidence, color can be produced in them, and the phenomenon of the rainbow appear.

Chapter XII

Some used to think that the moist cloud was colored throughout, because there is reflection in all the drops, and the bow is caused by reflection; moreover, because in accordance with the number of observers and diversity in the position of the same observer the bow appears everywhere. But to the first statement we must reply that everywhere there are conditions suitable for the appearance of the bow, but as an actual fact the bow appears only in raindrops from which there is reflection to the eye; because there is merely the appearance of colors arising from the fantasy and deception of the vision, as has been stated. Therefore real color is nowhere present in the moist cloud, nor is the appearance of color present except in the drops from which reflection comes to the vision. But a reflection comes from every drop at the same time, while the eye is in one position, because of the equality of the angles of incidence and reflection. To the second statement we must reply that we can imagine colors appearing everywhere from two causes, in one way because the color was fixed, just as in other things; and it would produce a species from itself to the eye, and it would then be everywhere, and thus wherever there were sprays one would see color. But such is not the case here, because there is no real color, but only a fantasy of vision; and therefore the cause of the appearance is an erroneous judgment of the vision alone. Therefore the bow appears only in the place from which reflection reaches the eye; and from this cause, not from the first one, it changes according to a change in the observer.

There are five principal colors, namely, white, blue, red, green, black. For red is equidistant from the extremes, and is midway with respect to white and black. For Aristotle's statement in his work De Sensu et Sensato that there are seven colors is true if we divide blue into several shades, as dark blue and purple, and similarly by dividing green into different shades; but the five principal colors are distinct by nature. For the number five is better than all other numbers, as Aristotle says in the book of Secrets, and this is true as far as distinguishing definitely the number of things is concerned, although the number three is better as regards the numeral quality found in anything. For we draw this from nature, as Aristotle says in the first book on the Heavens and the World, because in everything a trinity exists, as Aristotle there shows, both in the Creator and in the creature. Because the number five distinguishes things more definitely and better, nature for this reason rather intends that there shall be five colors. Therefore these five colors are in the rainbow, rather than other colors, in accordance with the general arrangement of nature, which carries into effect and purposes that which is better. The color of blue termed celestial is black with a certain sweetness of luster, and is therefore reckoned under black.

It is thought by scientists that these colors are caused by the humors and colors of the eye; for these colors exist merely in appearance, and the parts of the eye have some colors naturally, although they are weak, in accordance with the existence of which the colors appear in the bow. Moreover, there are five bodies in the eye, namely, three humors and two coats, the uvea and the cornea; the consolidativa takes no part in vision, and therefore the five colors appear according to the properties of these five parts. Sometimes those bodies do not have distinct colors. For they vary in the eyes of different people, and different bows appear to vary, one in one way, another in another in the same hour, also at different times according to the variation of the air between the eye and the bow in its arrangement of light and dark portions. Moreover, a proof that the colors of the bow can appear through the eye is the fact that, when a hexagonal stone is placed before the eye in a dark place, colors of this kind are formed, and therefore in a similar manner in suitable matter in a dark place in the cloud they can at all events appear.

After what has now been said the cause of the corona is more easily apparent, and likewise the cause of the phenomenon appearing in a rectangular figure, which Seneca calls a rod, and Aristotle a perpendicular; for these phenomena are colored and others not. Therefore Seneca says, "If you form the vapor erect, it is a rod [streak in the heavens]; if you bend it into the arc of a circle, it is the rainbow; if you bend it into a complete circle, it is a corona"; which Aristotle calls a circle around the sun and the moon, and a halo. They state another difference also, namely, that the rainbow is formed opposite the sun, the streak to the side of the sun, and the corona beneath it. But the statements in regard to the circle and corona can be made without misrepresentation. Concerning the perpendicular, however, and the rod [streak] it is different. For it is merely a small portion of the corona, which by reason of the excessive distance seems to be a straight line, when the matter to complete the corona is lacking. A mass, moreover, of dense vapor sometimes forms in the direction of the sun beneath it. This vapor is denser than the air, and yet is not of excessive density but of such density as is required for a phenomenon of this kind. I state, then, that when that vapor is denser than the air, and is of a nearly spherical form, equidistant from the earth as nearly as it can be owing to the nature of a heavy body, all the rays proceeding from the point $o*$ beyond the perpendicular od are refracted at the surface of the vapor between the straight path and the perpendicular drawn from the point of refraction. All the rays falling on one circular path around that axis are refracted at equal angles, because all the angles of incidence are equal, as a and f, and the angles of refractions within the body are equal, and this is true in regard to all angles of rays falling on the circumference, which passes through the points agf, and in the same way the rays falling on the circumference passing through bg are all refracted at equal angles, because they are incident at equal angles, as is evident by geometrical demonstration. The rays, therefore, of a circular path, as oa and of, and all rays that in the circumference pass through a and f, fall and travel after refraction in the body of the equidistant vapor. Then when the air, which is a rarer body, meets the concave surface of the vapor, the rays are refracted and deflected from the perpendicular drawn from the point of refraction, and meet necessarily at a point, as at o. The same is true of those rays that fall on another circular path, as ob and cg, and they are conterminous on the same circumference, and they intersect by a second refraction at a remoter point, as at d, because rays falling on a larger circular path intersect at a remoter point. And thus it is always true of other rays falling on other circumferences that all the rays of one circular path fall at a point different from the point at which the rays of the other circular paths meet. And just as the rays of one circular path at their entrance into the vapor form a circle on the vapor, so when they leave the vapor they pass from a circular base and meet in a point of the cone. For all this light coming from a point in the sun and passing through the vapor is broken up into an infinite number of rays and is like a cylinder in shape, and has a circular form at both ends while it is in the vapor. But after it has passed out of the vapors the rays are deflected into the form of a cone, whose base is at the end of the cylinder of light, and its

* No figure is given in the MSS.

vertex falls on the earth. If, therefore, the eye receives the vertex of a cone, it will see the base of this cone, and because that denser vapor is of such a density that it is visible, especially since it has light in itself, it can be seen beneath the bases of the cone, and therefore in a circular form.

But just as many experiments are needed to determine the nature of the rainbow both in regard to its color and its shape, so too are they required in this investigation, where we must note that rays can be considered in two ways, namely, either as coming from a point and to a circle in the vapor which intersect at the vertex of a cone; and other rays that fall from the same point and to another circle form another cone, and so on. But the vertices of all these cones fall on the axis and the perpendicular coming from that point from which the refracted rays come, and incomplete cones are formed, nor do the rays pass to the points of intersection because of the interposition of the observer, and therefore no one will see by means of these incomplete cones. Wherefore if several people are looking at a corona, we must choose one of the two explanations, either that from other points of the sun rays come to be refracted into a cone, so that to the individual observers rays come from separate points in the sun, or that from the base of a cone whose vertex falls on the eye of an observer, other cones formed from accidental rays come to the other observers; so that the base of the principal cone which comes to the eye of one person is seen by others by means of an accidental cone, just as those in a corner of a house see by means of accidental rays the light falling through a window. But this second explanation cannot be the correct one, because a judgment by means of principal rays and one by means of accidental rays cannot be equal, but those viewing the corona at the same time form equal judgments. Moreover, each one judges that the sun is the center of the corona; therefore each one sees the sun, but accidental rays do not lead the sight to an object but to a species, just as a person in a corner of a house cannot see the sun, although he may see a ray falling through an opening. It is evident, therefore, that to the eye of an observer one cone comes whose rays come from a definite point in the sun, so that from one point rays come to one eye, and to a second eye from a second point, and to a third eye from a third point. But experiment explains all these things, just as in the case of the rainbow. Hence reasoning does not attest these matters, but experiments on a large scale made with instruments and by various necessary means are required. Therefore no discussion can give an adequate explanation in these matters, for the whole subject is dependent on experiment. For this reason I do not think that in this matter I have grasped the whole truth, because I have not yet made all the experiments that are necessary, and because in this work I am proceeding by the method of persuasion and of demonstration of what is required in the study of science, and not by the method of compiling what has been written on this subject. Therefore it does not devolve on me to give at this time an attestation possible for me, but to treat the subject in the form of a plea for the study of science.

In regard to the circle around a candle it is thought that it is formed by the vapors set free from the foods and drinks on the table; or that it can appear when the air is moist; or that it is produced at a distance from the candle in the vapors of the moist eye. Thus, therefore, any scientist will readily admit that experiment, not reasoning, determines the conclusions in regard to these matters. But I now pass to the second prerogative of this Experimental Science.

CHAPTER ON THE SECOND PREROGATIVE OF EXPERIMENTAL SCIENCE

THIS mistress of the speculative sciences alone is able to give us important truths within the confines of the other sciences, which those sciences can learn in no other way. Hence these truths are not connected with the discussion of principles but are wholly outside of these, although they are within the confines of these sciences, since they are neither conclusions nor principles. Clear examples in regard to these matters can be given; but in what follows the man without experience must not seek a reason in order that he may first understand, for he will never have this reason except after experiment. Hence in the first place there should be readiness to believe, until in the second place experiment follows, so that in the third reasoning may function. For if a man is without experience that a magnet attracts iron, and has not heard from others that it attracts, he will never discover this fact before an experiment. Therefore in the beginning he must believe those who have made the experiment, or who have reliable information from experimenters, nor should he reject the truth, because he is ignorant of it, and because he does not arrive at it by reasoning. I shall state, then, those things that I hold to have been proved by experiment.

Example I

MATHEMATICAL science can easily produce the spherical astrolabe, on which all astronomical phenomena necessary for man may be described, according to precise longitudes and latitudes. The device of Ptolemy in the eighth book of the Almagest is used with reference to circles as well as stars, as I have stated, by means of a certain similitude, but the subject is not fully explained by that device, for more work is necessary. But that this body so made should move naturally with the daily motion is not within the power of mathematical science. But the trained experimenter can consider the ways of this motion, aroused to consider them by many things which follow the celestial motion, as, for example, the three elements which rotate circularly through the celestial influence, as Alpetragius states in his book on Celestial Motions, and Averroës in the first book on the Heavens and the World; so also comets, the seas and flowing streams, marrows and brains and the substances composing diseases. Plants also in their parts open and close in accordance with the motion of the sun. And many like things are found which, according to a local motion of the whole or of parts, are moved by the motion of the sun. The scientist, therefore, is aroused by the consideration of things of this kind, a consideration similar in import to that in which he is interested, in order that at length he may arrive at his goal. This instrument would be worth the treasure of a king, and would supersede all other astronomical instruments and clocks, and would be a most wonderful instrument of science. But few would know how in a clear and useful manner to conceive of such a miracle and of similar ones within the confines of mathematical science.

Experimental Science

Example II

ANOTHER example can be given in the field of medicine in regard to the prolongation of human life, for which the medical art has nothing to offer except the regimen of health. But a far longer extension of life is possible. At the beginning of the world there was a great prolongation of life, but now it has been shortened unduly. Many have thought that the reason for this prolongation and shortening of life is found in the influence of the heavens. For they considered that the arrangement of the heavens was best at the beginning, and that as the world grows old all things decay. They think that the stars were created in more advantageous positions, in which stars have their dignities, which are called house, exaltation, triplicity, face, and boundary; and in a better relationship of these to one another in accordance with the diversity of aspects or the invisible projection of rays. They also think that they have gradually receded from this position, and that in accordance with this recession they impose a shortened span of life up to some fixed boundary, at which there will be a state of rest. But this idea has many contradictions and difficulties, of which I must now speak.

Whether this shall prove to be true or not, another reason must be given, which is ready at hand for us and is plain, which cannot be contradicted, and which we know by experience. Therefore in regard to this we must strive, that the wonderful and ineffable utility and splendor of experimental science may appear and the pathway may be opened to the greatest secret of secrets, which Aristotle has hidden in his book on the Regimen of Life. For although the regimen of health should be observed in food and drink, in sleep and in wakefulness, in motion and in rest, in evacuation and retention, in the nature of the air and in the passions of the mind, so that these matters should be properly cared for from infancy, no one wishes to take thought in regard to them, not even physicians, since we see that scarcely one physician in a thousand will give this matter even slight attention. Very rarely does it happen that any one pays sufficient heed to the rules of health. No one does so in his youth, but sometimes one in three thousand thinks of these matters when he is old and approaching death, for at that

accordance with the property of the remedies retarding the accidents of old age and senility and mitigating their evil. The first limit can be passed but the second cannot be.

Because of these two limits the Scripture says more than once, "Thou hast set its bounds which cannot be passed"; for it is impossible for the ultimate limit to be passed, but the first limit can be passed, although it is rarely passed; but the second limit cannot be passed. The proper regimen of health, therefore, as far as a man can possess it, would prolong life beyond its common accidental limit, which man because of his folly does not protect for his own interest; and thus some have lived for many years beyond the common limit of life. But a special regimen by means of remedies retarding the common limit mentioned, which the art of directing the health does not exceed, can prolong life much further. What is possible is shown by Dioscorides, who says that there may be some medicine to protect man from the swiftness of old age and from cold and from the drying up of his members, so that by its means the life of man may be prolonged. In the Tegni near the end Hali maintains this. Again he says, "Those who have lived a long time have used medicines by which their life has been prolonged." Avicenna, moreover, speaks in regard to such matters as follows in the second book of the Canon, "There is a medicine that settles and divides every constitution as it should be." But medical authorities have not given those medicines, nor have they been stated in their books, since these writers pay attention only to the art of caring for the health, and that, too, insufficiently as regards the elderly and the aged, as has been stated. But learned men devoted to experimental science have given thought to these matters, influenced thereto not only by their utility but by the action of animals which in many ways avoid a premature death, as, for example, the stag, the eagle, the snake, and many other animals that prolong their life by natural action, as authors state and experience has shown. Influenced by these examples they believed that God himself granted this power to brutes for the instruction of mortal man. Therefore they lay in wait for animals, in order that they might learn the powers of herbs, stones, metals, and other things, with which they improved their bodies in many apparently miraculous ways, just as we gather with the utmost certainty from the books of Pliny, Solinus, Avicenna on Animals, Tullius on the Divine Nature, from the philosophy of Artephius, and from other books and various authors, and many people have had experience in this matter. For in Paris lately there was a scientist who sought for snakes and took one and cut it into small portions, except that the skin of the belly on which it crept remained intact. This snake crept as it was able to a certain herb by the touch of which it was immediately cured. The experimenter collected the herb of wondrous virtue. Since human reason is superior to all the wisdom of animals, scientists thus encouraged by the examples of animals have thought out better and greater means.

And especially was this wisdom granted to the world through the first men, namely, through Adam and his sons, who received from God himself special knowledge on this subject, in order that they might prolong their life. We can learn the same through Aristotle in the book of Secrets, where he says that God most high and glorious has prepared a means and a remedy for tempering the humors and preserving health, and for acquiring many things with which to combat the ills of old age and to retard them, and to mitigate such evils; and has revealed these things to his saints and prophets and to certain others, as the patriarchs, whom he chose and enlightened with the spirit of divine wisdom, etc. And below he says that there is a medicine called the ineffable glory and treasure of philosophers, which completely rectifies the whole human body. This medicine is said to have been discovered by Adam or by Enoch and secured through a vision, as he himself states, although it has not been fully attested which of these first produced this medicine. But these matters and the most secret of secrets of this kind have always been hidden from the rank and file of philosophers, and particularly so after men began to abuse science, turning to evil what God granted in full measure for the safety and advantage of men.

Many examples, moreover, of these facts are written. Artephius, who traveled over all the regions of the East in his search for knowledge, found Tantalus, teacher of the king of India, seated on a golden throne and discoursing on nature and on the motions of the heavens. This same Tantalus humbled himself and became a pupil of Artephius, who is said in the book of his own philosophy to have lived actually for many centuries by means of secret experiments. Pliny, moreover, in the twenty-second book of the Natural History states that a man stood in the presence of Augustus, who had prolonged his life beyond a hundred years. To the astonishment of the bystanders he was strong, robust, and active to such a degree that the emperor in wonder asked him what he did so as to live in this way. The man replied in a riddle, as Pliny says, that he had applied oil on the outside and mead on the inside. Moreover, as stated in the book on the Accidents of Old Age, in the time of King William of Sicily a man was found who renewed the period of his youth in strength and sense and sagacity beyond all human calculation for about sixty years, and from a rustic ploughman became a messenger of the king. While ploughing he found a golden vessel in the fields hidden in the earth, which contained an excellent liquor. Thinking the liquor was dew from the sky he drank it and washed his face, and was renewed in mind and body beyond measure. And in the book just mentioned it is recorded that a man anointed with an excellent unguent the whole surface of his body with the exception of the soles of his feet, and lived for several centuries without decay except in his soles, which he had neglected to anoint, and for this reason he nearly always rode. Moreover, the author of this book bore witness that he had seen a man, and had talked with him, who had lived for several centuries, because he took a medicine prepared by scientists for a great king, who lost hope for himself and wished the medicine to be tried on an ignorant person. Thus the man's life was prolonged, and he had official letters from the Pope of that time and from others in regard to this fact.

Therefore the excellent experimenter in the book on the Regimen of the Aged says that if what is tempered in the fourth degree, and what swims in the sea, and what grows in the air, and what is cast up by the sea, and a plant of India, and what is found in the vitals of a long-lived animal, and the two snakes which are the food of Tyrians and Aethiopians, be prepared and used in the proper way, and the *minera** of the noble animal be present, the life of man could be greatly prolonged and the conditions of old age and senility could be retarded and mitigated. But that which is tempered in the fourth degree is gold, as is

* Old French word meaning mine used here probably in the sense of blood.

Experimental Science

stated in the book on Spirits and Bodies,* which among all
things is most friendly to nature. And if by a certain experiment
gold should be made the best possible, or at any rate far better
than nature and the art of alchemy can make it, as was the vessel
found by the rustic, and it should be dissolved in such water as
the ploughman drank, it would then produce a wonderful action on the body of man. And if there is added that which swims
in the sea, namely, the pearl, which is a thing most efficacious
for preserving life, and there is added also the thing that
grows in the air.† This last is an *anthos* [flower] and is the
flower of seadew, which possesses an ineffable virtue against the
condition of old age. But the *dianthos* that is put in an electuary
is not a flower, but is a mixture of leaves and fragments of wood
and a small portion of flower. For the pure flower should be
gathered in its proper season, and in many ways it is used in
foods and drinks and electuaries. To these must be added what
is cast up by the sea. This last is ambergris, which is spermaceti,
a thing of wondrous virtue in this matter. The plant of India
is similar to these, and is the excellent wood of the aloe, fresh
and not seasoned. To these ingredients there is added that
which is in the heart of a long-lived animal, namely, the stag.
This is a bone growing in the stag's heart, which possesses
great power against premature old age. The snake which is
the food of the Tyrians is the Tyrian snake from which Tyri-
aca‡ is made, and whose flesh is properly prepared and eaten
with spices. This is an excellent remedy for the condition of
old age and for all the corruptions of the constitution, if it is
taken with things suitable to one's constitution and condition,
as we are taught in the book on the Regimen of the Aged. Aristotle, moreover, in the book of Secrets recommends strongly the
flesh of the Tyrian snake for our ills. The snake that is the food
of the Aethiopians is the dragon, as David says in the psalm,
"Thou hast given it as food to the tribes of the Aethiopians."
For it is certain that wise men of Aethiopia have come to Italy,
Spain, France, England, and those lands of the Christians in
which there are good flying dragons, and by the secret art they
possess lure the dragons from their caverns. They have saddles

* *I.e.,* gases and solids.
† Bacon does not complete these sentences, but the sense is clear enough.
‡ Antidote against poisonous bites.

and bridles in readiness, and they ride on these dragons and drive them in the air at high speed, so that the rigidity of their flesh may be overcome and its hardness tempered, just as in the case of boars and bears and bulls that are driven about by dogs and beaten in various ways before they are killed for food. After they have domesticated them in this way they have the art of preparing their flesh, similar to the art of preparing the flesh of the Tyrian snake, and they use the flesh against the accidents of old age, and they prolong life and sharpen their intellect beyond all conception. For no instruction that can be given by man can produce such wisdom as the eating of this flesh, as we have learned through men of proved reliability on whose word no doubt can be cast.

If the elements should be prepared and purified in some mixture, so that there would be no action of one element on another, but so that they would be reduced to pure simplicity, the wisest have judged that they would have the most perfect medicine. For in this way the elements would be equal. Averroës, moreover, asserts in opposition to Galienus in the tenth book of the Metaphysics that if the mixture was made with an equality of the miscibles, the elements would not act or be acted on, nor would they be corrupted. Aristotle also maintains this view in the fifth book of the Metaphysics, where he has stated definitely that no corruption occurs when the active potencies are equal; and this is an assured fact.

For this condition will exist in our bodies after the resurrection. For an equality of elements in those bodies excludes corruption for ever. For this equality is the ultimate end of the natural matter in mixed bodies, because it is the noblest state, and therefore in it the appetite of matter would cease, and would desire nothing beyond. The body of Adam did not possess elements in full equality, and therefore the contrary elements in him acted and were acted on, and consequently there was waste, and he required nourishment. For this reason he was commanded not to eat of the fruit of life. But since the elements in him approached equality, there was very little waste in him; and hence he was fit for immortality, which he could have secured if he had eaten always of the fruit of the tree of life. For this fruit is thought to have elements approaching equality; and therefore it was able to continue incorruption in Adam, which would have happened if he had not sinned. Scientists, therefore, have striven to reduce the elements in some form of food or drink to an equality or nearly so, and have taught the means to this end. But owing to the difficulty of this very great experiment, and because few take an interest in experiments, since the labor involved is complicated and the expense very great, and because men pay no heed to the secrets of nature and the possibilities of art, it happens that very few have labored on this very great secret of science, and still fewer have reached a laudable end.

Those men, however, of whom mention has been made, who prolonged their life for centuries, had a medicine of this kind prepared with more or less skill. For Artephius, who, it is stated, lived a thousand and twenty-five years, had a better medicine than the aged ploughman, in whom his youth was renewed for sixty years. That liquor which the rustic drank is thought to have approached an equality of elements far beyond ordinary foods and drinks; but yet it was far from possessing full equality. For there are many degrees in the approach to final equality, which the medicine of Artephius failed to secure, as well as that which caused the man to live for five hundred years who had the papal letter in attestation of so great a miracle, of whom mention was made above. Nor is it strange if Aristotle did not live so long, nor Plato, nor many other famous philosophers; since in the Categories Aristotle says he was ignorant of the quadrature of the circle, which bears no comparison to a secret of this kind. Avicenna, moreover, says in the third book of the Physics that he did not yet know the category of habit; and now I judge that this is easily learned, and we wonder that these men were ignorant of matters so evident. For all wisdom is from the Lord God; and therefore sometimes to the simple are granted things that the most learned and famous cannot know. But medicine cannot give us these things nor does it mention them; but the greatness of the secret belonging to an experimental science of this kind has proved them. What, then, the remedies are and what things they contain, are discovered especially in the book of the Secrets of Aristotle and in the philosophy of Artephius, and in the book on the Conditions of Old Age, and in the treatise on the Regimen of the Elderly and the Aged, and in the books of Pliny, and elsewhere in many ways.

Example III

IN the third place, the dignity of this science can be exemplified in alchemy. For that whole art is scarcely so perfected that the greater metals may be produced from the lighter ones, as gold from lead, and silver from copper. But that art never suffices to show the natural and artificial grades of gold and the modes of its grades. For experimental science has brought both to light, since it has discovered both the four natural grades and their seventeen modes and the artificial ones. By experiment it can be produced beyond twenty-four. Thus the vessel in which the liquor was contained, by means of which the ploughman became the messenger of the king, had a purity of gold far beyond the twenty-four, as its test and worth showed. But when those twenty-four degrees are found in a mass of gold, the gold is the best that can be produced by nature. But when there are twenty-four degrees of gold and one part of silver or one degree, the gold is inferior to the former, and thus the diminution of the degrees of the gold goes as far as sixteen, so that there are eight grades of gold with an admixture of silver. But the mineral power in the belly of the earth is not able sometimes to digest matter into the nature of gold, and does what it can by digesting it into the form of silver. And that I am not led astray in this matter by my imagination is proved by the fact that men are found in several parts of the world who are clever at producing those sixteen modes, and have discovered pieces and masses of gold in those seventeen modes. They then made a mixture of silver and air with gold in the aforesaid modes, so that they might have seventeen lumps of gold made artificially, by means of which they might learn the natural modes of gold. Since this art is not known to the majority of those who are eager for gold, many frauds consequently are perpetrated in this world. The art of alchemy not only omits these modes, but this gold of twenty-four degrees is very rarely found, and with the greatest difficulty. There have always been a few who during their life have known this secret of alchemy; and this sci-

ence does not go beyond that. But experimental science by
means of Aristotle's Secrets of Secrets knows how to produce
gold not only of twenty-four degrees but of thirty and forty
degrees and of as many degrees as we desire. For this reason
Aristotle said to Alexander, "I wish to disclose the greatest
secret"; and it really is the greatest secret, for not only would
it procure an advantage for the state and for every one his desire because of the sufficiency of gold, but what is infinitely
more, it would prolong life. For that medicine which would
remove all the impurities and corruptions of a baser metal, so
that it should become silver and purest gold, is thought by scientists to be able to remove the corruptions of the human body
to such an extent that it would prolong life for many ages. This
is the tempered body of elements, of which I spoke above.

CHAPTER ON THE THIRD PREROGATIVE OR THE DIGNITY OF THE EXPERIMENTAL ART

BUT there is a third dignity of this science. It arises from those
properties through which it has no connection with the other
sciences, but by its own power investigates the secrets of nature.
This consists in two things; namely, in the knowledge of the
future, the past, and the present, and in wonderful works by
which it excels in the power of forming judgments the ordinary
astronomy dealing with judgments. For Ptolemy in the book
introductory to the Almagest says that there is a more certain
road than that through the ordinary astronomy, and this is the
pathway of experiment, which follows the course of nature, to
which many of the philosophers who are believers are turning,
just like Aristotle and a host of the authors of judgments
formed from the stars, as he himself says, and as we know by
proper practice, which cannot be gainsaid. This science was discovered as a complete remedy for human ignorance and inad-
vertence; for it is difficult to get accurate astronomical instruments, and it is more difficult to get verified tables, especially
those in which the motion of the planets is equalized. The use,
moreover, of these tables is difficult, but still more difficult is
the use of the instruments. But this science has discovered the
definitions and the means by which it can answer easily every

question, as far as the power of a single branch of philosophy can do so, and by which it can show us the forms of the celestial forces, and the influences of the heavenly bodies on this world without the difficulty of the ordinary astronomy. This part of the science relating to judgments has four principal divisions or secret sciences.

Moreover, certain bear witness that activities of this science which display philosophy consist in changing the character of a region, so that the habits of its people are changed. One of such witnesses was Aristotle himself, the most learned of philosophers. When Alexander asked him in regard to the nations which he had discovered, whether he should exterminate them because of the ferocity of their character, or should permit them to live, he replied in the book of Secrets, "If you can alter the air of those nations, permit them to live; if you cannot, then kill them." For he maintained that the air of these nations could be changed advantageously, so that the complexions of their bodies would be changed, and then their minds influenced by their complexions would choose good morals in accordance with the freedom of the will. This is one of the secrets.

Moreover, certain assert that change is effected by the sun. There is, as an illustration, the example of Aristotle when he said to Alexander, "Give a hot drink from the seed of a plant to whomsoever you wish, and he will obey you for the rest of your life." Some maintain that an army may be stupefied and put to flight. Of this number is Aristotle, who says to Alexander, "Take such a stone, and every army will flee from you." They bear witness that these statements and innumerable others of this kind are true, not meaning that violence is done to the freedom of the will, since Aristotle, who maintains this view, says in the Ethics that the will cannot be coerced. The body, moreover, can be changed by the influence of things, and the minds of people are then aroused and influenced to desire voluntarily that to which they are directed; just as we see in the book of Medicine that through potions and many medicines people can be changed in body and in the passions of the soul and in the inclination of the will.

There are, moreover, other inventions belonging more to nature which do not have as their object a marvelous change in the will, and they are diversified in character. Some of these possess an excellence of wisdom with other advantages, as, for example, perpetual baths most suitable for human use that do not require any artificial renewal; and ever-burning lamps. For we see many things that cannot be impaired by fire, nay, that are purified by fire, like the skin of the salamander and many other things of this kind, which also can be so prepared that they are externally luminous of themselves, and retain the power of fire, and give forth flame and light. Moreover, against foes of the state they have discovered important arts, so that without a sword or any weapon requiring physical contact they could destroy all who offer resistance. There are many kinds of these inventions. Some of these are perceived by no one of the senses, or by smell alone, and of these inventions Aristotle's book explains that of altering the air, but not those of which I spoke above. These last are of a different character, since they act by means of an infection. There are others also that change some one of the senses, and they are diversified in accordance with all the senses.

Certain of these work a change by contact only and thus destroy life. For malta, which is a kind of bitumen and is plentiful in this world, when cast upon an armed man burns him up. The Romans suffered severe loss of life from this in their conquests, as Pliny states in the second book of the Natural History, and as the histories attest. Similarly yellow petroleum, that is, oil springing from the rock, burns up whatever it meets if it is properly prepared. For a consuming fire is produced by this which can be extinguished with difficulty; for water cannot put it out. Certain inventions disturb the hearing to such a degree that, if they are set off suddenly at night with sufficient skill, neither city nor army can endure them. No clap of thunder could compare with such noises. Certain of these strike such terror to the sight that the coruscations of the clouds disturb it incomparably less. Gideon is thought to have employed inventions similar to these in the camp of the Midianites. We have an example of this in that toy of children which is made in many parts of the world, namely, an instrument as large as the human thumb. From the force of the salt called saltpeter so horrible a sound is produced at the bursting of so small a thing, namely, a small piece of parchment, that we perceive it exceeds the roar of sharp thunder, and the flash exceeds the greatest brilliancy of the lightning accompanying the thunder.

There are also very many things that slay every poisonous animal by the gentlest touch, and if a circle is made around these animals with things of this kind the animals cannot get out, but die, although they are not touched. But if a man is bitten by a poisonous animal, by the application of the powder of such things he can be healed, as Bede states in his Ecclesiastical History and as we know by experience. And thus there are innumerable things that have strange virtues, whose potencies we are ignorant of solely ·from our neglect of experiment.

But there are other inventions which do not possess such advantage for the state, but are to be looked upon as miracles of nature, such as experiments with the magnet, not only on iron, but on gold and other metals. Moreover, if the experiment on iron were not known, it would be viewed as a great miracle. And surely in respect to the action of the magnet on iron there are phenomena unknown to those who use the magnet which show in a wonderful way the dissolutions of nature. Just as also from these the faithful experimenter knows how to experiment on the mutual attraction of other things, as, for example, the stone that passes to the acid, and bitumen that ignites from fire placed at a distance from it, as Pliny states in the second book of the Natural History; and certain other things that are mutually attracted although locally separated. This is truly wonderful beyond all that I have seen and heard. For after I saw this, there has been nothing difficult for my intellect to believe, provided it had a trustworthy authority. And that this fact may not be hidden from your Reverence, this phenomenon occurs in the parts of plants divided and locally separated. For if a sapling of one year's growth is taken, which springs forth beside the roots of the hazel, and is divided longitudinally, and the divided parts separated by the space of a palm or four fingers, and one person holds on one side the extremities of the two parts, and another similarly on the other side, always with an equal and gentle grasp, so that the parts are kept opposite each other in the same position they had before the division, within the space of half a mile* the parts of the twig begin to approach each other gradually, but with greater force at the end of the experiment, so that at length they meet and are united. The ends, however, remain apart, because they are prevented from meeting owing to the force exerted by those holding the parts. This is a very wonderful thing. For this reason magicians perform this experiment, repeating different incantations, and they believe that the phenomenon is caused by virtue of the incantations. I have disregarded the incantations and have discovered the wonderful action of nature, which is similar to that of the magnet on iron. For just as the one attracts the other because of the similar nature of the iron and the magnet, so do the parts in this case. Hence the natural force, which is similar in both parts of the twig, causes them to unite. If they were arranged in the required way, they would meet at the extremities just as in the middle and more quickly, as, for example, if the ends were minutely pierced and threads passed through the ends, so that they could be suspended in the air without hindrance. This is true not only of hazel saplings but of many others, as in the case of willows and perhaps in that of all saplings if they were arranged in the required manner. But since in such matters the mind thinks more aptly than the pen writes, I forbear for the present. I am here merely writing down the statements of scientists and noting their achievements. The genius of these men I admire more than I understand.

Concluding thus the subject of this science experimental without restriction, I shall now show its advantage to theology, as I have done similarly in the case of the other sciences. Since I have now shown the intrinsic nature of this science, it is evident to all that next to moral philosophy this science is the most useful, and it is so in the first place to theology itself in its unrestricted sense because of the literal and spiritual meaning in which it consists. For I showed above that the literal meaning consists in expressing the truth in regard to created things by means of their definitions and descriptions, and I likewise showed that reasoning does not arrive at this truth, but that experiment does. Wherefore this science next to moral philosophy will present the literal truth of Scripture most effectively, so that through suitable adaptations and similitudes the

* Time taken to walk half a mile.

spiritual sense may be derived, owing to the peculiar nature of the sacred Scripture and in accordance with the methods employed by the sacred writers and by all sages.

Then this science as regards the commonwealth of believers is useful, as we saw in its special knowledge of the future, present, and past, and in its display of wonderful works on behalf of Church and state, so that all useful activities are promoted and the opposite are hindered both in the few and in the multitude, as was explained. And if we proceed to the conversion of unbelievers, it is evidently of service in two main ways with numerous subdivisions, since a plea for the faith can be effectively made through this science, not by arguments but by works, which is the more effective way. For to the man who denies the truth of the faith because he cannot understand it I shall state the mutual attraction of things in nature, just as I described it. Likewise I shall tell him that a jar may be broken without human force, and the wine contained in it remain motionless and without flow for three days; and that gold and silver in a pouch, and a sword in its scabbard may be consumed without injury to their containers, as Seneca states in the book of Natural Questions. I shall tell him, moreover, that the birds called kingfisher in the depth of winter compel the stormy sea to be calm and restrain itself until they have laid their eggs and brought forth their young, as Basil and Ambrose in the Hexaemeron and philosophers and poets state. For these facts and similar ones ought to influence a man and urge him to accept the divine verities. Since if in the vilest creatures verities are found by which the pride of the human intellect ought to be subdued so that it may believe them although it does not understand them, conviction should follow, or injury will be done to infallible truth, since a man ought rather to humble his mind to the glorious truths of God. Surely there is no comparison.

But there is still another very useful way; since the formation of judgments, as I have said, is a function of this science, in regard to what can happen by nature or be effected in art, and what not. This science, moreover, knows how to separate the illusions of magic and to detect all their errors in incantations, invocations, conjurations, sacrifices, and cults. But unbelievers busy themselves in these mad acts and trust in them, and have believed that the Christians used such means in working their miracles. Wherefore this science is of the greatest advantage in persuading men to accept the faith, since this branch alone of philosophy happens to proceed in this way, because this is the only branch that considers matters of this kind, and is able to overcome all falsehood and superstition and error of unbelievers in regard to magic, such as incantations and the like already mentioned. How far, moreover, it may serve to reprobate obstinate unbelievers is already shown by the violent means that have just been touched upon, and therefore I pass on.

We must consider, however, that although other sciences do many wonders, as in the case of practical geometry, which produces mirrors that burn up every opposing object, and so too in the other sciences, yet all things of such wonderful utility in the state belong chiefly to this science. For this science has the same relation to the other sciences as the science of navigation to the carpenter's art and the military art to that of the engineer. For this science teaches how wonderful instruments may be made, and uses them when made, and also considers all secret things owing to the advantages they may possess for the state and for individuals; and it directs other sciences as its handmaids, and therefore the whole power of speculative science is attributed especially to this science. And now the wonderful advantage derived from these three sciences in this world on behalf of the Church of God against the enemies of the faith is manifest, who should be destroyed rather by the discoveries of science than by the warlike arms of combatants. Antichrist will use these means freely and effectively, in order that he may crush and confound the power of this world; and by these means tyrants in times past brought the world under their sway. This has been shown by examples without end.

But I now cite the one example of Alexander the Great in place of all other examples that might be cited, who when he set out from Greece to conquer the world had only 32,000 foot soldiers and 4500 horsemen, as Orosius states to Augustine in his book Ormesta Mundi, bringing war with so small a force upon the whole world. It is uncertain which is the more wonderful, that he conquered or that he ventured the attack. In his first battle with King Darius he overcame 600,000 Persians with a loss in his army of 120 horsemen and nine foot soldiers.

In the second battle he conquered 400,000 men, and of his own army 130 foot soldiers and 150 horsemen fell. After this he easily subdued the rest of the world, which had become terrified. But Orosius says that he conquered not less by skill than by the valor of the Macedonians. Nor is it to be wondered at, since Aristotle was with him in these wars, as we read in the life of Aristotle. Seneca, moreover, states in the Natural Questions that Alexander conquered the world under the guidance of Aristotle and Callisthenes, who were his teachers in all knowledge. But Aristotle was his chief teacher; and it is easily apparent from what has been said how by the paths of knowledge Aristotle was able to hand over the world to Alexander. Moreover, the Church should consider the employment of these inventions against unbelievers and rebels, in order that it may spare Christian blood, and especially should it do so because of future perils in the times of Antichrist, which with the grace of God it would be easy to meet, if prelates and princes promoted study and investigated the secrets of nature and of art.

PART SEVEN OF THIS PLEA

MORAL PHILOSOPHY: FIRST PART

I HAVE shown in what precedes that the knowledge of languages, mathematics, perspective, and experimental science are most useful and necessary in the pursuit of wisdom. Without these branches no one can advance as he should in wisdom, taken not only in an unrestricted sense, but also in relation to the Church of God and to the other three activities already described. I now purpose to disclose the principles of a fourth science that is better than all those previously mentioned and nobler. This science is preëminently active, that is, formative, and deals with our actions in this life and in the other. For all other sciences are called speculative. For although certain are active and formative, they are concerned with the actions of art and nature, not with morals, and they investigate the verities of things and of scientific activities which have reference to the speculative intellect and are not concerned with things pertaining to the active intellect, which is called active because it directs action, that is, good or evil action. Hence the term active is here taken in a restricted sense as applying to the actions of conduct, in accordance with which we are good or evil; although if we take the term active in a broad sense for all formative science, many other sciences are active. But this science is called in a self-explanatory way active because of the chief actions of man, which relate to virtues and vices, and to the felicity and misery of the other life.

This active science is called the moral science and the civil science, which instructs man as to his relations to God, and to his neighbor, and to himself, and proves these relations, and invites us to them and powerfully influences us thereto. For this science is concerned with the salvation of man to be perfected through virtue and felicity; and this science aspires to that salvation as far as philosophy can. From these general statements it is evident that this science is nobler than all the other branches of philosophy. For since it is the final inner purpose of human wisdom, and since the purpose is the noblest part in anything, this science is of necessity the noblest. Similarly this science alone or in chief measure is concerned with the same questions as theology; because theology considers only the five aforesaid, although in a different way, namely, in the faith of Christ. This science, moreover, contains a great deal of excellent testimony in regard to this same faith; and from afar surmises its principal articles to the great aid of the Christian faith, as what follows will make clear. But theology is the noblest of the sciences; therefore that science which is most closely related to it is nobler than the others. But that the very great utility of this science may be apparent, we must investigate its parts, to the end that we may draw what we wish from the parts and the whole.

Since, moreover, moral philosophy is the end of all branches of philosophy, the conclusions of the other sciences are the principles in it in accordance with the relationship of preceding sciences to those that follow; because the conclusions of preceding sciences are naturally assumed in those that follow. For this reason it is fitting that these conclusions in preceding sciences should be carefully proved and attested, so that they may be worthy of acceptance in the sciences that follow, as is evident from metaphysics. Therefore the principles of moral philosophy are attested in preceding sciences; and for this reason these principles should be drawn from the other sciences, not because they belong to these sciences, but because these sciences have prepared them for their mistress. Hence wherever they are found they are to be ascribed to moral philosophy, since in substance they relate to morals. And although they may be stated in other sciences, this is by grace of moral philosophy. Wherefore all such are to be considered in regard to moral philosophy and ascribed to it. Therefore if we wish to use them as they were intended to be used, they must be collected in moral science from all the other sciences. Nor is it strange if philosophers through the whole of speculative philosophy have diffused ethical principles, because they knew that these related to man's salvation; and therefore in all the sciences they have diffused beautiful thoughts, so that men might always be directed to the blessing of salvation, and that all might know that the other sciences are sought after only for the sake of that science which is the mistress of human wisdom. Therefore if I adduce from other places authorities other than those contained in books on morals, we should consider that these ought properly to be placed in this science. Nor can we deny that they have been written in books of this science, since in Latin we do not possess except in parts the philosophy of Aristotle, Avicenna, and Averroës, who are the principal authors in this subject. For just as theology perceives that truths bringing salvation belong to it, wherever it finds them, as I stated at the beginning and touched upon later, so also does moral philosophy claim as its right whatever it finds written elsewhere pertaining to it. This science is called moral science by Aristotle, and by others civil science, because it shows the rights of citizens and states. And since cities used to bear sway over countries when Rome ruled the world, this science is called civil from city [*civitas*], although it formulates the rights of kingdom and empire.

This science, moreover, in the first place teaches us to lay down the laws and obligations of life; in the second place it teaches that these are to be believed and approved, and that men are to be urged to act and live according to those laws. The first part falls under three heads; for first comes naturally man's duty to God and in respect to angelic beings; secondly, his duty to his neighbor; and thirdly, his duty to himself, just as the Scripture states. For in the first place in the books of Moses are the commands and laws in regard to God and divine worship. In the second place are those regarding a man's relationship to his neighbor in the same books and in those that follow. In the third place instruction is given in morals, as in the books of Solomon. Similarly in the New Testament these three alone are contained. For a man cannot assume other duties.

Not only on account of the first but of all that follows is it necessary that the principles of this science, by which the others are verified, should be set forth at the beginning. Certain of these principles are purely principles and are capable of being expressed only metaphysically. Others, although they are principles with respect to what follows, either are first conclusions of this science, or although they rejoice in some privilege of a principle, yet because of their very great difficulty, and because they meet with less contradiction,* and because of their very great utility with regard to what follows, ought to be sufficiently demonstrated. Just as Aristotle in the beginning of his

* See Bridges' note on the meaning, Vol. II, page 226.

natural philosophy proves the first principle of that science, namely, that there is motion in opposition to those who maintained that there is only the one immovable. But we must note that metaphysics and moral philosophy are very closely allied; for each is concerned with God, the angels, life eternal, and many questions of this kind, although in different ways. For metaphysics through the common principles of all sciences investigates qualities metaphysically, and through the corporeal investigates the spiritual, and through the created discovers the Creator, and through the present life deals with the future life, and furnishes much introductory matter to moral philosophy. Metaphysics inquires into these subjects because of civil science, so that we have accordingly the right to unite this science with metaphysics, in order that the principles that must be explained in metaphysics may be assumed here, lest I should confound sciences differing from each other if I try to prove in this science what properly belongs to metaphysics.

I state, therefore, that God must exist just as this fact must be proved in metaphysics: second, that God's existence is naturally known to every man; and third, that God is of infinite power and of infinite goodness, and coupled with this that he is of infinite substance and essence, so that it follows that he is best, wisest, and most powerful. Fourth, that God is one in essence and not more than one. Fifth, that not only is God one in essence but triune in another way, which must in general be explained by the metaphysician, but here must be unfolded in special doctrinal form. Sixth, that he has created all things and rules in the realm of nature. Seventh, that besides corporeal things he has created spiritual substances which we call intelligences and angels; because intelligence is a term denoting a nature, but angel is a term denoting an office. This science inquires also how many there are, and what are the activities of these intelligences, in accordance with their relation to metaphysics, as far as it is possible for them to be known by human intelligence. Eighth, that besides angels he has made other spiritual substances which are the rational souls in men. Ninth, that he has made these immortal. Tenth, that the felicity of the other life is the highest good. Eleventh, that man is capable of this felicity. Twelfth, that God has the moral direction of the human race, just as he directs all else in the realm of nature.

head in three equal Persons, but he proved that he exists in this way. These truths are evident from his book on Divine Things. Porphyrius, moreover, as Augustine says in the tenth book on the City of God, chapter XXIX, predicated a Father and his Son, which he called the paternal intellect and mind, and the medium of these, whom, as Augustine says, we think he himself calls the Holy Spirit, and following his custom he calls them three Gods, where, although he employs his terms loosely, he yet perceives the truth to be maintained. Augustine, moreover, in the same book, in chapter XXXII,* states that a certain Platonic philosopher, whose name he does not mention, recited the beginning of the Gospel according to John as far as the Incarnation of Christ, in which the distinction in the divine Persons is clearly stated. Augustine also in the tenth book on the City of God, chapter XXXVI and chapter XXXVII, asserts that Porphyrius states in the first book on the Return of the Soul that sins cannot be purged except by the Son of God. Aristotle states in the beginning of the Heavens and the World that in divine worship our object is to magnify one God through the number three, excellent by reason of the properties of the things that have been created. And therefore since every creature, as is evident from the metaphysics, is a vestige of the Trinity, there must be a Trinity in the Creator. And since Aristotle completed the philosophy of his predecessors as far as his times permitted, he must have had a far more definite perception concerning the blessed Trinity of Persons, so as to confess the Father and the Son and the Holy Spirit. For this reason in the law of Aristotle there were three sacrifices and three prayers, as Averroës says in his commentary on the beginning of the Heavens and the World. This is also made clear by the politics of Aristotle, which is the Book of Laws. Avicenna, moreover, the chief expositor of Aristotle, maintains in the principles of moral philosophy that there is a Holy Spirit.

But he was able to perceive the truth far more clearly concerning the Father and the Son, because it is more difficult to understand the procession of the Holy Spirit from two distinct persons than the generation of one of these from the other. For this reason philosophers were more deficient in their comprehension of the Holy Spirit than in their knowledge of the

* See Bridges' note, Vol. II, page 230.

Father and the Son. And therefore those who were able to gain a knowledge of the Holy Spirit knew much more about the other Persons. Ethicus the philosopher in his book on Things Divine, Human, and Natural, maintains that in God are the Father, and the Word of the Father, and the Holy Spirit; and that there are three Persons, namely, the Father and the Son and the Holy Spirit. This dogma must also be held by reason. This reasoning, however, should not have been given before those things that have to be expressed concerning God in particular, nor before the authorities of the great philosophers, which are introduced for this same purpose in this science as in a place appropriate for them.

I say, therefore, that God is of infinite power, and infinite power is capable of infinite action; therefore something infinite can be made by God, but not anything by substance, because in that case there could be a plurality of gods. The contrary to this has been demonstrated in the section on mathematics. Therefore that which is begotten by God must be God, since it has the essential nature of the begetter; yet it is different in person. And since that which is begotten has infinite power, since it is infinite goodness, it is able to bring forth infinite goodness; therefore it is able to bring it forth in another person. Then, therefore, either the Father brings forth the same person; and in that case the Holy Spirit will proceed from both, or he will be brought forth from the Son alone; and then he will not appertain to the Father, nor will there be full relationship, and in that case there will not be complete accord in the divine Persons, which is contrary to reason. Moreover, there cannot be parity of love according to this view, because the Father would love the Son more than he loves the Holy Spirit, because he begets the Son, and does not bring forth the Holy Spirit. But since the Holy Spirit is God, because he has the divine nature, an infinite love must be due him; and therefore the Father will love him just as he does the Son with an infinite love. And also since the love of the Father cannot be less than an infinite love, because his love is in accordance with his power, it remains, then, that the love of the Father for the Holy Spirit will be as great as that of the Son for the Holy Spirit. Wherefore both the Holy Spirit and the Son must be brought forth from the Father. That, moreover, there are not nor can there be more persons, cannot and ought not to be explained here, but should be assumed, until it is proved in the fourth part of this science, on which the full measure of persuasive argument will be bestowed. But it was necessary that the trinity of Persons, namely, the Father and the Son and the Holy Spirit, should be proved and expounded here, because it is the fundamental principle in this science for establishing divine worship and for many other things. Nor should it be stated, on the other hand, that no science must prove its principles. For how this is to be understood has been explained above. But the other questions that can be asked in regard to God and in which there should be probable doubt, are the conclusions of the fourth part, and therefore they will be determined there.

Not only have the philosophers spoken of God unrestrictedly, but of God incarnate, who is the Lord Jesus Christ, and of those things that pertain to him. For truths of this nature are necessary for the human race, and there is no salvation for man except through a knowledge of these truths. And therefore it was necessary for the salvation of all from the beginning of the world that truths of this kind should be known as far as suffices for salvation. I state this fact because some men have more knowledge, some less, of truths of this kind. It was fitting also that philosophers devoted to wisdom should know something of this truth, whether they were to be saved or not; so that the world might be prepared and made ready for this perfect truth, in order that it might be more easily received when the time came. And the plea in regard to it was stated in greater fullness in a preceding section, and for this reason a general plea suffices here, in order that by experience we may learn that the philosophers had knowledge of many remarkable facts in regard to Christ and the glorious Virgin. Moreover in the section on astronomy the formal judgment of Albumazar was cited from the sixth book of the larger Introduction, where he asserts on the authority of all from the beginning of philosophy that a Virgin should bring forth a son who would be called Jesus Christ. Moreover, in the book of Conjunctions he made a similar statement. But this judgment, although it is stated in the section on Astronomy and there verified like a conclusion, is properly a principle in this science. Hence this science receives this noble principle that has been proved in astronomy; and in this way this science is served, as a mistress by her maidservant. The same is true in certain other sciences, as we note from what precedes, and as we shall state below. Porphyrius, moreover, said that sins cannot be taken away except by the Son of God, as stated above. Moreover, on that statement, "His divinity proved from the instruction of Plato's scholars," the expositor says that in the tomb of Plato a statement written in golden letters was found on his breast containing these words, "I believe in Christ who will be born of a virgin, will suffer for the human race and will rise again on the third day." But the philosopher Ethicus also in the book already mentioned says, "The just shall deserve to see their Lord Christ and their King and the marks and prints of the nails, and the Word of the Father and the Beginning, creating all things with him." The human mind can be influenced to accept the truth of the virgin birth, because certain animals remaining in a state of virginity conceive and bear young, as, for example, vultures and apes, as Ambrose states in the Hexaemeron. Moreover, mares in many regions conceive by virtue of the winds alone, when they desire the male, as Pliny* states in the fifth book of the Natural History, and Solinus tells us in his book on the Wonders of the World. Aristotle maintains in the second book on Vegetation that the fruits of the female palms mature from an odor coming from the male trees.

Since a knowledge of Antichrist pertains to the Christian faith, because this faith holds that Antichrist will come, whom Christ will destroy, therefore the statement has been added to the articles of the faith that we believe Antichrist will come. Therefore one principle of this science is concerned with the coming of Antichrist in confirmation of the things pertaining to the Christian faith. Ethicus the philosopher therefore states that about the time of Antichrist there will be a race of the stock of Gog and Magog opposite the fertile districts of the North around the Black Sea, the worst of all the nations, which in company with the worst seed of those shut up behind the Caspian gates of Alexander will cause a great devastation of this world, and will meet Antichrist and will call him God of gods. Albumazar also in the book of Conjunctions verifies similarly this principle, stating and showing that a leader shall

* Pliny, IV, 22; VIII, 42.

come with a foul and magical law after the law of Mahomet, who shall destroy the other laws for a time. But he shall not last long, owing to the magnitude of the evil. This has been explained above. Without doubt careful consideration must be given to this principle of this science. For the race of the Tartars has come forth from those places, as we know, since they dwelt behind those gates to the northeast, shut up in the mountains of the Caucasus and of the Caspian, and are leading with them peoples who already are masters from the mountains mentioned as far as the confines of Poland, Bohemia, and Hungary, countries far this side of the fertile lands of the North. For it is true that other races have emigrated from those places and have invaded the world to the south as far as the Holy Land, just as the Tartars are now doing, as Jerome writes in his letters and the histories tell us. Moreover, the race of the Goths and of the Vandals which later invaded the South are from the regions of the North. Therefore the invasion of the Tartars is not sufficient to fix the time of the coming of Antichrist, but other facts are required, as what follows will explain.

Another principle concerns the judgment to come. For an article of the Christian faith refers to this, in regard to which the philosopher Ethicus has said, "The devil, who had been established in the beginning and had been the first to fall, will be punished before all wicked men and will be shut up in hell. Since he shone forth first in the order of creation, and was illustrious as a miracle of God's ways, he will be the first to suffer all the penalties in the last terrible judgment to come, such as have been appointed for him from the beginning in the hollow of the lake, and have been reserved for the judgment before the tribunal of the king, in order that the wicked may see the very truculent author of their death."

Another principle relates to the creation, which, since it requires proof in metaphysics, is known; therefore it is to be touched upon here only as regards morals. Aristotle in his book on the Regimen of Kingdoms expressly assumes it and names Adam and Enoch, and therefore knew of the first man and the beginning of the world. Albumazar, moreover, in his book on Conjunctions, doing an excellent service for moral philosophy, assumes a first man, namely, Adam, and shows how long was the period from him to the deluge, and how long from the deluge to Christ, and how long from Christ to Mahomet, and how long from him to the foul law. Avicenna also explicitly assumes the creation. Moreover, Ethicus the philosopher says, "First of all God made all creatures, and with a supreme effort formed a massive whole, and those things which he made out of nothing he amplified in many ways." Trismegistus also in his book on Deity says to Asclepius, "In the Creator are all things before he had created them," so that he is in agreement with John the Evangelist who says, "In himself was the life of that which was made." Yet this Trismegistus lived near the time of Moses and Joshua, as Augustine states in his book on the City of God.

In regard to the beings first created we find another principle of this science; of this kind are the angels, good and bad. In the first place, therefore, because of the motions of the heavenly bodies, which they have discovered to be about sixty, philosophers have assumed that there are that many good angels, because those motions are voluntary and therefore are caused by angels. This, moreover, is evident from the Metaphysics of Aristotle and of Avicenna. In the second place, they have passed on to a further consideration and have found an almost infinite number corresponding to us, just as individuals in this world below are multiplied under one species, and are distinguished from one another in number, as sensible individuals, as we find stated in the book on Causes; with a difference, however, because the angels are separated from one another in a way that they do not suffer corruption, but remain in a stable being. These individuals, however, that are known to us are separated from one another in a way that they finally suffer corruption. Moreover, if we wish to wonder further at the words of Ethicus, we can state, as he himself does in his book, that there are twenty orders of angels; who he also assumed stand in the celestial glory.

But far more is Apuleius of Mandara to be wondered at in his book on the God of Socrates, in which in his exposition of many wonderful things regarding the nature of angels he transcribes the opinion of Plato in the Symposium, namely, that to each man there is an angel deputed to guard him against all evils, and to urge and arouse him to what is good. And after the soul has been separated, the angel becomes a witness before

Moral Philosophy

God as the judge of all the good and evil things which that soul did in the body. He asserts, moreover, that angels carry the petitions of men to the heavenly beings and bring back gifts from them to men; and that one angel is charged with one duty, another with another; and he makes many statements of this kind in the following words: "There are certain divine powers in an intermediate state between men and gods, through whom our desires and merits reach the gods. They are bearers hence of prayers and thence of gifts, who quickly carry our petitions hence to the region beyond, and thence bring back the answers; or they are certain agents acting for both parties, and each of them, according to his special function, provides that salvation be brought us by these messengers, either by confirming dreams, or by directing those set over us, or by clearing up what is too obscure for us, or by inspiring prophets, or by other means which we recognize as from God. We must judge that all these things are done by the divine will, power, and authority, but by the ministry and activity of the angels. From this host of angels Plato then states one is assigned to each man during his life as a witness and a guardian, who, manifest to the mind, is always present as a judge not only of his acts but also of his thoughts. And when our life is over that same angel who was assigned to us must hasten thither and carry as it were his guardianship to judgment; and he must assist there in pleading the case and sentence must be given in accordance with his testimony." "I then admonish you all who hear this divine opinion of Plato according to my version, so form your minds with regard to all your acts and thoughts, that you may know that a man has nothing secret in his soul nor beyond it because of those guardians. Nay, your angel carefully perceives all things, sees all things and understands them, this guardian, individual overseer, household observer, personal defender, intimate advocate, constant watcher, personal judge, inseparable witness, condemner of what is evil, approver of what is good, provider in your uncertainties, forewarner in your doubts, defender in your perils, aid in your needs, who is able in dreams, and in signs, and in person when necessity requires, to curtail your ills, prosper your good, control prosperity, ease adversity." For this is a wonderful statement and wholly favorable to the Christian, and contains nothing unworthy either in the letter or the spirit. May we clearly see that it contains well-known articles belonging to the faith; nor should the philosopher be here interpreted in a worse sense, since his statement evidently contains nothing except that which is consistent with the truth in a wonderful way. I make this statement because others sometimes try to obscure Catholic sentiments found in books of the philosophers. But we should receive gladly such statement in testimony of our faith; and since it is certain that these men learned them through a revelation made to them and to the holy patriarchs and prophets, as we have already shown.

Porphyry, moreover, as Augustine states in the tenth book of the City of God, said that there are angels who descending from above proclaim divine messages to men, and that there are others who on earth declare those things that belong to the Father and state his majesty and profundity. Concerning the devil and his angels philosophers have said many things. For the philosopher Ethicus has expressed a trustworthy opinion about him, as stated above, in regard to his creation, his sin, and his primordial and final damnation after the judgment. He has also ventured to say that the tenth order fell after sin into the punishment of hell. Apuleius and Plato and others distinguish two kinds of daemons, since *daemon* in Greek is the same as *sciens* [versed] in Latin. Therefore also there are *calo-daemones* and *caco-daemones,* that is, good and bad daemons. For *calon* means good and *cacon* means bad. Concerning the good we are to understand what has been said with reference to the guardianship of men. But the evil ones are devils by name and yield to the irrational passions of the mind, according to Apuleius; whence they are subject to displeasure and torment of mind and pleasure from evil and rage and the other malign impulses. These are they of whom the poets speak, as Apuleius states, and whom they represent to be gods and the lovers of some people and hateful to others; and certain of them are incubuses and lead men to sins and vices, and afterwards to the punishment of hell, of which Hermes Trismegistus and the philosopher Ethicus speak.

The immortality of the soul is touched upon in metaphysics. But we must mention it here in reference to morals and particularly in reference to the resurrection of the body, concerning which the metaphysician could not express an opinion, either general or particular. Moreover, not only Aristotle and Avicenna have given general conditions for the immortality of souls of which mention was made previously, but philosophers in treating of morals have spoken of it. For in the first place Cicero in the Tusculan Disputations states as a philosophical proposition the immortality of the soul, and through that whole book investigates it, and considers various arguments for it which are manifest from that book, nor can they be given here because of their great length. And similarly in his book on Old Age this same question of immortality is settled by Marcus Tullius. Moreover, in his book on the Divine Nature, Hermes Mercurius beautifully says, "The God and father of all and lord, and he who alone is all in all, gladly reveals himself; not, however, as regards his locality nor quality nor quantity; but the intelligence alone of the mind illuminates the man who, with the darkness of error dispersed and the brightness of truth perceived, identifies himself with a full sense of the divine intelligence. Freed by his love of this from the share of nature in which he is mortal he conceives a confident belief in a future immortality." Moreover, Avicenna says in the Morals that Mahomet spoke of the glory of the body; but we know, as he says, that the glory of our souls is greater, since we are not asses, reckoning only the delights of the body; and therefore he finds fault with his own lawgiver and wishes another to investigate who promises not only the glory of our bodies, but rather that of our souls. In this Seneca agrees throughout, and Socrates and Plato, as is evident in the Phaedo. Avicenna, moreover, says in the Morals that the resurrection of our bodies must be assumed, as the entire man will be glorified in soul and body if he obeys the commands of God. Not only Avicenna and others of the school of Aristotle have perceived this truth, but Democritus also, who belonged to an earlier age and was a philosopher of great repute, as Pliny states in his Natural History, book VII. Moreover, Plato himself has also said that souls cannot exist forever without bodies, but return to them, just as Augustine teaches in the twenty-second book of the City of God. Varro also in his book on the Race of the Roman People states that many philosophers have said that the same soul will return at length to the same identical body. If, therefore, Plato maintained that souls return to bodies, and Varro that the soul returns to the same body, and if Porphyry, the greatest of philosophers according to Augustine, maintains that a purged soul will never go to evil nor to this world but to God the Father; the resurrection must then follow from the statements of the philosophers.

This conclusion, moreover, is necessary, since from the source of philosophy they have elicited the fact that virtue belongs to the entire union formed of soul and body, that is, man, not to soul only nor to the soul in man, but to man through the soul, just like understanding and building, as Aristotle says in the first book on the Soul.* And they have therefore assumed that felicity belongs to the entire union, whence they have not assumed that man is a soul in a body but in reality is composed of soul and body, so that the essence of man is formed of soul and body, and that his essence is not soul alone in a body. For that which is nobler as regards man they have assumed to be the precise subject of virtue and felicity, but this is a union as far as possible of this kind, since he himself who is composed of soul and body is a noble substance. And although spiritual felicity and virtue are in man by reason of his soul, yet they do not belong to the soul, so that they have their place there, but they are in man because of the united man himself; and therefore they have maintained that felicity which is man's goal, completes the whole man, both as respects the body, as due to it, and as respects the soul. And therefore they have maintained that the body is at length united with the soul, so that both may be perfected in accordance with its special character. For they knew by reason that form is appropriated by its own matter, and contrariwise. And therefore incorruptible form appropriates incorruptible matter, and contrariwise. For they knew that the desire of form is not satisfied except in its own matter. And they have assumed that the desire of the soul is wholly satisfied by felicity. Wherefore they have assumed that it would be in a body.

The reasonings and persuasive arguments of philosophers on this point are of this nature. For they knew that the power of God is infinite, and therefore it can cause the same body to return. And the agent of finite power is able to make the same

* *De Anima,* I, 4, 12.

thing in species, as, for example, nature from a corrupt seed makes other seeds of the same species. Wherefore much more so will the agent of infinite power be able to make the same thing in number [*i.e.,* the same individual]. For infinite power infinitely exceeds finite power. But the production of the same thing according to number infinitely exceeds the production of the same thing according to species. But Aristotle says in the ninth book of the Metaphysics that the living is formed from the dead if a resolving takes place to the first matter. Since, therefore, God is able to cause this resolving, as is evident, a resurrection can take place. Likewise we have a strong supporting argument in the phoenix, which after being reduced to its own ashes comes to life again and becomes a phoenix. But a stronger one is drawn from the worm, which after birth quickly dies, and again coming to life remains immortal, as the philosophers and sacred writers state, and as we learn from the books of the Hexaemeron which determine the works of the six days.

In regard to the felicity of the other life and the misery prepared for the evil, the moral philosopher must assume principles in addition to that which has been touched upon in metaphysics. For these questions must be considered in metaphysics in general, but here in particular. For excellently do the philosophers determine the causes by which we are hindered from a knowledge of eternal life. These hindrances are four in number: sin, care of the body, trammels of the sensible world, and lack of revelation. For revelation is not a matter within our power. But on the question whether there be an eternal promise, they have been able to secure some knowledge, as I have said, and also in general on the question of the reality and nature of this future life. They have not, however, been able to give us particular and definite instruction on this subject, chiefly because of the four reasons first stated. Hence Avicenna in the Fundamentals of Moral Philosophy after many statements concludes, "Our condition as regards these matters is like that of a deaf man who has never heard in his privation of the power of imagining the delight of harmony, although he may be certain of the reality and nature of its sweetness." And not only is the intellect in this condition in knowing, but also the desire and the will in longing for, loving, tasting, or enjoying the sweetness of eternal life, to quote the words of Avicenna. For he compares us to a paralytic to whom delicious food is brought, but he does not perceive its sweetness until he is cured of his paralysis and the disease removed. Such is our condition, he says, with respect to the sweetness of life eternal, both because of our sins and our union with a mortal body; for sins affect the desire of the rational soul, and the weight of the body burdens it. Hence Avicenna gracefully says that we in our age and in this body have been plunged in many vices, and therefore do not perceive that delight, although there are in us some of its causes. And therefore we do not seek after it nor are we attracted to it, until we have removed from our necks the yoke of pleasure and anger, and their sister vices, and thus shall we taste something of that delight; and thus perhaps we shall gain too slight a perception of it, as through something interposed, because revelation is still necessary. Therefore he says that then shall we have a clearer perception, especially when the questions concerning God, and the felicity and immortality of our souls, and the resurrection of our bodies have been settled; and similar truths of high import have been revealed to us. Then, as Avicenna says, "The comparison of our perfect delight with our imperfect one will be like a comparison of the delight of our senses in smelling the odors of delicious foods with the delight we experience in actually eating them."

But the attention paid by the soul to the body, as he says, causes the soul to forget itself and that which it ought to love; just as a weak man is forgetful of that which it is necessary to restore in place of that which is taken from him. For, as he himself states, the body seizes upon the substance of the soul and makes it foolish, and causes it to forget its natural longing and search for the perfection that befits it, and its perception of the delight of its own perfection. Not that the soul has been impressed on the body and immersed in it; but because there is a bond between these two, which is the natural desire to direct the body and to excite its affections.

The third hindrance is the attention one bestows on this world of sense, although a man may not sin nor be occupied with bodily interests. For since we are given over to the world of sense, we neglect the insensible and spiritual world, as Avicenna shows. In these statements he clearly and cogently touches upon the causes that hinder us in our consideration and love of felicity.

On the other hand, his words point out to us what our aids are in knowing and loving and tasting the delight of future felicity. The first of these is the purification of the soul from sins. And the second is the withdrawal of the soul from its natural desire to direct the body. And the third is the elevation of the mind from this world of sense, that it may cleave to the world of intelligence. And the fourth is the attestation through revelation and prophecy in regard to those things about which the human mind cannot form judgment, such as the questions of high import of which he is speaking. For in such matters, as he says, "We believe the testimony of the prophet and the legislator who receives the law from God." He who possesses these four would not place felicity in this world but misery and death, as will be explained clearly below; and with Aristotle, Theophrastus, and other true philosophers would have leisure for the contemplation of future felicity, as far as a man can, in order that a good and merciful God might reveal the truth in fuller measure, just as we have proved that he revealed it to others besides those who were born and reared under the old dispensation or the new one, as must be stated in metaphysics. Since, moreover, they perceived that for a knowledge of felicity it is necessary to separate themselves from sins and from excessive love of the body and from the world, in order that they might be able to receive from God the fourth aid, namely, enlightenment within, so that they might understand the articles of the truths of the faith, casting all else aside they gave themselves up to a wise contemplation of future felicity.

For wisdom, as Aristotle states in the fourth book of the Ethics, is almost the same as felicity, since wisdom is not mere knowledge but is an intellectual force, as he himself determines, producing rather an affection for future felicity than an understanding and a beginning of it, since both are the knowledge and love of God. But wisdom possesses both of these as far as it is possible in this life, and felicity comprehends them imperfectly. For this same fact is evident in regard to felicity and is made manifest in regard to wisdom by the first book of the Metaphysics and by the sixth and the tenth books of the Ethics. Therefore Aristotle himself, the most excellent of all philosophers, renounced all things, that he might have leisure for contemplation suited to a sage, because this life resembles most the divine life; and therefore it was seen by the sage to be the most worthy, as Cicero writes in reference to Aristotle in the fifth* book of the Academics; and similarly in reference to Theophrastus, his successor in philosophy.

After they were prepared for divine enlightenment and had received it they maintained that this felicity is a beatitude of the whole man both in body and soul, which eye has not seen nor ear heard, as Avicenna says. This felicity is a state perfect in the aggregation of all good things, as the philosophy of Boetius teaches in the third book of the Consolation. Moreover, in the same book he proves that this can only be through participation in the highest good, which is God, because complete participation in good does not exist except in a participation in God who is the perfect good. Therefore men cannot be blessed and happy except by enjoying the goodness of God. Therefore his philosophy contains a noble corollary, namely, that the blessed are gods; but there is only one God of nature with many, namely, all the blessed, sharing his deity. Aristotle, moreover, in the first book of the Moral Philosophy teaches that human desire cannot have its limit in any good except in the highest good by which it is terminated; because the desire of the rational soul transcends all finite good and passes on to the infinite good. Therefore of necessity it participates in the highest and infinite good, which is God, if its desire must be satisfied. But it must evidently be satisfied through felicity, wherefore the soul must enjoy God for ever. And then as regards the speculative intellect, the soul will become, according to Avicenna, an intelligible world, and there will be described in it the form of the whole universe and the order of all things from the beginning, namely, God, both through all spiritual substances and the heavens, etc., until there is perfected in it the arrangement of the universe, so that it may thus pass into the world of intellect, perceiving that which is perfect beauty and true grace. And as regards the active intellect he says that it will be perfected in pure goodness, and its delight will not be of the kind of delight pertaining to the senses, which is

* Bridges suggests that the reference may be to *De Finibus,* lib. V, cap. 25.

caused alone by bringing together the surfaces of sensible bodies affecting our senses; nay, it enters the soul, and is infused into its substance, and is a delight befitting the natural disposition that is in pure and spiritual living substances. It is, moreover, more excellent and more noble than any other delight; and this is the delight of felicity, as he affirms.

Not only have they spoken of the felicity, but also of the misery of the other life which is reserved for the wicked. Hence they have maintained that God has prepared for those who obey him a promised felicity which eye has not seen nor the heart of man apprehended; and for the disobedient a dreadful punishment, as Avicenna states. Moreover, Cicero, Trismegistus, Socrates, and many others have spoken expressly of these promises. Hence Cicero says in the first book of the Tusculan Disputations* that two paths and two courses are open to men. Those who have kept themselves upright and pure and have had the least possible contact with the body and in their human bodies have imitated the divine life find the return easy to him from whom they came forth, namely, to God. But the path of those who have defiled themselves with human vices is at length far removed from the counsel of God. Hermes Mercurius in his book on the Divine Nature speaks as follows: "After the departure of the soul from the body has taken place, the judgment and test of its merit pass to the supreme power, which on perceiving the soul to be good and just permits it to remain in places suitable for it. But if this supreme power perceives the soul to be smeared with the stains of faults and marred with vices, it thrusts the soul down to the depths and delivers it up to eternal punishments, so that in this case eternity is a disadvantage to the soul that has been brought under the yoke of eternal punishment by an unalterable sentence." Therefore we learn that we must stand in awe and fear and be on our guard lest we be ensnared by these things. For unbelievers after their transgressions will be compelled to believe not by words but by examples, not by threats but by the actual suffering of punishments. Ethicus the philosopher and Alchimus in their books teach that the wicked are to suffer in hell with the devil, in

---

* *Tusculan Disputations,* lib. I, cap. 30. Here as in many other passages Bacon has substituted the singular of the word God for the plural.

order that the impious may see the very savage and furious author of death, whom they followed into many useless and harmful desires. The just will deserve to see their Lord God, as I explained above.

The principles having been stated with respect to what follows, although they are conclusions with respect to the statements given previously, and with respect to others of this kind, we must now pass to the laws of divine worship before we consider the other rights, public or private, in human society. Moreover, it is evident that because of our reverence for God a worship without end is his due. This is due him also because of the blessing of our creation, which is the effect of his infinite power, and because of future felicity. Because of the first, Avicenna says in his Moral Principles that obedience to God's precepts is his right; because of the second, he says that obedience must be given to the commands of him to whom creation belongs. Because of the third, he says that God has prepared a promised felicity for those obedient to him and for the disobedient a terrible future punishment. Worship is also due him because of the cleansing of the human race from sins by the Son of God, a cleansing of which Porphyry has spoken, since this is more than the mere act of creating. Also because of the acceptance of our humanity in the unity of the Divine Person, of which Albumazar, Plato, and Ethicus have spoken, for this must be infinite joy to us; and because of the prints of the nails and the passion and the redemption, which Plato and Ethicus have affirmed. And not only this but all that has been stated previously influences men to worship God and leads them to conclude that this worship should be rendered.

For this reason Marcus Tullius in the first book of the Tusculan Disputations says, "What else in fact is philosophy, the mother of all arts, if not, as Plato says, the gift, as I say, the invention of God? She taught us in the first place his worship, and then the rights of mankind on which human society is based." The same writer also says in the second book on the Divine Nature, "The best and likewise the most sacred, the most pure and pious worship of God is for us to reverence him always with a pure, blameless, unpolluted mind and voice. For not only the philosophers but our ancestors as well have separated superstition from religion. For those who were wont to

[656]

pray whole days and to sacrifice, that* they themselves and their children might survive, were called superstitious, a word which afterwards became more general. But those who paid diligent attention to all that pertains to the worship of God and, as we may say, read over again these matters were called *religiosi,* religious, from *relegendo,* reading over again; as *eligentes,* those making a choice, from *eligendo,* making a choice; *legentes,* readers, from *legendo,* reading; and *intelligentes,* intelligent, from *intelligendo,* understanding. The one is a term of reproach, the other of praise." For Augustine in the fourth book on the City of God accepts and explains this opinion of Cicero in regard to superstition and true religion, and in the eighth book of the same work, his opinion regarding religion and the religious; maintaining that they were called religious because they choose God and revere him, again and again making the choice through a true and continuous worship.

Moreover, in this worship, according to Avicenna and others, temples, prayers, oblations and sacrifices, and fasts must be appointed, and also very great peregrinations to the seat of the legislator, in order that he may be kept in memory and held in veneration. Aristotle also in his considerations of this worship says that never should we be more modest than when we are engaged in divine worship; if we enter temples let us be composed, if we are about to approach the sacrifice let us lower the countenance, if in our prayer we are to give an indication of modesty. Therefore Avicenna says, "The teacher ought to instruct one who prays in the proper means by which he may be prepared for prayer, just as a man is wont to prepare himself to meet a human king in cleanliness and with a becoming appearance. Such a teacher should cause his pupil to form the habit of cleanliness and of presenting a becoming appearance, and should train him in the manner of a man preparing himself to meet a king with humility and downcast look, with limbs restrained, and without needless turning of the body and disturbance." Philosophers such as Avicenna and others decide that great festivals should be appointed, for the reason that they cause nations to assemble and give them boldness in the law and inspire an emulation of it. Such festivals also give an opportunity

* It is to be noted that Bacon has substituted *ipsi et sui liberi* for *sibi sui liberi.*

for the prayers of the multitude to be heard; and because of these festivals they discover blessings from God. And similarly for the same reasons general fraternities should be formed.

How, moreover, in particular prayer can fitly be offered Hermes Mercurius teaches in his book on Divine Matters, beginning thus, "God himself lacks nothing excellent, but let us adore him by giving thanks. For thanks when rendered by mortals are God's highest incense." He also says, "Thanks be to thee, thou supreme and most excellent Being, by thy grace alone have we obtained the light of thy knowledge. O sacred name and the one name to be honored, by which God alone must be blessed because of a paternal religion, since thou deignest to give to all paternal care and religion and love and all things that tend to make life sweeter, and grantest us rational sense and intelligence. Sense that we may come to know thee; reason that we may search thee out more clearly; intelligence that we may rejoice in knowing thee, and also that after being saved by thy divine power we may rejoice, because thou hast revealed thyself wholly to us. Let us rejoice because thou hast seen fit to consecrate us to eternity while we are still in our bodies. For the knowledge of thy majesty is the only source of human rejoicing. O true life of life! O universal productiveness of nature! we know thee, eternal in thy duration. Therefore in this whole prayer adoring thee we ask this only that thou wouldst keep us ever in the love of the knowledge of thee and never suffer us to be parted from this kind of life. With this prayer we turn to a pure supper free from animal food."

On the sacrifices, oblations, and ceremonies of these people we need not dwell, because they were superstitious and useless for the most part, except in so far as they took some things from the priests of the Jewish law. Hence also the philosophers themselves practiced such customs because of civil statutes and because of popular prejudice, not because of their truth, as Seneca states in the book which he composed against superstitions. For although as a senator he was obliged to dissemble in regard to the public statutes, yet he says that ceremonies of this kind do not pertain to the advantage but the custom of the people at large; and that no person of discernment should give them consideration in his private life. Also the observances of the Jews he considered absurd and unbecoming a wise man, just as God also allowed them to have these ceremonies rather lest they should become idolaters than because of their truth, as the sacred writers bear witness. And thus the fundamentals of the first part of Moral Philosophy are brought to a close.

MORAL PHILOSOPHY: SECOND PART

CHAPTER I

Concerning the observance of the laws of marriage and of the state.

THE second part treats of the laws and statutes regulating human relations. In the first place, the preservation of the human species is considered in the line of propagation with a view to bind the people by laws in their increase. Therefore legislators give the laws of marriage and determine how they must be made and how obstacles may be removed; and especially do they decree that fornicators and sodomites be excluded from states, who are inimical to the fabric of the state, since they draw men away from that which is a better thing in states, namely, marriage, as Avicenna and others maintain.

In the next place, laws are given in accordance with which the mutual relationship existing between subjects and prelates and princes is arranged, and that between slaves and their masters as regards every class of servitude and ownership. Laws are also given in accordance with which the fathers of families must live in directing their offspring and family, and the master as regards his pupils. Next, teachers are appointed and artificers in the different sciences and arts; and from the youths to be instructed those best fitted to pursue studies and perform duties of this kind according to the advice of wise men are selected; and the rest are assigned to military duty to execute justice and check malefactors. And it is necessary, as Avicenna says, that in instituting law this should be the first intention, namely, to arrange the state in three parts, those who administer, those who serve, and those skilled in the law, and that in each of these groups a dignitary be appointed. After him other dignitaries inferior to him should be appointed, and after these still others until nearly all are included, to the end that no one should be useless in the state, but that each one may have an honorable status, and that from each profit may be derived by the state. Hence in Plato that state is said to be most justly organized in which each citizen comes to know his proper function. Therefore, as Avicenna says, the prince of a state ought to prohibit idleness and lack of occupation. Moreover, those who cannot be restrained should be expelled from the state except in the case of infirmity or old age; and then a place should be assigned in which people of this kind should remain and have a keeper appointed over them. It is necessary, moreover, that in the state there should be a means of collecting a public fund, which in part should come in accordance with the law governing contracts, partly from fines inflicted for malicious prosecution, partly from the estates and spoils of rebels, partly from other sources; and that this public fund should be secured in part for those who are not able to make a living owing to infirmity and old age, and in part for teachers of law and medicine, and in part for public uses.

And then the legislator teaches men to frame laws relating to patrimonies, inheritances, and wills; because Avicenna says that the substance necessary for life is partly branch, partly root. But the root is patrimony and anything bequeathed and given by will, of which three roots patrimony is the most secure. But the branch of substance comes from gains derived from the various kinds of business. Then laws should be published regarding contracts in all kinds of business, buying, selling, giving out and taking contracts, borrowing, lending, expending, saving, and the like, so that in contracts whatever can do harm may be excluded, as Avicenna says.

Then laws must be framed in accordance with which in all causes and cases justice may be shown and the cases closed, so that peace and justice may be fostered among citizens. Afterwards, as Avicenna says, pursuits must be prohibited by which inheritances and property are lost, and the peace and concord of citizens are disturbed; and those practicing these pursuits are people who wish to get the upper hand in the case of some gain, as, for example, the wrestler, the gambler, and the like. Similarly, pursuits should be prohibited which are in opposition to what is advantageous, as he shows in his instruction in regard to thieving, pillaging, and other acts of this kind.

And further ordinances should be passed, as Avicenna states, that men should aid and defend one another, and be united against the foes of law in the effort to subdue them. If, moreover, another state or government has good regulations and

laws, therefore no attack is made on it, except that the time will
come when there must be no other law than that one, the estab-
lishment of which, since it is the best, must then be extended
throughout the whole world. In this statement the Christian
law is hinted at, as will be explained below. If, moreover, there
are some among these who are at variance with the law, let
them first be corrected, in order that they may come to their
senses; but if they are unwilling to do so, let them be put to
death.

CHAPTER II

THE last point required here is that the legislator should arrange for his successor. This is done, according to Avicenna, in
this way. For he must do this with the consent of the nobles
and of the people; and he should choose a man who can rule
well and is prudent and of good morals. He should be courageous, kind, skilled in management and in the law, than whom,
in fact, no one is more skilled, and this fact should be evident
to all. But if after this men should so disagree that they desire
to choose another, they have actually denied God, and for this
reason the legislator should place in his law enactments that the
whole state should with one accord attack and slay any one
who wishes to obtrude himself by power or money. But if they
shall have the power to do this and shall not have done it, they
have actually contradicted God, nor is he blood-guilty who kills
such men, provided that the facts are already known to the people. But if the man who should receive the office is not worthy
and this fact has been proved, let another be appointed.

Thus terminates the statement of the application of the principles of the second part with what follows as consequences to
the principles in general. In this part the civil law is included,
which is now in force among the Latins, as is evident from the
principles of this part. Moreover, it is certain that the Latins
received their rights and laws from the Greeks; namely, from
the books of Aristotle and Theophrastus his successor, with the
exception of the laws of the twelve tables which in the first
place came from the laws of Solon the Athenian.

MORAL PHILOSOPHY: THIRD PART

Chapter I

Concerning the guidance of a man in reference to himself.

THE third part of moral and civil science is concerned with personal conduct, to the end that every one should keep his life pure and free from the foulness of vices because of future felicity and the horror of eternal punishment. It is clearly evident that this should be the third part, since it is plain that that part which contains the worship of God is the first, as I have stated. But public good takes precedence of private good, as Aristotle says in the first book of the Metaphysics. But the part preceding contains the public good; this part urges upon men private good. For love is the greatest virtue, and is ordained for the common good, and peace and justice are its companions, virtues which transcend the morals of individuals. For man is a social animal and it is in accordance with his own nature, as Avicenna says in the fifth book on the Soul, that he should not live alone like a beast which in its life suffices itself alone. Therefore the laws regulating men with regard to the last topic are more important.

According to Aristotle and Averroës, in the tenth book of the Metaphysics, a hermit who is not a part of the state, but lives for himself alone, is neither good nor bad. And Cicero in his book on Duties, quoting the words of Plato, highly commends his statement that we were not born for ourselves alone. Our country claims part of our origin, and friends a part, and as it is a tenet of the Stoics that all things are created for the use of men, they taught that men were generated for the sake of men, so that they might be able to benefit one another. Since Cicero himself says in the fifth book of the Academics, "Nothing is so noble as the imparting of benefits." For it is innate in man to have some organized society, a relationship expressed by the Greeks in the word *politicon*. Hence in his book on the Happy Life Seneca says, "This statement is required of a man, that he benefit all if it can be done, or many; if not, a few; if not, his nearest relatives; if not, himself." Wherefore the second principal part of moral philosophy must be concerned with public laws, as I have stated; and the third part will deal with the life and integrity each one should strive after. This, moreover, is the proper arrangement according to Nature's dignity and for simplicity of statement, although Aristotle does not adopt this method in his books; because he proceeds by the path of inquiry, and therefore from what is better known to us, not to Nature. But since we have been informed through him and others what the power of this science requires, we can arrange its divisions in accordance with the order that Nature's dignity demands.

Moreover, under this heading philosophers have said many admirable things in regard to the virtues and vices, so that every Christian may be confounded when we perceive that unbelievers had such lofty conceptions of the virtues, and we seem basely to fall short of the glory of the virtues. But we should be much encouraged to aspire to the acme of virtue, and inspired by noble examples we should produce still nobler fruits of the virtues, since we have a greater aid in life than the philosophers themselves, and we are assured that we receive incomparably greater assistance through the grace of God. I shall first quote certain passages relating to the virtues and vices in general, and shall then pass to special branches.

Chapter II

ARISTOTLE shows in the first book of the Ethics that virtue is twofold; one, according to him, is in the sensitive part of the soul, in so far as it is obedient to reason, or in reason dominating the parts of the sensitive soul, and so regulating them that they obey its rule. Virtue of this kind is called moral and habitual, by which men form good moral habits. He teaches, moreover, in the second book of the Ethics that there are twelve moral virtues, and he treats of these in the fourth book and calls them means, because each of these is a mean between two vices opposite to each other and to the virtue. For one extreme falls short of the virtue and the other passes beyond it; as is the case with avarice, which falls short of liberality, and with prodigality, which exceeds it. For the liberal man gives only what he should give, the miser gives nothing or very little; the prodigal scatters abroad his all. Such is the case also with the vices that form the extremes for the other means.

These twelve according to Aristotle are as follows. First is fortitude in attacking what is terrible and in bearing what is adverse. Second is chastity both in the things pertaining to taste and in those pertaining to touch. Third is liberality as relating to moderate expenditures. For the fourth virtue is munificence, which is concerned with important matters, like temples, divine worship, hospitals, and other public blessings. And just as munificence and liberality differ in respect to money, so do magnanimity and a certain other virtue in respect to the merit and honor of virtue. Hence the magnanimous man is one who is not cast down by adversity nor puffed up by prosperity, but glories only in virtue. Hence magnanimity is the ornament of all virtues, as Aristotle says, by which a man raises his mind above all things human, and this virtue is of merited worth in all, nor does the magnanimous man meditate on injury or enmities. For he does not consider the avenging of injuries, nor does he preserve the memory of evils, nor does he deign to consider anything worthy of his anger, nor does he trouble himself about the folly and negligence of men, but overlooks all things by the greatness of his mind; nor does he rejoice in regard to honor done him, or only moderately, since for perfect virtue, as Aristotle says, a reverence equal to it is not found, nor as much as it deserves; nor is he disturbed by anything, since there is nothing that is extraordinary in his sight, prepared as he is for retributions and benefits, like God as much as a man can be.

The sixth mean, which bears the same relation to liberality as liberality does to munificence, has no name in Latin, but is concerned with matters of less merit than is magnanimity, and becomes any man according to his station. The seventh virtue is gentleness, which restrains angry passions. The eighth is friendliness in social intercourse, to the end that a man be pleasing to his fellow man without adulation, and that he be not envious or disagreeable but forbearing. The ninth is sincerity, which removes from a man pretense and deceit, so that he is such in his heart as he appears to the outside world. The tenth consists in cheering others in the proper way, to the end that scurrility be excluded, and that a man be not boorish and rude, disquieted and glum toward the friendly advances of others. For quiet relaxation and friendly cheer with a vein of humor are necessary in human intercourse, as the philosopher says. The eleventh is a sense of shame at sins, which is especially needful for young people, so that they may not easily incline to vices. Therefore Aristotle says, "We praise youths with a sense of shame." For Seneca in his book of the first Letters relates the story of a youth who sinned, and when a sage asked whether the youth had a sense of shame, and received the reply that he had, he said, "Well, then the situation is saved." The twelfth is justice.

And besides these virtues there are other nobler ones which do not depend on sense but belong absolutely to pure reason, and therefore are called intellectual virtues, which are intellect, knowledge, art, prudence, and wisdom. But these may be considered purely in the region of speculation, when they are directed to truth alone. And in this view they are not virtues but intellectual and cogitative attitudes of mind, or they may be directed to matters of practice, and accordingly they have as their object the good. And thus they are virtues, namely, when they aim at the salvation of the soul; and this is the case when they are concerned with divine worship and public good among citizens, and integrity of life and morals, and the consideration of the life eternal and of like matters. Intellect is an acquired mental condition concerned with the principles underlying practice, and knowledge is an acquired mental condition concerned with conclusions. Art is the knowledge of good works in their outcome, and prudence is the acquired mental condition directing such works. But wisdom is the perfect knowledge of spiritual blessings together with the sweetness of love, a sweetness in which there is peace of the human mind as far as it is possible for the mind to enjoy such in this life; and therefore this is the beginning of future felicity, and is almost the same as felicity, as Aristotle says in the sixth book of the Ethics.

In the same book he states that in every kind of virtue there is one that is natural and another that is acquired, just as we find a man chaste by nature and courageous, and the same is true in regard to the other virtues. He also makes a similar distinction at the end of the tenth book; and he there says that the natural virtues are not derived from ourselves, but are given us by divine grace. This is a wonderful statement. Therefore still more are the acquired virtues derived from God, which are far more noble, although the habit of virtuous action preserves and strengthens and moulds them, for which reason they are called the virtues of habit and are said to depend on our actions.

The ancient philosophers uphold virtue as the whole good and the only good of man in this life, as Seneca teaches throughout in his book on the Happy Life, and Cicero everywhere in the fifth book on the Tusculan Disputations. He also solemnly assures us in his book on the Paradoxes that he will never consider anything good except virtue. He confirms the view by the judgment of one of the Seven Wise Men. When all his fellow citizens were fleeing from their homes owing to a hostile attack, and they asked him why he was not carrying his possessions with him as the rest were doing, he replied, "I am carrying my all with me"; meaning that nothing was his except virtue. This man was Bias of Priene, as Valerius Maximus informs us in the fourth book. Seneca also in his book to Serenus on the topic, "How neither injury nor contumely happens to a wise man," states that the philosopher Stilbon, on being asked by the tyrant who had invaded his state and had seized all his temporal possessions whether he had lost anything, replied, "Nothing, for my all is with me"; and he bore witness that he was not only unconquered but had suffered no loss. For he had with him his real blessings, on which no hand is laid. But those things which were scattered and carried off as plunder he did not consider his, but the mere accidents of fortune following its nod.

Moreover, virtue is the life of man: since Seneca says in the First Letters that men die before they begin to live, speaking of those who busy themselves in sins up to the time of their natural death. For this reason the very noble Apuleius in his book on the God of Socrates expresses astonishment that men do not care for their souls so that they may live. He says, "I am surprised at nothing so much as at the fact that, although men wish to live in the best way and although they know that they live in the mind alone, and that they cannot live in the best way without cultivating the mind, they do not, however, cultivate their mind. Thus, if a man wishes to see clearly, he must take care of his eyes; if you wish to run swiftly, you must take care of your feet; similarly each of your members must receive special care. When I see all men acting on this principle, I do not know how adequately to explain to myself and to express my wonder why they do not also cultivate their mind by means of reason. The art of living is equally necessary for all, not so the art of painting and of harp-playing; and the same is true of the other arts, not to go through them all, which you may be ignorant of without shame. But when you say, I am not ashamed of my ignorance of the correct way to live—but you will never venture to say this. And chiefly must we wonder that those things which they are least desirous of seeming to be ignorant of, they never the less neglect to learn, and they fail to learn this same art and at the same time hold an ignorance of it reprehensible."*

This statement is directed chiefly against those who pose as models and teachers of morals to others; of whom Aristotle says in the Elenchi, "They make very fine speeches, but their wishes are at variance with their words." Cicero in the second book of the Tusculan Disputations asks in regard to such people, "How few of these philosophers will you find whose life and manners are conformable to the dictates of reason! who regard their profession, not as a means of displaying their learning, but as a rule for their own life! who conform to their own precepts and obey their own decrees! You may see some carried away by such levity and vanity, that it would have been better for them to have remained ignorant; some covetous of money, others eager for glory, many slaves of their lusts, so that their discourse is strangely at variance with their mode of life, which indeed seems to me a most disgraceful thing. For just as if a professed teacher of grammar should speak ungrammatically; or if he who wishes to be considered a musician sings out of tune, such inconsistency being all the worse since each of them fails in the very subject in which he professes to be expert; so a philosopher who fails in the conduct of his life is the more disgraced, because he errs in the very branch which he claims to teach, and does not regulate his own life by the rules he professes to teach." When Zaleuchus, the lawgiver of the Locrians, with remarkable justice and zeal for virtue wished that the law which he had made inflicting the loss of both eyes as a penalty

* "This quotation like many others made by Bacon," as Bridges says, "is nearly but not quite accurate."

for adultery should be complied with in the case of his own son, the state refused because of the integrity of the father. But the righteous judge put out one of his own eyes and an eye of his son to avoid breaking the law which he had made. Valerius Maximus records these facts in the sixth book.

But all philosophers maintain that the grace of virtue by its own wondrous beauty should attract each man, since it is becoming, as Cicero says in his book on Duties, that by its own power it draws us and allures us by its own worth. Apuleius also, in the third book on the Teaching of Plato, says that virtue is beauty of mind. Cicero in the fourth book on the Tusculan Disputations says, "As in the body there is a certain proper formation of limbs, together with a certain sweetness of complexion, which is called beauty, so in the mind beauty consists in an impartiality, and constancy of opinions and judgments, joined to a certain firmness and stability, following virtue or preceding virtue itself." Apuleius says that virtue is not only beauty of mind but health and strength also. Cicero also holds the same opinions, as is evident from many passages in the second, third, fourth, and fifth books on the Tusculan Disputations.

Although it is impossible or difficult for the man who has become hardened in vicious habits to experience a change of heart, as Aristotle says at the end of the Ethics, yet Seneca says in the second book on Anger, "There is nothing so hard and so difficult, that the human mind cannot master it and render it familiar by constant practice. For none are so iron-hearted and of such an independent frame of mind that they may not be brought under control by discipline. Whatsoever the mind has imposed upon itself it has obtained. Some have gained such control of themselves as never to laugh. Others have forbidden their bodies the use of wine or fluid of any kind. Still others satisfied with a short sleep prolong the period of wakefulness tirelessly. Some have learned to run on very slender and steep ropes, and to carry great weights beyond the ordinary strength of man, and to dive into the sea to a great depth without any change of breath. There are a thousand other things in which perseverance overcomes every obstacle." And he shows that nothing is difficult if the mind has enjoined patience upon itself. For as Averroës says in the second book of the Physics, many have become accustomed to nourish themselves on poison, as Aristotle writes in the book of Secrets. For he himself discovered that a beautiful girl sent to Alexander with other gifts had been fed on poison. Therefore persistent labor conquers all things, as Vergil says.

There is, then, no difficulty in virtue for him who loves it. For virtue is eager for danger. Virtue considers the end it has in view, not what it will be called upon to suffer, as Seneca writes in his work De Copia Verborum, and makes the same statement in another book in which he inquires why many misfortunes happen to the good. And he makes there the additional statement, "Since that which it is destined to suffer is part of the glory. Soldiers glory in their wounds and rejoice to show their blood flowing from wounds that are not mortal. He who returns wounded attracts more attention than those who return unharmed from the battle-line, although they have been in the same engagement." He states, moreover, in the seventh book on Benefits that it is easy to know and to possess the virtues, as far as they themselves and nature are concerned; and he adds, "Whatever will make us better and happy, nature has placed in plain view or within easy reach, if a man has consecrated his mind to virtue. And whithersoever virtue summons he considers the path easy, if he is a social animal and views the world created for the common good as one household, and always lives as though in the public eye, more fearful of himself than of others. Such a man withdrawn from the storms of tribulations has set his foot on a firm and peaceful soil. He has made useful knowledge his own. For of no thing is the discovery difficult except of that whose only reward when discovered is in the discovery itself." And this lies in the domain of the purely speculative, not in matters pertaining directly to the happy life. Seneca, moreover, in the second book on Anger, refuting those who seek the solace of vice instead of the difficult path of virtue, speaks as follows, "There is nothing in the vices which you may say cannot be removed; we are ill with curable maladies, and nature aids us, created as we were to be whole, if we desire to be cured. Nor is the road to the virtues hard and rough, as it has seemed to some; we advance along an easy path since God himself is our aid. Much harder is it to do what you are doing. What is more restful than peace of mind, what more laborious than anger? what milder than forbearance, what more vexatious than cruelty? Chastity enjoys leisure, lust is very much preoccupied. Finally the guardianship of all the virtues is easy, the vices are cultivated at a great cost." Cicero, moreover, in the third book on the Tusculan Disputations says, "The knowledge of the virtues is innate and if permitted to increase, Nature herself would conduct us to the happy life." Seneca expresses the same sentiment in the book of the First Letters. That virtue, however, as he says in the first book on Anger, is surest which has greatly distrusted itself for a long time and has controlled itself and has advanced slowly and intentionally.

CHAPTER III

THEY discourse about sin in common just as they do about virtue. For Cicero in the fifth book on the Disputations says, "No one is permitted to sin"; because sins hinder complete perfection of mind and acquisition of eternal felicity, since Algazel says in the Logic this felicity comes from perfection of soul. Now perfection of the soul consists of two things, cleanness and adornment. Cleanness is the purification of the soul from filthy habits and sanctification from foul impressions; adornment consists in depicting on the soul the certitude of divine truth and the being of the whole universe in its sequence, by means of a revelation in which there is no error nor concealment; like a mirror, for example, which does not possess perfection unless a beautiful form is apparent in it; but this is not possible unless it has been cleansed completely from dirt and rust and beautiful forms afterwards placed before it. The soul, then, is like a mirror; for there are depicted in it the forms of the whole universe when it is clean and has been freed from foul habits. These are the words of Algazel. Sins, therefore, render a man blind, because every evil man is ignorant, as Aristotle says in the second book of the Ethics. Socrates says that it is not possible for any one to do a base act except through ignorance; since when he reaches the state of a desire for sin, he loses his knowledge and his intellect is in abeyance. So great is the depravity and turpitude of sin that the Philosopher has said, "If

Opus Majus

I were to know that the Gods would pardon and that men would pardon, I would refuse to sin." For this reason Cicero says in the second book of the Academics that men select darkness and solitude for committing sins, because the very baseness of sin deters by its foulness. Seneca, moreover, in the fifth book on Natural Questions says that because of their shamefulness crimes shun the sight of themselves, for concealing which no night is sufficiently dark. Apuleius also, in the third book on the Beatitude of Plato, says, "Evil or sin is filthiness of soul, and not only this but weakness and disease." Cicero expresses the same thought in many ways in the Tusculan Disputations.

Sin not only blinds, defiles, and weakens the rational soul, but lowers it to the level of the brutes, as the philosophers show in many passages. Hence Seneca in his book on the Happy Life says, "I place men in the same class whom a dull nature and ignorance of themselves have reduced to the level of brutes. There is no difference between them, since brutes do not have any reason, and such men have a depraved reason and one that is clever to their own hurt and in the wrong direction." Moreover, philosophy proves in the fourth book of the Consolations that evil men lose their identity, because the identity of a thing consists in retaining its order and preserving its nature. But sin is contrary to the order of nature, therefore evil men cease to retain their identity. It is necessary, therefore, to thrust down below the rank of mankind those whom their wickedness excludes from human status. The result is, then, that you cannot regard as a human being the man whom you see transformed by vices. And the philosopher infers that you would compare to a wolf the robber who is inflamed with greed and employs violence in possessing himself of the property of other people. You will compare to a dog him who is insolent and wags a quarrelsome tongue. He who lurks by the way and finds delight in pilfering is on an equality with foxes. If a man roars in uncontrolled anger, he may be regarded as having the intelligence of a lion. He who is timid and ready to flee, fearing what need not be feared, may be considered as similar to deer. The lazy and stupid dolt lives the life of an ass. The fickle and inconstant man who changes his pursuits differs in nothing from the birds. He who is plunged in defiling and unclean lusts is foully possessed by the pleasure of a hog. Therefore it comes to pass that he who ceases to be a man by the loss of his goodness is turned into a beast.

Since, moreover, we gladly excuse as far as possible our sins, whether they be small or great, many or few, Seneca in the second book on Anger asks, "Which vice, pray, has lacked an advocate?" but we do not thus excuse the vices of others. For in the same book he says, "We keep the vices of others in view, but our own in the background." And since with the holy thou shalt be holy and with the innocent man thou shalt be innocent, Seneca says in the book of the Second Letters, "Nothing else so clothes our minds with the garments of respectability and recalls to rectitude those who are wavering and inclining to evil as association with good men." And in the third book on Anger, "We form our habits from our associates, and as certain diseases of the body pass from one person to another by contact, so the mind gives its evils to those with whom it comes in contact. The drunkard inspires his messmates with a love of wine. Association with the impure weakens the character even of a strong man, if it be permitted. Avarice passes on its poison to those near it. The virtues conversely have the same action in softening everything with which they have to do. A mild region and more salubrious climate do not confer so great a benefit on bodily health as that derived by the morally weak from association with better people. You will understand how strong such influence is if you see that wild animals grow tame by living with us, and that no savage beast retains its ferocity if it has dwelt for a long time in the habitation of man. There is the added fact that not only does a man who lives with peaceful men become better by their example, but he does not find occasions for his vice and does not practice it."

Moreover, in the same book for the correction of all vices he says that all the senses must be brought to a condition of stability. For they are patient if the mind, which must be called daily to render an account, has ceased to corrupt them. Sextius followed the practice, when the day was over and he had retired to rest at night, of questioning his own mind, "What one of your faults have you corrected today? What vice have you withstood? In what way are you better? Can anything be better or finer than this habit of examining the whole day? How wonderful is that sleep which follows self-examination; how tranquil, deep, and free it is after the mind has been praised or admonished; and as spy and secret censor of itself finds out about its own behavior." And in the same book he says about himself, "I take advantage of this opportunity and daily before myself plead my case when the lamp has been removed. I go over with myself the whole day, and I consider what I have said and done, I hide nothing from myself, I pass over nothing. For why should I have any fear of my mistakes, when I can say, See that you do not do that again, I pardon you this time?"

Moreover, since that man is happy who dashes his little ones against the stones, Seneca says to Marcia, "All our vices will become fixed within us, unless they are crushed as they spring up. The violence of a disease should be checked at its outbreak by a gentle remedy, but we must take more vigorous measures against chronic disorders. For wounds are easily cured while they are fresh with blood." And since this matter should receive particular attention in the period of our youth, Aristotle says in the second book of the Ethics that it makes no little difference that we are trained in this way or in that from our youth. For he compares the innocence of youth to a green twig, which can be bent in every direction and its curvature easily removed. And Seneca says in the second book on Anger, "It is easy to mould minds while they are still tender; for with difficulty are we freed from vices that have grown along with us." Seneca likewise says to Helvia, "In this case mould both the manners and nature of the young girl. Precepts that are impressed at a tender age sink more deeply. You will bestow much upon her even if you give her nothing but your example." And therefore in the second book on Anger he says, "Everything that is tender clings to the things nearest and grows to resemble them. The manners of youth soon repeat those of their nurses and tutors. A boy brought up in the home of Plato, on returning and seeing his father vociferating and shouting, said, I never saw this in the home of Plato. I do not doubt that he would have imitated more readily his father than he did Plato, had he been brought up in his father's house."

Moral Philosophy

CHAPTER IV

IF we consider what the philosophers have said and done in particular in regard to habits of this kind, we find much that is most pleasing. All their teachings are reduced to a contempt of riches in opposition to avarice, or to a despising of honors as opposed to pride, or to the shunning of pleasures as opposed to luxury and gluttony, or they have reference to the violent feelings and passions of the mind and are directed against anger, envy, and sloth; to the end that thus the seven mortal sins may be avoided. All these sins except anger relate to prosperity. For the mind grows feeble in the midst of riches and pleasures while it delights itself in these sins. For as regards avarice, pride, luxury, and gluttony it is evident that they are aroused by a strong desire for enjoyment. Envy also springs from the good and the prosperity of another. Sloth, however, owes its being to the fact that the mind is absorbed in pleasures and in the other interests incident to prosperity. For in such circumstances a man loses interest in the true good which consists in virtue, and finds every virtuous effort disagreeable. Inert and lazy becomes the man for whom death of the soul is at the portals, to bring quickly to a close his spiritual life. Anger alone has no regard for prosperity and battles in adversity. For this reason I shall touch first upon their statements pertaining to the contempt for prosperity; then I shall consider how adversity should not be dreaded.

Aristotle, the greatest of philosophers, accordingly is the most conspicuous example, who in contempt of the world with all its riches and honors and pleasures left his native land and ended his life in exile. Theophrastus, his noted successor in philosophy, did the same thing, as Cicero states in the fifth book on the Tusculan Disputations. But these were not the only instances, but there were many others among the most noted philosophers and fathers of philosophers, as Xenocrates, who was head of the old Academy, according to Censorinus in his book on the Natal Day, and Carneades, who founded the third Academy called the new one. For the disciples of Plato were called the Academics from the place in which Plato studied, and they were divided into many schools after the death of their master. But these were not the only ones; there were many

other famous men, whom Cicero names to the number of sixteen: and still others in endless numbers, as he himself says,
passed their years in exile and in constant travel abroad, who
once having set out never returned home. Socrates, on being
asked of what country he was a citizen replied, "I am a citizen
of the world"; for he considered that he was an inhabitant and
a citizen of the whole world, as Cicero states in the fifth book
on the Tusculan Disputations. Seneca accordingly says to Marcellus in exile, "It is not a misfortune if you are without a
country. You were trained to know that every place is a philosopher's native land. The lowly hut to be sure contains the virtues. It will be more beautiful than any temple since we shall
see in it justice, continence, prudence, piety, a plan of duties
properly coördinated, a knowledge of things human and divine.
No place is narrow which contains this number of such great
virtues." Ptolemy also, in the maxims given in the Almagest,
says, "He is superior among men who does not care under
whose power the world is." Nor is it strange if this philosopher
speaks thus who spent most of his labor in learning about the
heavenly bodies and the principal divisions of the world. For
he proves in the first book of the Almagest that the whole earth
has no sensible size in comparison with the heavens, a fact
established more fully above. Seneca says to Helvia, "The mind
is narrow which earthly things delight. For the higher men
rear their towers, and the larger they build the roofs of their
dining halls, the more do they shut out the heavens." Xenophon, the pupil of Socrates, said, according to Censorinus, that
to be in need of nothing is a characteristic of God, but to be in
need of as little as possible is the next thing to God.

Seneca in the fifth book of the Natural Questions, rightly
judging the earth but a point in respect to the heavens, a fact
proved by astronomy, considers of no moment and reduces to
naught all things which are distributed in this world among
men, as compared with heaven for which man was made. He
accordingly says,* "He who now broadens and prepares his
mind and makes it worthy of fellowship with God, possesses the
complete and perfect good of the human lot; when treading
under foot every evil he seeks what is above and enters into

* This quotation is from the prologue to the first book of *Naturales Quaestiones.*

the bosom of nature, he delights wandering among the very stars to view the pavements of the rich and the whole earth with its gold, not that only which it has produced, but that which it reserves in secret for the avarice of posterity." "This is a mere point which is divided by sword and fire among so many nations. Oh how ridiculous are the boundaries of mortals! The Dacian may not pass beyond the Ister. The Euphrates must restrain the Parthians, and the Danube divide the Sarmatian and the Roman territories, the Rhine is to set a bound for Germany. The Pyrenees are to rear their crest between Gaul and Spain. Between Egypt and Ethiopia a vast uninhabited stretch of sand must lie. If any one should give human understanding to ants, will they not divide one anthill into many provinces? When you see armies marching with flags flying and the cavalry now scouting ahead, now spread out from the flanks, that is merely the running to and fro of ants busying themselves in their narrow path. What difference is there between them and us except the extent of a small body? This is only a point on which you sail, on which you reign, on which you make war. Above are the vast spaces into the possession of which the mind is admitted; and as though freed from chains returns to its origin. And this is a proof of its divine origin that divine things delight and interest it, not as things alien to it but as its own possessions. It will then despise the narrow confines of its former abode. For the space from the remotest parts of Spain to India is traversed in a very few days if the ship have a favorable wind. But that celestial region requires a journey of thirty-six thousand years for the fastest star."

Moreover, Apuleius in his book on the God of Socrates fitly says that all good things, external and belonging to the body, are to be despised and not to be taken into account in praising a good man. His words are, "In considering men do not set any value on things that do not really belong to them, but consider the man himself within, view him as my poor Socrates. Now I call those things not really his which his parents procured, and which fortune bestowed, no one of which I join to the merits of my Socrates, neither high birth, nor lengthy lineage, nor riches that cause others to envy. Therefore you may number all gifts together; is he high born? You are praising his parents. Is he rich? I do not trust fortune. Nor do I enumerate such gifts further. Is he in good health? He will be worn out by sickness. Is he active? He will pass into old age. Is he handsome? Wait awhile and he will not be. But is he trained in the liberal arts and is he especially learned, and wise, as far as a man is permitted to be, and of good counsel? At length now you are praising the man himself. For this is neither a heritage from his father, nor is it dependent on chance, nor is it assistance dependent on the will of others, nor is it a transitory thing from the body, nor is it changed by age. All these things my Socrates had, and for this reason he despised the possession of all else." Therefore Cicero in his book on the Paradoxes glories in the fact that he never counted gold or silver or honor or anything belonging to this world among blessings. Sallust, moreover, in his book on Catilina says, "Fortune makes all things famous according to its caprice rather than in accordance with fact. First there was the desire for money, then for empire. These became as it were the sources of all evils. For avarice has destroyed faith, probity, and the other good qualities; in place of these she has taught us pride, cruelty, neglect of God, and to consider that all things are to be bought and sold. Avarice has a fondness for money, which no philosopher has desired. This vice steeped as it were in noxious poisons weakens the body and mind of man; always boundless, insatiable, it is lessened neither by plenty nor want." And Seneca in the third book on Anger says, "In regard to money there is the utmost vociferation; this wearies out the forums, mingles poisons, places swords in men's hands, this is gathered from our blood, because of it the throng presses upon the tribunals of the magistrates, kings rage and overthrow states: the law courts echo with the roar of the cases, judges summoned from far distant regions sit to determine which one of the two litigants has the juster avarice." And in his work De Copia Verborum he says, "The avaricious man's only correct action is performed when he dies." Sallust in the book mentioned above says, "The ambition for power has forced many men to become false; to have one thing locked in their heart and another ready on their tongue. And when men passed their lives in the land without greed, all were satisfied with what they had. But when insolence of power appeared, fortune changes along with character." Therefore Seneca addressing those who were proud because of the blessing of fortune says, "All things which force you, swollen with pride and superior to the common lot, to forget your own frailty, things which you guard with iron bars, which plundered from the blood of others you defend with your own, because of which after the rupture so often of the ties of marriage, friendship, and colleagueship the world was crushed between the two contenders, all these things I say are not yours. Already they are looking to another owner; either an enemy, or an unfriendly successor, or fire or some other misfortune will assail them. Do you ask how you are to make them yours? By bestowing them as gifts. Take thought then for your possessions and make your ownership of them sure and impregnable; you will render them not only more respectable but more secure. That in which you reckon yourself rich and powerful, as long as you are in possession, rests under a sordid name; it is house, or slave, or money. When you have donated it, it becomes a benefaction." And therefore he asks in the book of the First Letters, "Who is worthy of God except the man who has despised riches?"

CHAPTER V

CONCERNING the sensual pleasures philosophers make many excellent statements. Cicero in his book on Old Age speaks as follows: "Since God has given to man nothing more excellent than mind, nothing is more hostile to this divine gift than sensual pleasure. For such pleasure hinders deliberation, is hostile to reason, and blindfolds the eyes of the mind. For the great Archytas of Tarentum, a Pythagorean and a teacher of Plato, was of the opinion that no one can doubt that a man so long as he is enjoying sensual pleasure is incapable of handling any matter requiring thought, reason, and reflection, since such pleasure, if indulged in too much or too long, extinguishes completely the light of the soul."* Hence Cicero in the third book on the Tusculan Disputations says,† "But these definers say

---

* Bacon has changed the order of sentences in this quotation, as he frequently does in quotations from classical authors. See *De Senectute*, XII, 40, 41.

† *Tusculan Disputations*, IV, 9, 21.

that the source of these disturbances is lack of moderation, which is a defection from the entire intellect and from correct reasoning, a state so averse to the dictates of reason that the appetites of the mind can in no way be governed and restrained." Moreover, Pliny for this reason says in the fourteenth book of the Natural History, "After pleasure has begun to live life fails." Aristotle also in his book on the regimen of Life said to Alexander, "Avoid the inclinations to bestial pleasures, for the carnal appetites incline the mind to the corruptible pleasure of the bestial soul if no discretion be used. Therefore the corruptible body will rejoice, and the incorruptible intellect will be saddened. The inclination to carnal pleasure therefore generates carnal love. But carnal love generates avarice; avarice generates the desire of riches; the desire of riches generates shamelessness; shamelessness generates presumption, and presumption generates infidelity. And therefore pleasure brings with it stains on the soul of man, by which the soul is darkened." Aristotle for this reason also says in the book of Problems that we are called incontinent and blameworthy more on account of taste and touch than because of the other senses, since we are overcome by the basest pleasures and by those in which we participate with the brutes. For the latter take no delight in seeing and hearing and smelling, as does man. For they do not seek an odor for itself, but because of the food to which they are led by the odor. But a man not suffering from hunger finds delight in a perfume, as in the case of roses and other odoriferous flowers. He also takes great delight in hearing and in seeing; but brutes take pleasure only in what is known to pertain to taste or to touch. For this reason regulations and directions for correct living are drawn up in regard to the pleasure of both taste and touch; and we are praised more when we abstain from these pleasures, and we are blamed because of them since they are low and bestial. Moreover, Seneca says in the second book on Anger,* "When pleasures have corrupted both mind and body, no form of adversity seems tolerable, not because it is hard, but because a soft man is enduring it." For this reason since there are two principal modes of pleasure, one in lust, the other in intoxication and drunkenness,

* *De Ira,* II, 25.

Moral Philosophy

Cicero asks in the fifth book on the Tusculan Disputations,* "Why should you not call that man most miserable whom we see raging and inflamed with lustful passions, madly craving all things with an insatiable desire, and thirsting the more keenly and ardently the more deeply he drinks everywhere from the cup of pleasure?" Seneca, moreover, says in the seventh book on Benefits† that "pleasure is fragile, brief, exposed to disgust, the more eagerly quaffed the more quickly subsiding into the opposite, a thing of which we must either repent or be ashamed, in which there is nothing splendid nor befitting the nature of man next to God, a thing that is low belonging to our base members, foul in its end." And Seneca in the second book of the Declamations says, "The young man sins, the voluptuous old man is mad, for he brings dishonor on his old age, and is rendering the age of youth more imprudent." And Cicero in the fourth book on the Tusculan Disputations, teaching how to cure this lustful person, shows the worthlessness of such pleasure in these words,‡ "Now the cure for one who is affected in this manner, is to show how light, how contemptible, how very trifling he is in what he desires; how he may turn his affections to another object, or accomplish his desires by some other means; or else to persuade him that he may entirely disregard it: sometimes he is to be led away to objects of another kind, to study, business or other different engagements and concerns: very often the cure is effected by change of place, as sick people that have not recovered their strength are benefited by change of air. But above all things the man thus afflicted should be advised what madness love is: for of all the perturbations of the mind there is no one which is more vehement; for, (without charging it with debaucheries, adultery, or even incest, the baseness of any of these being very blameable; not I say, to mention these,) the very perturbation of the mind in love is base of itself, for, to pass over all its acts of downright madness, what weakness do not those very things which are looked upon as indifferent argue, injuries, suspicions, unfriendliness, war, then peace again" renewed, all of which follow upon men inspired by lust? Hence it follows that

* *Tusculan Disputations*, V, 6.
† *De Beneficiis*, VII, 2.
‡ *Tusculan Disputations*, IV, 35. Yonge's translation.

Opus Majus

"The man who seeks to fix
These restless feelings, and to subjugate
Them to some regular law, is just as wise
As one who'd try to lay down rules by which
Men should go mad.

Now is not this inconstancy and mutability of mind enough to
deter any one by its own deformity? We are to demonstrate, as
was said of every perturbation, that there are no such feelings
which do not consist entirely of opinion and judgment, and are
not owing to ourselves. For if love were natural, all would be
in love, and always so; nor would one be deterred by shame,
another by reflection, another by satiety." For this reason Aristotle in the Secrets of Secrets says to Alexander, "Kind Emperor, do not yield to the desire for sexual intercourse with
women, since such intercourse is a characteristic of swine. What
glory is it for you if you practice a vice that is characteristic of
unreasoning animals and follow the actions of brutes? Believe
me without question that sexual intercourse involves the destruction of our bodies, the shortening of life, the corruption
of the virtues, the transgression of the law, and the adoption
of effeminate manners." Therefore, that every flaw of character
may be avoided, Seneca says to Helvia,* "If you consider that
sexual desire was given man not for his enjoyment but for the
purpose of propagating the race, every other desire will pass
by that man unscathed whom this secret and ruinous passion
deep-seated in our very vitals has not harmed."

Concerning the pleasure taken in gluttony Seneca speaks
fittingly to Helvia,† "Oh, how wretched are those whose appetite is not excited except at the sight of expensive foods! But
not their fine flavor or the pleasure they give the palate but their
rarity and the difficulty in procuring them render such foods
dear. Otherwise, if they care to return to a sane state of mind,
what need is there of so many arts ministering to the belly?
What need to ravage forests, what need to search the deep?
Everywhere are the different kinds of food, which nature has
distributed in all places. But men pass by these as though they
were blind, . . . and although they can appease their hunger

* *Ad Helviam*, XIII.
† *Ibid.*, X.

at a small cost, they whet it at a great one. From far and wide they bring together all that is known to pampered gluttony; and they convey from a remote ocean that which is admitted with difficulty into a stomach weakened by dainties. May God confound those, the luxury of whose gluttony thus passes beyond the boundaries of their own land." Moreover, Seneca says in the book of the First Letters regarding intoxication and drunkenness,* "Oh, how many things men do when intoxicated for which they blush when sober! Consider drunkenness to be nothing else but voluntary insanity. Prolong the drunkard's state to several days, will you have any doubt of his madness? Drunkenness undoubtedly elicits, kindles, and discloses every vice; it removes the sense of shame that hinders our evil purposes; . . . when the power of wine overpowers the mind, every hidden evil comes forth to view. It is then that the lustful man brooks no delay in gratifying the demands of his passions; it is then that the unchaste man proclaims his disease; it is then that the ill-natured man does not restrain his tongue or his hand." And since such is the case Aristotle says in the second book of the Ethics that a twofold malediction is due the drunkard. And after many statements on this subject Seneca says in the place quoted above, "Cruelty generally follows wine drinking, for a man's soundness of mind is corrupted and he is made savage. As prolonged illnesses render it difficult for the eyes to bear even a very weak ray of the sun, so continued spells of drunkenness bestialize the mind. For when people are frequently beside themselves, the habit of insanity becomes fixed, and the vices produced by wine retain their ascendancy without it." Seneca, moreover, in the first book on Natural Questions writing against those with a luxurious and perverted taste in drinking says,† "Good God, how easy it is to slake a natural thirst! do you consider such the thirst of voluptuaries?" As though he were to say their thirst is not a thirst but a fever. "And indeed it is the more severe in this way because it is detected neither by touching the veins nor by heat diffused over the skin; but luxury dries up the heart itself, an unconquerable evil."

I wish now at the end to add to the authors cited a letter of

* *Epist.*, lib. XII, 1.
† *Naturales Quaestiones*, IV, 13.

the philosopher Anacharsis assailing pleasure, which he wrote to the rich Hammo in these words:* "Anacharsis to Hammo greeting. My clothing is the same as that with which the Scythians cover themselves; the hardness of my feet supplies the want of shoes; the ground is my bed, hunger my sauce, my food milk, cheese, and flesh. So you may come to me as to a man in want of nothing. But as to those presents you take so much pleasure in, you may dispose of them to your own citizens, or to the immortal gods." Cicero in the fifth book of the Tusculan Disputations quotes this letter with approval. Seneca in the book of the First Letters says, "He who comes forth into the light of this world, should be content to live on bread and water." And in his book on the topic, Why many evils happen to good men, he exhorts us to shun luxury, "Shun luxury, shun an enervated prosperity, by which the mind is cloyed, and unless something happen to admonish of our human lot, it falls into a state of torpor like continued drunkenness." Moreover, in the Phaedo of Plato we read that he who frees as much as possible his soul from association with the body and is least under the influence of carnal pleasures is manifestly a philosopher. The meditation of philosophers is the freedom and separation of the soul from the body. He teaches us that the man has confidence in regard to his own soul who permits carnal pleasures to depart as though they were strangers, and adorns his mind not with an embellishment that is foreign but with one belonging to it, temperance, justice, fortitude, liberality, and virtue. Wherefore Cicero in his work on the Immortality of the Soul concludes for many reasons that the "whole life of philosophers is a meditation on death"; to separate the soul from the body, what else is it than to learn how to die? and therefore he continues, "Let† us separate therefore ourselves from our bodies, that is, let us accustom ourselves to die, and thus while we remain on earth we shall be enjoying a life like that of heaven, and when we are borne thither from these chains . . . then finally shall we live." For this "life in fact is death," as he himself elegantly puts it. Moreover, Seneca says to Marcia,‡ "Tarrying in the body is never dear to great souls; they long

* *Tusculan Disputations*, V, 32. C. D. Yonge's translation.
† *Ibid.*, I, 31.
‡ *Ad Marciam*, XXIII, XXIV.

ardently to go forth and break loose, they endure with difficulty these narrow bounds, wandering as they do through the whole universe and accustomed from their lofty pinnacle to look down upon human affairs. Hence it is that Plato exclaims that the whole soul of the philosopher reaches out to death, desires it, meditates on it, always is carried away with a longing for it." "These things that you see about us, bones, tendons and skin stretched over them, face and ministering hands, and all the rest with which we have been enveloped, are chains of our souls and shadows; by these the soul is overwhelmed, routed, stained, kept from the truth and from what is its own, and driven to what is false; its whole struggle is with this flesh that weighs it down; it presses forward to that place whence it was sent forth; there eternal rest awaits it." Therefore Avicenna says in his Morals, "A man will not be set free from this world and its allurements, unless after becoming wholly dependent on that celestial world he desires that which is there, and the love of those things that are there withdraws him completely from the consideration of that which is behind him."

Chapter VI

I HAVE spoken of prosperity and how the six mortal sins are nourished by it. Now I must speak of adversity and how anger contends with it, although anger suffers a base defeat. In the first place, I shall state the principles regarding those matters that are to be considered relating to the remedy for anger, and in the second I shall take up the main points in regard to the glorious endurance of adversity. The first step in resisting anger is the comprehension on our part of its horrible consequences, so that each of us bearing these in mind may make the avoidance of this vice his special study. Anger is a very serious sin. For the angry man blasphemes God, loses his neighbor, confounds himself, scatters abroad his temporal blessings, and is not deterred in venting his rage by the fear that he is neglecting his eternal good and making himself liable to the punishments of hell. First, then, we must consider that anger is contrary to all human nature. For the description of man marking him as such is that he is an animal kindly by nature. Therefore Seneca in the first book on Anger proves that anger is contrary to human nature in this way :* "If we consider man, what do we find milder than he is while he is in the right frame of mind? But what is more cruel than anger?" He continues, "Anger is eager to inflict punishment, but the presence of such a desire in the very peaceful breast of man is by no means in accordance with his nature." But elsewhere he reasons thus: "Man is born to help his fellow man, but anger is instrumental in his ruin." He, that is, man, "wishes to associate with his fellow man, anger tries to separate them: he wishes to benefit, anger wishes to harm: he wishes to aid even those who are unknown to him, anger desires to destroy those who are dearest: he is ready to expend himself in relieving the misfortunes of others, anger is prepared to run into danger, provided it can involve others. Who then is more ignorant of nature than he who assigns this savage and destructive vice to nature's best and most faultless work," namely man? "For human life consists of favors, and is bound together into common fellowship and assistance by concord, and not by fear but by mutual love." And in the first book he compares men in anger to beasts, which are different from men in their nature. He says,† "Anger displays itself and appears in the face; and the greater it is the more manifest is its expression. Do you not see that in the case of all animals, as soon as they rise to attack, signs precede, and their whole bodies cease to retain their usual quiet habit? The jaws of the boar are covered with foam, his teeth are sharpened by rubbing, the horns of the bull are tossed in the air and the dust is scattered by the stamping of his feet, the lion roars, and the neck of the angered snake swells, the look of the mad dog is forbidding." Moreover, he expresses the opinion in his third book that angry men are further removed from human kindness than are other beasts. "The‡ face, believe me, of a wild beast, whether goaded by hunger or by the dart piercing its vitals, even when half dead it makes a final attack with its jaws on the hunter, is less repulsive than the face of a man inflamed with anger." Morcover anger is contrary to man's nature, because it first destroys and confounds his own substance. For in the first place it alters a

* *De Ira,* I, 5.
† *Ibid.,* I, 1.
‡ *Ibid.,* III, 4.

man externally as regards his whole body into a foul and horrible appearance. Hence Seneca in the opening part of his book writes as follows:* "You have asked me, Novatus, to write how anger can be controlled, and not without reason do you seem to me to have feared this especially foul ungoverned state of mind. In other passions there is an element of rest and peace, but this state of mind is marked by violent agitation and passion of grief." And in the second book on Anger he says,† "Nothing, however, will profit so much as first of all to view the hideousness of the thing. Nor is the appearance of any other passion more repulsive. It defiles the most beautiful face, renders savage the most tranquil brow. All beauty departs from those angered; and if they are neatly dressed, at the dictate of anger they will pull their garments awry and pay no heed to their persons; and their hair smooth cither by nature or art becomes rough along with their disordered mind. Their veins swell, their breast heaves with their rapid breathing, angry ejaculation of the voice distends the throat. Then the limbs become restless, the hands shake, the whole body is agitated. In what state do you suppose the mind is whose external appearance is so repulsive? How much more terrible within the breast is its look, how much keener its spirit, more eager its passion, destined to burst itself unless it find outward expression? We should picture anger to ourselves as similar to the fire-breathing monsters which the poets have imagined in the lower world —anger which raises its voice loudly with hissing, bellowing, and raucous sounds, which labors under universal hatred of itself, being especially anxious, if it cannot do harm otherwise, to bring ruin on lands, seas, and sky." And in the third book he says,‡ "It is necessary, therefore, to expose its foulness and ferocity and place before our eyes how monstrous is man raging at man"; and "how we have described the angry man's countenance as fierce and now pallid with the blood withdrawn and banished from the surface, and now red with all the color and energy brought into the face as though covered with blood, the veins swollen, and the eyes now restless and darting from their sockets, now fixed and set in a stare. Add the sound of his teeth

* *Ibid.*, I, 1.
† *Ibid.*, II, 35.
‡ *Ibid.*, III, 3, 4.

as they clash not differing from the noise made by boars sharpening their weapons by grinding them together. Add the cracking of his joints as his hands crush each other, and his oft smitten breast, his rapid breathing and deep-drawn groans, his swaying body, uncertain words, his lips quivering with sudden exclamations and sometimes compressed, and hissing forth some dreadful imprecation." Moreover, anger is contrary to man's nature because it injures the body with many afflictions and scourges it with deformities. For Seneca says at the end of the second book, "We must see how many anger has injured by its own action. Some have ruptured their veins by excess of passion, and a shout raised beyond one's strength has caused a hemorrhage, and humor discharged into the eyes with too much force has destroyed the sight, and the sick have suffered a relapse." And we have seen frequently healthy men under the influence of violent anger attacked by various maladies.

But similarly anger is unnatural in man as regards his soul. For the intellectual soul has two divisions; one is speculative and employs reason; the other is active and fitted for the love of virtue. Anger disturbs the first and is especially inimical to it, and frequently reduces it to madness and insanity. For in the second book Seneca says,* "Reason gives time to both sides of a question and seeks for time to investigate the truth. Anger is precipitate. Reason wishes that the decision be rendered in accordance with justice. Anger cares nothing for the just decision rendered by reason. Reason considers nothing except the case in hand. Anger is influenced by foolish and irrelevant matters. Rage does not brook control; it is angered at truth itself if truth appears to oppose its wish. With shouting and uproar and tossings of the body it pursues with insults and curses the objects of its hate. Reason does not act in this way, but, if it be necessary, Reason silently quietly destroys families including wives and children that are dangerous to the state, pulls down houses and levels them to the ground, and roots out names inimical to liberty. All these things Reason does without gnashing its teeth and shaking its head or any other indecorous act."

Moreover anger reduces reason to insanity and madness. For

* *De Ira,* I, 18, 19. (Not from the second book.)

Moral Philosophy

Seneca at the end of the second book on Anger says,* "There is no quicker road to insanity. Many accordingly have continued in their state of passion and have never recovered their banished reason. Madness drove Ajax to death, anger drove him to madness." And in the third book he says,† "What then? Does any one call that man sane who caught up as it were by a tempest does not walk but is driven along; and enslaved by an evil passion does not entrust to another his vengeance, but exacts it himself, mad alike in mind and deed?" And in the first book he says,‡ "That you may know that those are not sane whom anger possesses, look at their appearance. For as there are definite indications of madness, the bold and threatening look, the gloomy brow, the savage face, the hasty step, the restless hands, the changing color, the frequent and labored sighs, so are the same signs visible indicative of anger: the eyes blaze and flash, a deep flush covers the whole face as the blood surges up from the depths of the breast; the lips quiver, the teeth are pressed together, the hair is rough and erect, the breathing labored and strident, the joints emit a sound as they are bent, with groaning and bellowing and abrupt speech in words offering little explanation and hands frequently clapped together, and stamping on the ground with the feet and the whole body agitated and making dire threats, the face foul and horrible to look upon. . . . You are in doubt whether the vice is more detestable or hideous." Finally anger is altogether unnatural in man, since the angry man does not shrink from exposing himself to every kind of danger and has no fear of death, but freely runs the risk of death in order that he may take vengeance. Hence at the end of the second book he says, "Angry men are prepared both to fight with swords and to fall upon them." And at the beginning of the third book he says,§ "The angry man is destructive not without his own destruction and sinks those things that cannot be sunk except with him who sinks them." Not only does he destroy himself but he loses his neighbor; and not only does he drive his enemies to death, but he is the cause of the death of his friends. Seneca in the second book gives

* *Ibid.*, II, 36.
† *Ibid.*, III, 3.
‡ *Ibid.*, I, 1.
§ *Ibid.*, III, 3.

us an excellent example illustrating this matter. A tyrannicide on being captured by the tyrant deceived him with such caution, that the tyrant himself slew all his own friends;* and the tyrant at length dies. Seneca says, "The incident of the tyrannicide is well known who on being thwarted in his attempt and seized was tortured by Hippias, so that he might disclose his associates. The tyrannicide thereupon named the friends of the tyrant surrounding him, to whom he knew the tyrant's safety was especially dear. After ordering all those who had been named to be killed, the tyrant asked if there was any other survivor. You alone, said the tyrannicide. For I have left no one else to whom you are dear. His anger, therefore, caused the tyrant to aid the tyrannicide and slay with his own sword his guard."

Just as anger confuses the speculative part of the soul and is unnatural to it, so also does it affect the active part and far more so. For this part of the soul has virtue as its dower, and in it virtue has its place; and anger is a vice. Since, therefore, according to Seneca in his book of the First Letters, and according to Cicero in his book on Duties, and according to the same author in the second book on the Tusculan Disputations, all the virtues are interconnected; so that he who has one has them all owing to the general conditions of their association, although they differ in their special conditions, of necessity anger does not permit any virtue to accompany it, since anger excludes kindness which is joined chiefly to other virtues. This is what Seneca says in the second book on Anger, "You must first remove virtue from your mind, before you entertain anger, since vices do not associate with virtues; and a man can no more be at the same time both angry and good, than he can be sick and well." Finally anger destroys the noblest virtues, namely, kindness, clemency, magnanimity, piety, joy, and peace of mind. For Aristotle in the fourth book of the Ethics teaches that kindness is a virtue the opposite of anger. And Seneca says in the first book on Clemency,† that no one of all the virtues is more befitting man than clemency, since there is none more human. But anger excludes clemency, because it degenerates into cruelty;

---

* Bridges' text reads *inimicos*. The sense of the passage requires *amicos*.
† *De Clementia*, I, 3.

and cruelty is rightly the opposite of clemency, as Seneca says in the second book.

Although clemency is fitting in all, yet, as Seneca says, clemency befits no one more than a king and a prince. For the kings of Israel are clement, says the Scripture. For as Seneca says,* "To have power to injure is a pernicious force; the greatness of that man is firm and secure whom people know to be as truly for them as he is above them: from whom as he proceeds they do not flee, as though he were some dangerous animal, but they emulously run to him as to a bright and beneficent star"; and he adds, since "savage and inexorable anger does not befit a king." "It is proper for a prince to hold the same position with reference to his subjects as God does to him." "If† God forgiving and just does not immediately follow up the faults of sinners, how much juster it is for a man placed over men to exercise his power with clemency, and to consider whether the aspect of the world is more pleasing to the eye and more beautiful on a calm and clear day or when all things are shaken by frequent peals of thunder; . . . and yet the appearance of a quiet and well ordered government is not different from that of a calm and bright sky!" "This is true clemency," as he infers,‡ "to have no stain—a clemency that did not have its origin in regret for cruelty. This is in the midst of the greatest power the truest moderation of mind. Clemency renders princes not only more honorable but safer. Tyrants rage at will; kings not unless with reason and from necessity. Clemency creates a great distinction between a king and a tyrant. No one can have faithful and willing servants, whom he uses not otherwise than as beasts." For severity long continued loses authority. "On the other hand there is the man in whose mind there is nothing inimical, nothing savage; who exercises his power peacefully and beneficially; affable in his speech, easy to approach, amiable of countenance which especially wins popular favor, . . . of whom men speak the same in private as in public."

Moreover, Seneca cites a fine example. He says,§ "Nature invented the idea of a king, as we may learn both from other

* *Ibid.*, I, 3.
† *Ibid.*, I, 7.
‡ *Ibid.*, I, 7.
§ *Ibid.*, I, 19.

animals and from the bees, whose king has a spacious couch in their midst and in the safest place. As the superintendent of the work of others he does none himself; and on the loss of their king the whole swarm separates; nor do they permit more than one king at a time, and by means of combat they discover the better candidate. The king is distinguished in appearance and unlike the others both in size and beauty. Bees are very subject to anger and for their size are most pugnacious, and they leave their stings in the wound: the king himself has no sting. Nature did not wish him to be savage nor seek a revenge that would be so costly, and took away his weapon, and left his anger unarmed: this is an important example for great kings . . . since the mind of men ought to be as much more under control as it is capable of doing more serious harm. Would that the same law applied to man, so that his anger would be broken with his weapon, and that he could not do harm more than once." And he infers, "He is in error who thinks that a king is safe when nothing is safe from the king. Security must be obtained by mutual security. There is no need for a king to hedge himself about with walls and towers . . . clemency will render a king safe in the open. The love of his subjects is an impregnable fortification. For what is more beautiful than to live with the good will of all?" "We* exhort, therefore, that if clearly injured he retain his self-control, and remit the penalty, if he can do so with safety, and that he be far more willing to pardon injuries to himself than those to others. For as he is not generous who is liberal with what belongs to another, but he who takes away from himself what he bestows on another, so I shall call clement, not the man who is easy going in the matter of another man's grief, but him who when he is stirred by goads applied to him does not spring forward." And again Seneca says,† "The mere act of clemency on the part of a ruler causes a feeling of shame at wrong-doing." "And not less disgraceful to a prince are many acts of punishment than many deaths to a physician." For "by nature the human mind is stubborn and resists what is unpleasant and difficult, and follows more readily than it is led. And as spirited horses of noble stock are controlled with a light rein, so integrity of its own free will

* *De Clementia*, I, 20.
† *Ibid.*, I, 22, 24.

and motion follows clemency." And at length directing his speech to the Roman prince he says,* "The kindness of your disposition will be handed down and gradually diffused throughout the whole of your empire, and all things will be formed in your likeness, as health derived from an excellent source spreads among all men."

Thus, then, I have introduced certain facts to show the beauty and nobility of clemency, in order that the principal proposition may be made clear, namely, the madness of anger, which destroys this glorious virtue, and turns it into cruelty. Now I wish to make some statements in regard to the other virtues enumerated above with clemency, all of which frenzied anger destroys. That one especially united to clemency is magnanimity, which, as Aristotle teaches in the fourth book of the Ethics, is the ornament of all virtues. It is characteristic of this virtue that he who possesses it is forgetful of injuries and disregards them, as stated above, and does not deign to give way to anger nor consider any one worthy of his anger. Hence Seneca says in the second book on Anger,† "It is the mark of a great mind to disdain injuries; the most insulting way to exact vengeance is not to let him who has injured us appear worthy of our vengeance." And in the book on the Four Cardinal Virtues Seneca says;‡ "If you are magnanimous, you will never consider that an insult has been offered to you. You will say of your enemy, He did not harm me, but he intended to do so: and when you see him in your power, you will think that you have been able to take your revenge. For you should know that to pardon is the most noble and greatest kind of vengeance." And in the second book on Anger he says,§ "It is characteristic of the small and pitiable person to attack the one who pains him. Mice and ants, if you move your hand towards them, turn their mouths; weak creatures think that they are hurt if they are touched." Accordingly in the first book he says,‖ "The most irritable are infants, old people and the sick; and everything that is impotent is querulous by nature." And

* *Ibid.,* II, 2.
† *De Ira,* II, 32.
‡ *De formula honestae vitae.*
§ *De Ira,* II, 34.
‖ *Ibid.,* I, 13.

in the third book he says,* "Sick people are never touched without a complaint. Anger is small and narrow. For no man is not inferior to him by whom he considers himself despised. But the great mind and the true appraiser of itself does not take vengeance for an injury because it does not feel any. As missiles fly back from a hard object, and solids are struck with pain to him who strikes them, so no injury causes a great mind to feel it, since it is weaker than that which it attacks. How much nobler as though impenetrable to every weapon to spurn all injuries and insults! For taking vengeance is a confession that one is hurt; it is not a great mind that is bowed by injury. Either a stronger man or a weaker injures you; if a weaker, spare him; if a stronger, spare yourself. There is no surer proof of greatness than to be unmoved by anything that can happen." For who abandoning himself to personal grievance and madness does not cast aside his sense of shame first? Who in his blind rush and assault on another has not cast away whatever feeling of shame he possessed?

Since, therefore, nothing so befits a man as magnanimity, as Seneca says in the second book on Clemency, and since anger confuses and brings to naught this most glorious virtue, man should root out completely anger from his mind, and this is especially true of a ruler. Since in the first book Seneca says† that "it is the mark of a great mind to put up with injuries although possessed of the greatest power, nor is anything more glorious than a prince who refuses to punish personal offences." And in the second book on Anger he cites an example pertinent to this point,‡ "That prince is magnanimous and steadfast who like some mighty wild beast listens unmoved to the barking of his subjects." He adds, moreover, in the third book,§ "There is no question but that he who disdains his assailants will free himself from the throng and will stand upon higher ground; for it is the part of true greatness not to feel that one has been assailed. Thus the huge wild beast regards indifferently the barking of dogs." For the lion does not deign to hasten at the shouts and din of the hunters. "Thus in vain the wave assaults

---

* *De Ira,* III, 5, 6.
† *De Clementia,* I, 20.
‡ *De Ira,* II, 32.
§ *Ibid.,* III, 25.

the huge rock. He who does not become angry, remains unshaken by injury; but he who yields to anger has been moved." Hence this is the advice he gives against anger, "Beware lest your magnanimity and strength relied upon by most men fail"; most particularly has he in mind those possessed of great authority. And in the third book he says,* "The higher part of the world and that which is the more orderly and is nearest to the stars is never gathered into a cloud nor driven into a storm nor whirled into confusion; it is free from disturbance of any kind. It is the parts below that are blasted with lightning. In the same way the lofty mind, always serene and unmoved in its tranquillity, checking every disposition within itself to anger, is modest, commands respect and is properly disposed. You will find no one of these qualities in an angry man." Hence anger has no greatness in it, as he says in the first book. "We† must not think that anger makes any contribution to magnanimity. For anger is not greatness but a mere swelling of the mind. Nor to bodies already strained by a supply of harmful liquid is disease a mere augmentation, but a destructive abundance. All whom an insane mind lifts above human thoughts believe that they are breathing something lofty and sublime: but there is nothing solid beneath; those things are prone to fall that have increased without foundations. Anger has nothing on which to stand: it does not spring from what is firm and destined to be permanent; but is full of wind and folly." "Like ulcered and diseased bodies groaning at the lightest touch, anger is especially the vice of women and children. . . . There is no reason why you should believe the words of men in anger whose din is great and threatening; within their mind is very timid, because they are disturbed and hurt at trifles. Hence an angry man resembles closely a crocodile, an animal that is very bold when one is timid and very timid when one is bold. For it flees from one who pursues it and pursues him who flees from it: exactly what happens in the case of those who are subject to fits of anger. For they tower over those who are submissive to them, but shrink away when they are resisted with spirit. Hence they would not be disquieted so frequently at trifles unless their minds were weak. Since, therefore, anger is incompatible with

* *Ibid.*, III, 6.
† *Ibid.*, I, 20.

magnanimity, a virtue most worthy of honor, anger must be banished completely from our hearts."

And not only is this true because of this virtue of magnanimity and the remaining virtues mentioned above, but also because of other virtues, namely, mercy, piety, patience, joy, and peace of heart. Cicero in his plea to Caesar that he would spare Marcellus says, "No one of your many virtues is more admirable or pleasing than your quality of mercy; men in no other way approach more nearly to God than by granting deliverance to their fellow men. Your fortune holds nothing greater than that you should be able, your nature nothing better than that you should wish, to save many." Therefore in the case of each one of us Seneca says in the third book,* "Who am I whose ears it is a crime against heaven to wound? Many have pardoned their enemies; am I not to pardon the lazy, the negligent, the talkative? Youth excuses the child, sex the woman, freedom the stranger, familiarity one of the household." "He is a friend: he did what he did not wish to do: he is not a friend, he did what he should have done. Let us yield to one who is more prudent: let us pardon one who is more foolish. On behalf of each offender let us make this reply to ourselves that the very wisest men commit many faults; that no one is so circumspect that his carefulness is not sometimes forgotten . . . no one so fearful of offences as not to fall into them while he is seeking to avoid them. But if the most prudent sin, who is without a good excuse for his error? He is unjust who reproaches individuals with a vice that is general. The color of the Aethiopian is not conspicuous among those of his own race, nor is red hair gathered in a knot unseemly in a German. You will judge nothing noteworthy or unbecoming in an individual which is customary in his race. These peculiarities which I have mentioned are excused owing to the custom of some particular district and corner of the world; consider now how much more reasonable is pardon in the case of faults that are common throughout the whole human race. We are all inconsiderate and careless; we are all unreliable, querulous, solicitous of favor. Why under milder words do I hide a public ulcer? We are all evil; therefore each one of us will find in his own bosom that which he complains of in another." "Let us be

* *De Ira*, III, 24, 25, 26, 27.

more considerate of one another: we are evil men living among
evil men. One thing can make us peaceful, an agreement to
observe mutual affability. That man has already harmed me, I
have not yet harmed him. But already you have perhaps injured some one; but you will do so. Do not consider only this
hour, this day. Look into your whole habit of thought; even if
you have done no evil, you have the ability to do it. How much
better it is for a wrong to be healed than avenged! Vengeance
consumes much time, exposes itself to many injuries, while it
is smarting under one. We are angry for a longer time than we
are injured; how much better it is to go off in the opposite direction and not oppose vices to vices! Would a man seem quite
consistent if he sought satisfaction from a mule with his heels
and from a dog with his teeth? Those creatures, you say, are
ignorant that they are offending. In the first place how unjust
is he in whose eyes the fact that the offender is a man is an
obstacle in the way of his obtaining pardon. In the second if
the fact that other animals lack sense protects them from your
anger, let any one who lacks sense be equally privileged. For
what difference does it make whether he has other qualities
unlike those of brutes, if he has like the brutes that which defends them in every fault, namely darkness of understanding?
He has offended; well, is this the first time? Is this the last?
He will offend, and another will commit an offence against him,
and all life will wallow in the midst of errors."

Therefore he says in the second book,* "Do not become angry
at individuals, we must extend a general pardon: indulgence
must be shown to the human race." "Does any one become
angry at children whose youthful years do not yet know the
distinctions in things? The excuse is a more weighty one and
a juster one that the offender is a man than that he is a child."
"What removes the anger of a wise man? The throng of
offenders. He perceives both how unjust and perilous it is to
be angry at a vice that is general." "The wise man will not be
angry at sinners, because he knows that no one is born wise.
He also knows that very few in any age turn out to be wise,
since he has the condition of human life under observation. No
sane man becomes angry at nature. For what if he should take
a notion to be surprised that apples do not grow in uncultivated

* *Ibid.*, II, 10.

thickets? What if he should be surprised that thorns and briars do not swell with some useful fruit? No one becomes angry when nature defends a vice. The wise man, therefore, is calm and just to errors, he is not the foe but the corrector of sinners, he looks upon all men in just as kindly a way as a physician does sick people." It is evident, therefore, that mercy and anger cannot be in accord.

Similarly also the other noble virtues, piety, patience, joy, and peace of heart, are incompatible with anger. And since there is no question about these, and our discussion of the other virtues that are related to these has been an extended one, there is no need to dwell upon them. Piety which is effective in all things, according to Aristotle, is destroyed by anger, because the mind of an angry person is impious and cruel owing to an excessive desire for vengeance. That it destroys patience and peace of mind is evident; and therefore it removes and quenches all good, and breaks every protection against adversity. For as long as a man retains patience and happiness of mind and peace, he fears nothing, he is disturbed in no manner, he does not feel an injury, but master of his own mind he will despise whatever is termed adverse. Therefore the angry man by his anger destroys himself both in soul and body in this way that anger of itself acts on its own subject by destroying whatever is laudable in him. But not only do angry people thus incur danger, they even when goaded by passion and frenzied by the desire for vengeance expose their life to every danger, and with no fear of death impetuously oppose themselves to the assaults of their enemies, and are ready to fight with swords and to fall upon them, as Seneca says in the second book. And not only do they lose themselves but those nearest to them; and not only those whom they reckon hostile about whom there is no question, but also those who are friendly. For, as Seneca says in the second book, "Men in anger invoke death upon their children, and are hostile to their closest friends and must be avoided by those dearest to them." He says, "Anger has brought grief to a father, divorce to a husband, and hatred to a magistrate." And he aptly cites instances where men in anger have attacked their own friends.

Moreover, in the third book he states that Praexaspes,* one

* *De Ira*, III, 14, 15, 16, 17.

of the dearest friends of Cambyses, advised the monarch, who was addicted to over-indulgence in wine, to drink more sparingly, saying that drunkenness is disgraceful in a king, whom the eyes and ears of all make note of. But the king ordered the son of his monitor to proceed beyond the threshold, bent his bow and pierced the heart of the youth. And he infers, "I do not doubt that Harpagus* gave some such advice to the Persian King, at which he took offence, and served up to Harpagus his own children as a banquet." "And Darius, who was first to obtain the Persian throne after the Kingdom had been wrested from the Magian, on being asked by the aged noble Oeobazus to leave as a solace to his father one of his three children and to employ the services of the other two, said that he would send them all to him, and cast them down slain in the sight of their parent." And he continues, "I shall cite to you the case of King Alexander, favorite pupil of Aristotle, who slew at a banquet Clitus, a very dear friend who had been brought up with him; Alexander also threw to a lion Lysimachus, a friend equally dear to him. Lysimachus, moreover, severely mutilated his friend Telesphorus by cutting off his ears and nose, and kept him for a long time in a cage as though he were some strange and very rare animal." When Alexander traveled around the world, under the guidance of Aristotle and Callisthenes, he put Callisthenes to death, one of his great men, as Seneca states in his book on Natural Questions. Moreover, he provoked Aristotle to such an extent, that he was forced to free himself and the world by poison which he had sent Alexander to drink, as Pliny narrates in the thirtieth book of the Natural History. But these few examples are sufficient, because they are well known and have been written in regard to those matters under discussion.

Chapter VII

NOT only does anger destroy its own subject and loses for him his neighbor and his friends, but dissipates his wealth, makes him negligent in regard to his good name, and careless of honor. For the love of vengeance surpasses every other affec-

* *Ibid.,* III, 15, 16, 17.

tion of the mind and overpowers every other vice. Since Seneca
says at the end of the second book on Anger,* "Anger has
spurned avarice, the hardest and least pliant of evils, forcing
it to scatter its wealth and set fire to home and possessions collected into a single heap. The ambitious man in fact has cast
away insignia valued at a great price and has rejected an honor
granted. There is no passion of the mind over which anger
will not bear sway." And not only does the angry man destroy
himself, his neighbor, the blessings of fortune, but he offends
and loses God. Not indeed so much because anger is a sin, but
because in particular men in anger blaspheme God, of which
there are numberless examples, and there have been and will
be. And in contrast to such people, Seneca in the second book
on Anger says,† "God does not wish to harm nor is he able.
For his nature is mild and peaceful, as far removed from doing
injury to another as to himself. Therefore madmen and those
ignorant of the truth impute to him the raging of the sea, violent storms, and the persistence of winter. . . . No one of these
happens for the purpose of injuring us, nay, there is nothing
that is not for our preservation." Hence he states in the first
book‡ that "Caius Caesar because his revelry was disturbed by
thunderbolts challenged God to combat. How great was such
madness! He thought either that he could not be harmed even
by God, or that he could harm God."

Although many evils have been stated which arise from
anger, since a man loses his body, his reason, his virtue, his
neighbor, his possessions, his honor, and his God, yet its ex-
ceptionally bad quality can still further be shown in which it
surpasses all other sins. Hence Seneca says in the third book,§
"Anger must be compared with the worst vices, in order that its
nature may become apparent. Avarice acquires and hoards that
which a better man might use. The angry man, however, by his
anger loses more than the mere object of his wrath. Anger is
worse than extravagance since the latter enjoys its own pleasures, the former the pain of another. Anger surpasses malig-
nity and envy; for they wish that a man become unhappy, anger

* *De Ira,* II, 36.
† *Ibid.,* II, 27.
‡ *Ibid.,* I, 27.
§ *Ibid.,* III, 5.

wishes actually to make him so. They are pleased with fortuitous ills; anger cannot wait for fortune. Anger wishes to
harm the object of its hatred not merely that he be harmed by
some one else or by fortune." And at the beginning of the book
he says,* "Anger does not disturb men's minds in the manner
of other vices," "its impetuous and headlong violence does not
proceed gradually : anger is hasty and does not make its attack
on the objects only at which it aims, but vents its fury on everything that crosses its path. Other vices urge on our minds, anger
drives them headlong. Even if a man may not oppose his low
impulses, yet the impulses may cease of themselves. This vice
just like thunderbolts and hurricanes and all other irrevocable
things, because they do not proceed but fall, exerts its force
more and more. Other vices deviate from reason, but this vice
from sanity. Other vices have gentle means of approach and
grow without attracting attention; in anger there is an overthrow of our minds. Nothing, therefore, drives on a man more
than does anger, frenzied, as it is, and subject to its own violence, insolent when it succeeds, crazed when it is foiled. Reduced to a state of weariness not even by a repulse, when fortune saves its adversary, anger turns its teeth against itself. It
matters not what motive has aroused anger, for it passes from
trifles to the greatest excesses. It passes by no period of life, it
excepts no class of men. For certain races, thanks to their poverty have escaped luxurious living. Certain races because of
their active and wandering life have escaped sloth. . . . There
is no race that anger does not goad. . . . Finally other vices
seize upon individuals. This is the one passion that sometimes
lays hold of a people. Nowhere has a whole people burned with
passion for the female sex, nor has a whole state built its hope
on money or gain. Ambition seizes upon individuals. Frequently anger seizes upon men in a body. Men, women, old
men, children, princes and commons have had but one feeling,
and the whole multitude aroused by a very few words has out-
stripped the very man who incited them. They have rushed
forthwith for arms and fire-brands." And in the first book he
says,† "If you care now to view the effects of this vice, you
will find that no bane has cost the human race more dearly. You

* *Ibid.,* III, 1, 2.
† *Ibid.,* I, 2.

will behold murders, and poisons, and the mutual baseness of parties to an action and the ruin of cities, and the destruction of whole races . . . fires not confined within the walls of cities, but vast stretches of country lit up with hostile flames. Behold the foundations of the noblest cities scarcely discernible; anger has cast them down. Behold tracts solitary and deserted for miles without an inhabitant: anger has depopulated them." And since Seneca says in the third book,* "We shall protect ourselves against anger, if we represent to ourselves from time to time all its evils . . . it must be accused before us and condemned. Therefore its evils must be examined and brought to light"; for this reason in what precedes I have recounted all the fundamental evils of anger to the end that it may be completely rooted out, and that no vestiges of it may remain in our hearts.

Chapter VIII

Not only does a consideration of these evils warn us to renounce anger, but I shall cite some noteworthy examples of philosophers and of illustrious princes which properly have the effect of quieting down any man who is angry and banishing wrath from his mind. Solinus in his book on the Wonders of the World states among other marvels that Socrates, the parent of the great philosophers, never changed countenance, but always remained in the same habit of mind and face. And Seneca in the second book on Anger states the same fact with regard to Socrates. And Jerome writing against Jovinian touches on the subject of Socrates' bad wife. When Socrates was asked why he did not drive away so cross a wife, he said, "I am being trained at home so that I may be able to bear more easily injury and abuse abroad." And in the same place Jerome relates that on a certain occasion Socrates was drenched with dirty water from above after prolonged abuse from his wife, but merely remarked: "I knew that rain would follow that thunder." Cassianus tells us in his book of Dialogues of one who reproached Socrates because he was a corrupter of boys; but when his pupils wished to assault this detractor Socrates restrained

* *De Ira,* III, 5.

them with the words, "Well I am, but I keep myself under control." Seneca in the second book on Anger says, Socrates said to his slave, "I would beat you were I not angry." And in the third book he says,* "Men say that Socrates on receiving a cuff on the ear merely remarked that it was annoying that men did not know when they should go forth with a helmet." "Plato, the pupil of Socrates, when about to beat a slave with his own hand realized that he himself was angry and kept his hand suspended and stood in the attitude of one about to strike. On being asked by a friend what he was doing Plato replied, 'I am exacting punishment from an angry man.' " He had already forgotten the slave because he had found some one more deserving of punishment. Seneca tells this story in the third book on Anger, and he introduces after this another example. "Because of a certain offence Plato was considerably exasperated, 'Do you then, Speusippus, correct this young slave with blows; for I am angry.' For this reason he did not flog him. . . . 'I am angry,' he said, 'I shall do more than I ought, I shall go too far; this slave should not be in the power of a man who is not master of himself.' " And in the second book he gives an example that was quoted above, in regard to a boy brought up in Plato's home, who on returning to his own home and finding his father loudmouthed, said that he did not see such behavior at Plato's. And Archytas of Tarentum, the other teacher of Plato, being somewhat angered at his steward said, "How would I have treated you if I were not angry!" These words are quoted by Cicero† in the fourth book of the Tusculan Disputations. Moreover, Eusebius in the Chronicles says that Xenophon, the pupil of Socrates next in importance to Plato, said to one who reviled him on a certain matter, "You revile me: I on the witness of my conscience have learned to despise abuse." Diogenes the philosopher, as Seneca relates in the third book on Anger, when a forward youth spat on him as he was discussing anger, bore the insult meekly and like a philosopher. "I am not indeed angry," said he, "but I am in doubt, however, whether I should be." And Seneca continues, "How much better seems the reply of that sage who as he was pleading a case had discharged into the middle of his brow a mouthful of thick spittle by Lentulus, a

* *Ibid.*, III, 11, 12.
† *Tusculan Disputations*, IV, 36.

turbulent individual. He wiped off his face and said, 'I am in a position, Lentulus, to state to all men that those are in error who say that you do not possess mouth' " [*i.e.,* effrontery]. Democritus the philosopher resembled Socrates in the serenity of his countenance. For as Seneca tells us in the second book on Anger,* "Never did he appear in public without laughing: nothing in fact seemed serious to him of all that was being done with serious intent." But Heraclitus the philosopher, as Seneca states in the same passage, whenever he went out and saw so great a throng of people around him living wretchedly, nay, rather, perishing miserably, would weep and pity all.

Now these examples and the like refer to the philosophers. But there are deeds of others also that should be imitated. When Cambyses, a very evil king, had shot an arrow into the heart of the son and asked the boy's father whether he had a sure hand, the father replied that Apollo did not shoot an arrow with truer aim; he did not revile the king nor did he utter a word of sorrow, although he perceived that his own heart had been pierced as well as that of his son. For if he had said anything as an angered man, he could have done nothing as a father. Seneca relates this story in the third book on Anger. And he continues, "When the Persian king served up to his friend Arpagus as a banquet the latter's children and asked the father whether he was pleased with the food, Arpagus replied, 'At a king's table every dinner pleases' . . . from this I infer that anger arising from great wrongs can be concealed and forced to utter words at variance with one's thought."

He adds, moreover,† "But although for those who serve control of their passions and especially of this savage and unbridled one is advantageous, it is still more so for kings. For all is lost when fortune permits a man to go as far as anger dictates." "For what was easier for King Antigonus than to order two soldiers to be led forth, who while leaning against the tent of the king were doing that which men do with the greatest risk and also with the greatest satisfaction who are discontented with their king? Antigonus had heard all since between the speaker and the listener there was only a curtain. Gently pushing the curtain aside he said, 'Move further away

* *De Ira,* II, 10.
† *Ibid.,* III, 16, 22, 23.

DOCTORS OF THE UNIVERSITY OF PARIS

From *Chants Royaux* in the Bibliothèque Nationale, Paris

lest the king hear you.' The same king on hearing certain of his soldiers calling down curses on their king for bringing them into that particular road and into mud from which they could not extricate themselves, approached those who were in the most serious difficulty, and said to them, 'Now curse Antigonus, through whose fault you have fallen into these difficulties, but bless him who has rescued you from this morass.' Antigonus bore insults as tranquilly from his enemies as from his subjects. Accordingly when the Greeks were besieged in a certain small fortress, and relying on the strength of their position held the enemy in contempt and passed many jokes on the ugliness of Antigonus, now deriding his small stature and now his flat nose, he said, 'I rejoice and I hope that it is a good omen if I have a Silenus in my camp.' After conquering them by hunger, he enrolled in his cohorts those useful for war, the rest he sold; and he said he would not have done this save for the fact that it was expedient for these men who had such a bad tongue to have a master."

"If there was," as Seneca says in this passage, "any virtue in King Philip, father of Alexander, it was his patience under insults, a great aid in protecting a kingdom. For when Athenian envoys came to him and were asked what the Athenians desired, one of them replied, 'That you hang yourself.' And when the indignation of those present flared up at such a rude answer, Philip bade them be quiet, and that the envoy be dismissed safe and unharmed. 'But you other envoys,' said he, 'are to report to the Athenians that those exhibit far more haughtiness who make such statements than those who hear them without exacting vengeance.' " Alexander the Macedonian, grandson of Antigonus and son of Philip, although he was haughty and evil in his ways, yet, as Seneca says in the second book,* "after reading a letter from his mother, in which she warned him to beware of poison at the hands of Philip his physician, received the potion and drank it without fear. He relied on his own judgment rather in regard to his friend. I praise this in Alexander, because no man was more subject to anger. The greater the moderation in kings the more is it to be praised." Seneca in the third book says,† "It is recorded of

* *Ibid.*, II, 23.
† *Ibid.*, III, 11.

Pisistratus the Athenian tyrant that when a drunken table companion had declaimed vigorously against his cruelty, and there were not lacking those desirous of offering their hand to Pisistratus, and first one and then another tried to inflame his resentment, he bore the affront calmly and replied to those urging him on that he was no more incensed than he would have been had his detracter run into him blindfolded." Seneca in the second book relates the following anecdote in regard to Marcus Cato, who according to the histories was second to none in virtue and in wisdom was foremost among the Romans:* "When a man ignorant of his identity unintentionally struck Cato in the bath (for who knowingly would have done him an injury?) and offered an apology, Cato replied, 'I do not recall that I was struck': he thought it better not to acknowledge the injury than to avenge it." And in the third book he says,† "The deified Augustus did and said many things worthy to be remembered, from which we see that anger had no control over him. Timagenes, a writer of histories, had made certain statements against Augustus, against his wife and his whole house, and his pleasantries were not lost. For pleasantry of a daring kind is freely passed from mouth to mouth. Caesar frequently warned him to be more guarded in his speech. He put up patiently with the abuse; he never complained to Pollio, the host of his enemy. He merely said this to Pollio, 'Enjoy him, my dear Pollio, enjoy him.'" And Seneca concludes, "Therefore each one should say to himself, Am I more powerful than Philip? Yet an insult offered him was not punished. Have I more power in my home than the deified Augustus had in the whole world? Yet he was content to withdraw from his traducer."

Chapter IX

We have, however, remedies against anger drawn from a consideration of the evils inherent in it: moreover, we are influenced by the examples of the wise and powerful. In addition to these Seneca teaches us more direct remedies against this

* *De Ira,* II, 32.
† *Ibid.,* III, 23, 24.

vice. One of these is a knowledge of the facts before we give way to anger. For, as he says in the second book,* "Of those things that offend us some are told us, others we ourselves hear or see. We should not give ready credence to all that is told us; for many lie to deceive, many because they have been deceived. One tries to win favor by an accusation and feigns an injury in order that he may seem to have deplored its commission. There is the malignant man and he who wishes to separate firmly united friendships. . . . The question of a trifling sum would not be settled if you should act as judge, without a witness. The witness would have no standing except under oath. You will give both parties a chance to state the case, you will give them time, you will hear the case more than once. For the truth will be more evident, the oftener the case is reviewed. Do you condemn a friend at once? Before you hear him, before you question him, before he is permitted to learn who his accuser is or the charge, are you going to give way to anger? . . . The very man who told you will cease making the statement if he is required to prove it. 'There is no reason,' he says, 'to drag me into it. If I am brought into it I shall deny all; I shall never tell you anything in the future.' At the same time he both urges you on and himself withdraws from the contest and strife. He who is unwilling to speak to you except in private, is almost in the position of one who does not speak at all. What is more unjust than to believe in private and to be angry in public?" And again he says,† "Credulity causes a great deal of harm. In many cases we should not even listen, since in some things it is better to be deceived than to distrust." Of some things we are witnesses, but "suspicion and conjecture, two of the most deceiving provocatives, must be removed from the mind. That man greeted me with scant courtesy. This one did not embrace me. Still another broke off abruptly the conversation we had begun. This man did not invite me to dinner. I noticed aversion on the face of that man." "Suspicion will never lack a reason: we are in need of frankness and a kindly judgment in all things; we should believe nothing except that which meets our eyes and is manifest; and as often as our suspicion shall have appeared groundless, let us blame our credulity. For such cor-

* *Ibid.*, II, 29.
† *Ibid.*, II, 24.

rection will form in us the habit of not believing a story on insufficient evidence." And for this reason he says in the third book,* "We shall find many innocent if we begin to investigate before we yield to anger. But now we follow our first impulse; then although our suspicion is groundless, we persist, in order that we may not seem to have begun without cause; and unfairest of all is the fact that the injustice of our anger makes us the more obstinate. For we retain and augment our feeling of anger, just as though the excess of our passion were a proof of its justice. . . . You will find that very same thing in man which you see happen in the brutes. . . . The color red excites the bull, the adder rises at a shadow, a napkin angers bears and lions. All animals that are wild and savage are disturbed at trifles." And similarly he says in the second book,† "Trifles are a terror to such as have no stability in themselves. The motion of a chariot and the change in the appearance of the wheels drive lions back into their den. The squeal of a pig terrifies elephants." And in the third book he says,‡ "The same thing happens in the case of restless and stupid natures. They are struck by suspicion to such a degree that they call moderate favors injuries. In favors is found the most frequent, at any rate the most bitter, source of anger. For we become angry with our dearest friends because they have given us less than we expected, less than they have bestowed on another. . . . 'I have less than I hoped for . . . than I deserved.' This source of anger is especially to be dreaded; from it spring most destructive enmities and such as are likely to attack all that is most sacred. More friends than enemies slew the deified Julius, friends whose insatiable hopes he had failed to satisfy. . . . For no one has made a more generous use of victory from which he claimed nothing for himself except the power to regulate. But how could he have satisfied such insatiable desires, since all gauged their wishes to the full extent of the power of a single individual? . . . This has turned the arms of their own subjects against kings, and has driven the most faithful adherents to plot the death of those for whom and before whom they had vowed to die. No man is contented with his own lot when he

* *De Ira,* III, 29, 30.
† *Ibid.,* II, 11.
‡ *Ibid.,* III, 30, 31.

considers that of his neighbor. . . . So great is the injustice
of men, that although they have received much, the fact that
they could have accepted more they regard as an injury. He
gave me a praetorship: but I had hoped for a consulship. He
has given me that which he had to give some one: he has con-
tributed nothing of his own. Come, be thankful rather for what
you have received. Wait for the remainder and be glad that you
are not yet filled. We should reckon it among our pleasures that
there still remains something to hope for. . . . Consider how
many more you precede than you follow."

The second remedy is delay in exacting punishment. Hence
Seneca says in the second book,* "The greatest remedy against
anger is delay. Beg of anger at the beginning, not that it pardon, but that it judge; it will cool down if it waits." And in the
third book he says,† "Give yourself no license while you are
angry. Why? Because you wish for free license in all things.
Fight with yourself: if you cannot conquer your anger, it is
beginning to conquer you. If it is hidden, if an outlet is not
given to it, let us destroy its signs, and let us keep it as far as
possible hidden and secret. This will prove a great trial to us.
For anger is eager to leap forth and inflame the eyes and
change the face. But if we have allowed it to become manifest
on our exterior, it triumphs over us. Let it be hidden in the
lowest depths of our breast: let us carry it, let not it carry us.
Nay, let us turn all signs into their opposites. Let our look be
mild, our voice gentler than usual, our step slower. Gradually
the inner man is conformed to the outer. In Socrates a lowered
voice and restrained speech were indicative of anger. It was
then apparent that he was holding himself in check. . . . Let
us beg all our most intimate friends to treat us with the utmost
candor when we are least in a condition to brook it, and not to
lend themselves to our anger. Against this potent evil and one
that is pleasing to us . . . it is best to be on the look-out for
obstacles with which to oppose our known vices, and before all
else so to order our mind, that even when shaken by sudden and
very grievous blows it may either have no feeling of anger, or
bury such a feeling if excited by some great and unexpected

* *Ibid.*, II, 29.
† *Ibid.*, III, 12, 13.

injury in the depths of the heart and give no manifestation of its pain."

In the second book he likewise combines both the remedies just mentioned in a fitting and useful way. He says,* "Therefore against the first causes we must fight: for the cause of anger is the thought that we have been injured. To this thought, however, we must not give ready acceptance. Not even to what is open and manifest must we accede at once. For some falsehoods bear the appearance of truth. Time should always be given; time discloses the truth. Let us not lend ready ears to those who prefer charges: let this vice of human nature be noted by us and suspected, because we willingly believe that which we are unwilling to hear, and we yield to anger before we sit in judgment on the matter. What of the fact that we are influenced not only by charges but by mere suspicions? And become angry at innocent people by misinterpreting a look or a laugh? We ought then to plead the cause of the absent against ourselves and to hold our anger in suspense. For a delayed punishment can be exacted; an exacted punishment cannot be recalled." And he, moreover, says in the third book,† "It is not expedient to see all things, to hear all things; let many injuries pass unnoticed, most of which he does not receive who is ignorant of them. You don't wish to be angry? Then don't be inquisitive. The man who asks what has been said about him, he who digs up malicious remarks even though uttered in secret, disquiets himself. Our interpretation leads us to view certain things as injuries; therefore some of them should be postponed, others laughed at, and still others pardoned. Anger must be restrained in many ways: many things may be turned off into a laugh or a jest." And in addition to all these he sets forth a threefold argument against anger in the second book: for he argues as follows :‡ "It is wrong to injure your country; therefore it is also wrong to injure a fellow citizen, for he is part of your country. The parts are sacred if the whole is worthy of veneration. Therefore it is wrong to harm any man, for he is your fellow citizen in the larger city, that is, in the world." The second argument is drawn from a simile in reference to the

* *De Ira*, II, 22.
† *Ibid.*, III, 11.
‡ *Ibid.*, II, 31, 34.

members of the same body, and is as follows: "What if the hands should wish to harm the feet, and the eyes the hands? As all the parts are in accord, because the conservation of the whole depends on the preservation of the individual members, so men should spare their fellows, because they were born to form a society." The third argument is a most fitting and excellent one, the conclusion of which he places first. He says, "Therefore we must abstain from anger; either the man is an equal you are to attack, or a superior, or an inferior. To contend with an equal is a doubtful matter, with a superior is madness, with an inferior is paltriness." And he says,* "Is he a good man who has inflicted injury? Do not believe it. Is he a bad man? Do not imitate him. He will pay the penalty to another which he owes to you: and he who has sinned has paid the penalty to himself."

Many other matters should be considered with reference to anger, all of which are taken up mainly in the books of Seneca on Anger and on Clemency. But since the discussion in the present instance is in the nature of a plea and not of a complete presentation, I am for this reason concluding it at this point. I have spoken more fully on this vice, since it will always injure and confound the whole human race so long as man retains his mortal state. For the vice is a very bad one and particularly unnatural in man, flaring out to his peril. For this reason I have written at greater length and in more detail in regard to it.

CHAPTER X

SINCE the subject of anger has just been considered, which fights with adversity and is conquered, some virtues will be touched upon which conquer adversity and take no thought for this world's prosperity. Seneca composed a book to Lucilius whose title is, Since the world is ruled by providence, why do many evils happen to good men? in which he says, "When you see good men and such as are pleasing to God laboring, sweating, mounting the steep road, but evil men wanton and welter in pleasures, consider that we are pleased with the modest be-

* *Ibid.*, II, 30. Bacon substitutes *imitari* for *mirari* in this quotation.

havior of our sons, but with pertness of house-born slaves: that the former are restrained by a more rigorous training, and the latter are encouraged in their pertness. God treats a good man as a favorite, he tries him, hardens him, prepares him for himself. No evil can happen to a good man; opposites do not mingle. As so many streams, so great a quantity of rain water, and such an abundance of medicinal springs do not change the taste of the sea, do not even alter it; so the shock of adversity does not unsettle the spirit of a good man. He remains unmoved and gives to every event the coloring of his own character: for he is superior to all external happenings. I do not say that he is insensible to these things; but he conquers them, and his quiet and placid nature is supported against all adversity. He considers all adverse things as part of his training. . . . Virtue grows feeble without an adversary. Then are its greatness and its ability apparent when it shows its power of endurance. Whatever happens men should take in good part and should turn into good. It is not what you bear but how you bear it that matters. Do you not see how differently fathers and mothers show their affection? The former bid their children rise early and begin their studies, do not permit them to be idle on holidays, and draw the sweat from them, sometimes tears. But mothers desire to fondle their children and keep them in the shade: they are eager to save them from tears, labor, sadness. God views good men as a father, and loves them intensely, and says, Let them be trained by hardships, by pains, by losses to develop true strength. Animals fattened by inactivity grow weak: they succumb not only from labor, but from movement and their own weight. A happiness that is unimpaired can endure no blow. But after waging unceasing conflict with his own misfortunes, a man grows callous from the injuries he receives, he yields to no evil, but even if he falls, he still fights on his knees. . . . Behold two champions worthy the attention of a god, a brave man matched with an evil fortune."*

"Nothing seems to me more unfortunate than the man who has never been touched by adversity. For he has never had an opportunity to make trial of himself. . . . He is not considered fit to win a victory over fortune; as though fortune were to say, 'Am I to take that man as my opponent? He will lower his arms

* *De Providentia,* I, II.

at once. There is no need of exerting my full power against him . . . he cannot sustain my look . . . I am ashamed to fight with a man who is ready to be conquered.' A gladiator considers it a disgrace to be pitted against an inferior, and he knows that an opponent is conquered without glory who is conquered without danger. Fortune reasons in the same way: she seeks the bravest as her antagonists, she passes by certain with disgust, she attacks those that are most steadfast and upright, that against such she may direct her force. It is only adversity that discovers the shining example. . . . The greater the suffering the greater will be the glory: . . . prosperity falls to the lot of the common herd and to men of mean abilities."*

"But it is characteristic of a great man to overcome misfortunes and terrors common to mortals. But he who is always fortunate and passes his life without vexation of mind is ignorant of the other side of nature. You are a great man; but how do I know it if fortune does not give you an opportunity of showing your excellence? . . . I consider you an unhappy man because you have never been unhappy. You have passed your life without an opponent. No one will know what you could do; not even you yourself. For you cannot know yourself without trial. No man has learned his own ability without effort. Therefore some have voluntarily exposed themselves to adversity, which seemed to have forgotten them, and have sought for their virtue, destined to pass without notice, an opportunity to display itself. Great men," he says, "rejoice sometimes in adversity like brave soldiers in wars. . . . Courage is eager for danger; it thinks of its goal, not of what it is to suffer on the way: since that also which it is called upon to suffer is part of the glory. Soldiers take pride in their wounds; and joyfully display their blood flowing from wounds that are not mortal. Although those who return unscathed from battle have met the same danger, yet he who returns wounded, receives greater admiration. . . . You perceive the quality of the pilot in the storm, of the soldier in the battle. How am I to know what fortitude you possess against poverty if you are wallowing in riches? How am I to know your steadfastness when you are the object of ignominy, calumny and popular hatred if you are growing old amid plaudits? . . . Do not be afraid of those things that God applies as goads

* *Ibid.*, III.

to our characters: misfortune is virtue's opportunity. We may rightly call those wretched who grow torpid from excessive good fortune, whom as on an unruffled sea a lifeless calm detains . . . adversity presses harder on such as have never experienced it; the yoke is heavy on tender necks. The recruit pales at the thought of a wound; the veteran views his own blood undismayed; he knows that he has often been victorious after his blood was shed."

"God therefore hardens . . . trains those whom he esteems, whom he loves. But those to whom he seems indulgent he is keeping soft for evils yet to come. You are in error if you believe any one exempt: his own turn will come to the man who has long enjoyed prosperity. He who seems exempted is merely deferred. Why does God afflict all good people with ill health or grief or other misfortunes? Because in camp also the bravest are commanded to incur the greatest dangers. The general sends his finest troops to waylay the enemy by night. . . . No one of those who march forth says 'The general has done me an injustice'; but each one, 'He has a good opinion of me.' Those should say the same thing who are bidden to suffer afflictions that bring tears to timid and mean-spirited souls. Shun luxury, flee from good fortune weakening to our moral fibre, in which our souls become steeped and, unless something happens to warn us of our human lot, we remain in a state of torpor resembling a lasting intoxication. . . . Since all things that have passed beyond a due measure are harmful, excessive good fortune is most dangerous. . . . God follows the method in the case of good men that teachers employ with their pupils, exacting more work from such as are more promising. . . . Never is virtue's apprenticeship a mild one. Fortune lashes and lacerates us. Let us be patient: it is not mere brutality, it is a contest: the oftener we enter it the stronger we become. That part of our body is most robust which we have exercised most. We must offer ourselves to fortune, that we may be hardened against her by her own training. Gradually she will make us a match for her. Constant jeopardy will give us a contempt for dangers. Thus are sailors' bodies hardened from enduring the buffeting of the sea; thus do the hands of farmers become worn, the arms of soldiers acquire strength to hurl their weapons, the limbs of runners become agile; that member in each is strongest which he has exercised. The mind by endurance arrives at a point where it can despise the power of misfortunes. Why wonder that good men are shaken, that they may become steadfast. The tree is not firm nor strong unless it is subject to frequent assaults of the wind. For by the mere shaking it becomes firmly placed and more surely rooted. Fragile are the trees that have grown in the sunny valley. It is therefore for the advantage of good men themselves, in order that they may be undaunted, to be trained amid adversity and to bear with equanimity those things which are not ills except to the man bearing them ill."*

"This is God's purpose which he would show to the sage. . . . Good men labor, they sacrifice and are sacrificed and that too of their own free will; they are not dragged along by fortune, they follow her and keep pace with her. If they had known, they would have preceded her. . . . I can utter only one compaint in regard to thee, O God; thou didst not make thy will known to me before; for I would have taken up those tasks earlier which I am assuming after being summoned. . . . Dost thou wish some part of my body? Take it. I am offering no great thing. I shall soon leave it all behind. Dost thou wish my spirit? I shall not hinder thee in receiving again what thou hast given. Thou shalt receive from a willing hand whatsoever thou askest. What then? I should have preferred to offer it rather than to hand it over We have received that which is as perishable as we are. Always cheerful and steadfast let us believe that nothing which we lose is ours. What is a good man called upon to do? To offer himself to fate. It is a great consolation to be borne away with the universe. . . . Fire tests gold; misfortune good men."†

"Yet why does God permit any evil to befall good men? He removes all evils from them, crimes, disgraces, wicked thoughts, covetous designs, secret lust, and avarice threatening the property of another. God protects and sets them free. . . . Democritus cast away his riches, considering them as a burden on a virtuous mind. What then? Are you surprised if God permits that to happen to a good man which a good man at times wishes to happen to himself? . . . Imagine, therefore, that God says to you, what complaint have you to make of me, you who have

* *De Providentia,* IV.
† *Ibid.,* V.

chosen virtue? I have surrounded others with false blessings, and I have mocked their empty minds with what I may call a long and deceptive dream; I have adorned them with gold and silver and ivory; within they are destitute of good. Those men whom you look upon as fortunate, if you see them on the side they hide and not on that which they show, are wretched, sordid, base, after the similitude of their own walls adorned on the outside. Such felicity has no firm basis and exists in appearance only. It is only a shell and a thin one at that. Therefore while they are permitted to stand and appear to men as they themselves desire, they are brilliant figures and impose on their fellows. When something happens which disturbs and discloses them, it then becomes apparent how much deep and real deformity is hidden by a splendor not their own. The blessings I have given you are sure and lasting, the more you consider them and investigate them in every way, the better and greater will they appear. I have permitted you to despise what other men fear and to disdain what they wish. You do not shine on the outside, your excellence is within. Thus the universe despises all outside of itself, and rejoices in its own spectacle. Every blessing has been placed within. Your happiness consists in not having need of it. But you will say many things happen of a sad and dreadful nature and hard to bear. Because I was not able to withdraw you from them, I have armed your minds against them all. Bravely endure them; in this you are superior to God; he is exempted from the endurance of evils; you endure and triumph over them. While life is prayed for, learn of death."*

Chapter XI

Seneca, moreover, in his book to Serenus on the topic, Why a philosopher is affected by neither injury nor insult, maintains that a philosopher cannot receive injury or insult. And he proves this by the statement, "I have not meant to attribute to the sage an imaginary honor, but to place him in such a position that he can receive no injury. What then? Will there be no one to attack him, no one to disturb him? There is nothing in nature

* *De Providentia,* VI.

so sacred as not to be subject to sacrilege : but divine things on this account are not on a less elevated plane. . . . That is not invulnerable which is not struck, but that which is not injured : this I tell you is the distinguishing mark of the sage. Is it not certain that you can depend more on the strength that is not conquered than on that which is not assailed, since untried powers are doubtful, but you rightly regard that strength of character as most reliable which successfully resists all assaults? Thus you may rest assured that the sage is of a finer nature if he is harmed by no injury, than if no injury happens to him. I shall call that man courageous whom wars do not subdue nor hostile force terrify when directed against him; I do not call the man courageous who enjoys a luxurious ease among indolent people. This therefore I maintain, that the sage is subject to no injury. Accordingly it matters not how many shafts are hurled at him since he is invulnerable to them all. He resembles the hardness of certain stones which does not yield to iron. The diamond cannot be cut or marked or worn away, but actually dulls every tool applied to it. He may be compared to certain substances that cannot be consumed by fire, but even when enveloped in flame retain their rigidity and form; or to rocks projecting out into the deep which break the waves nor do they show any traces of the sea's violence although they have been lashed for so many ages."*

"Thus is the mind of the sage firm and gathers such strength, that it is as safe from injury as the objects to which I have compared him. . . . For the sage is too far removed from contact with baser things for any hostile violence to expend its force upon him. All the attacks of shamelessness, ill will, and pride directed against the sage are made in vain."†

"Let us distinguish, if you approve, Serenus, injury from insult. The former is more severe in its nature, the latter is milder and grievous only to weaklings. Men are not harmed by insult, only offended. Such are the weakness and vanity of some men's minds, that they consider nothing more bitter: thus you will find a slave who prefers to be beaten with a whip rather than slapped in the face, and who considers death and stripes more tolerable than words of insult. We go so far in our folly

* *De Constantia,* III.
† *Ibid.,* IV.

as to afflict ourselves not only with pain but even with the
thought of it. We are like children who are afraid of a shadow
or the ugliness of masks or an ill-favored face. . . . Injury has
the intention of harming some one. But wisdom leaves no place
for harm. In the sight of wisdom there is only one thing that
harms, namely, the baseness of sin, which cannot enter where
virtue and integrity are already established. Every injury is a
loss to him who is subject to it, nor can any one receive an injury
without some loss in prestige, in person, or in external interests.
But the sage can lose nothing. For he has stored away his all in
himself, he trusts nothing to fortune, he has his possessions in
safety, content with virtue, which has no need of fortuitous
things and therefore can be neither increased nor diminished.
For virtue in possession of the highest good can increase no
more, and fortune snatches away nothing except that which it
has given. But fortune does not bestow virtue, and therefore it
does not take virtue away. For virtue is free, inviolable, immovable, unshaken. Virtue so hardens a man against misfortunes, that he cannot even be bent, much less be conquered.
. . . Virtue does not lower its eyes nor change its expression
at the sight of either adversity or prosperity. Therefore the
sage will never experience a loss of which he will be sensible.
For he is in possession of virtue alone, of which he can never
be deprived. He uses all else as though merely borrowed: but
who is disturbed at the loss of what is not his? But if injury
can harm no one of the sage's possessions, because they are
guarded by his virtue, injury cannot befall the sage. King
Demetrius, surnamed Poliorcetes, had captured Megara. When
Stilbon the philosopher was asked by Demetrius whether he
had lost anything, he replied, 'Nothing; I have all my possessions with me.' And yet his patrimony had been plundered, his
daughters carried off by the enemy, his country reduced to a
foreign yoke, and he himself questioned by a king enthroned on
high and surrounded by the arms of a victorious army. But
the philosopher robbed the king of his victory, and bore witness that, although his city had been captured, he himself was
not only unconquered, but had suffered no loss: for he had in
his possession the true riches, on which no man could set hand.
But those things that had been pillaged and destroyed, he did
not consider his, but extraneous and subject to the caprice of

fortune; therefore he had not set his heart on these things as though they were his. For the possession of all that comes to us from without is hazardous and uncertain. The sage looks upon adversity . . . and bears prosperity with moderation, neither yielding to the former nor relying on the latter. He is one and the same under all circumstances, nor does he reckon anything his except the better part of himself. . . . Those defences which guard the sage are protected from flames and from every assault; they offer no entrance, they are lofty, impregnable, equal to God!"*

"You may not make your usual statement that this sage of ours is nowhere found. Such a beautiful human character is no mere fiction; nor are we imagining some exalted being who has no existence, but one whose existence is an assured fact and has been proved by us . . . seldom found perhaps, and then only after a lapse of many years. For great and exceptional phenomena do not frequently occur. For the rest I am afraid that Marcus Cato is even superior to our model sage. Finally, that which injures must be stronger than that which is injured. But wickedness is not stronger than virtue: therefore the sage cannot be injured. It is only evil people that try to injure the good. Good men live at peace with one another. Evil men are not so harmful to the good as they are to one another. But if only the weaker man can be injured, but the evil man is weaker than the good . . . injury cannot befall the sage. For you need not be reminded that no one is good except the sage. If Socrates, you say, was condemned unjustly, he received an injury. It is necessary to observe here that it may happen that some one does me an injury and I do not receive it; as, for example, if a man place in my city house an article he has stolen from my house in the country, he has committed a theft, but I have suffered no loss. . . . If a man has intercourse with his own wife under the impression that she is the wife of another, he will be an adulterer, although she will not be an adulteress. Some one has given me poison, but it has lost its efficacy owing to the fact that it has been mixed with food; by administering the poison he rendered himself guilty of a crime, even though he did no harm. . . . All crimes are accomplished facts, so far as their guilt is concerned, even before they have produced their

* *De Constantia,* V, VI.

effect. . . . If I have received an injury, one must of necessity have been done me. If an injury has been done, it does not necessarily follow that I received it; for many things can happen to ward off injury."*

"Moreover justice can suffer nothing that is unjust, because contraries cannot unite; . . . therefore injury cannot befall the sage. Nor is there any reason why you should be surprised at this: if no one can do him an injury, no one can confer even a benefit upon him. The sage lacks nothing that can be conferred upon him as a gift. . . . No one therefore can either harm or benefit the sage; since what is divine neither craves aid nor can suffer injury. Moreover, the sage closely approaches God, is like God with the exception that he is mortal. Striving to mount to those beings on high, well ordered, inaccessible to fear, ever moving in an equal and harmonious course, tranquil, beneficent, created for the general good, salutary to himself and to others, the sage will set his heart on nothing lowly; he will suffer no affliction who supported by reason passes through human vicissitudes with a divine courage. There is no source from which he may receive an injury. Do you think that I refer only to an injury received from man? I mean not even one received from fortune which after a contest with virtue has always been worsted. . . . And if the sage bears with equanimity the injuries of fortune, how much more will he endure those of men in power whom he knows to be the instruments of fortune?"†

"Now there is the added fact that no one receives an injury with an untroubled mind, but is perturbed when he experiences it. But the upright man is free from perturbation. He is master of himself‡ and of his deep and calm repose. For if an injury touches him, he is disturbed and hindered thereby. But the sage is free from anger which the appearance of an injury excites, nor would he be free from anger unless he was also free from injury, which he knows cannot happen to him. For this reason he is so firm and so happy, for this reason constantly elated with joy. So far is he from being saddened at the attacks

---

* *De Constantia,* VII.

† *Ibid.,* VIII.

‡ The reading *moderator sui* omitting *erroribus* seems to give better sense than the reading followed by Bacon.

made on him by men and things, that he views an injury as a means of experimenting on himself and testing his virtue."*

"After having passed through the first part, let us pass to the second," namely, insult. "An insult is less serious than an injury: we can complain of it rather than exact punishment for it, and the laws have not considered it worthy of a penalty. The resentment which it excites is the effect of an abject mind, which an action or a word is capable of dishonoring. A certain man refused to receive me at his home today, although he admitted others: he listened with a disdainful air to that which I had to say, or he openly laughed at it . . . and other affronts of this kind, which I can call only the complaints of a squeamish mind. Those affected by such insults are as a rule men who are pampered by luxury and prosperity. Characters weak and effeminate in nature owing to too much ease, and wanton from the lack of real provocation, are aroused by affronts, the greater parts of which are taken as such because of a faulty interpretation of their intent. Thus he who is affected by an insult shows that he possesses neither prudence nor self-confidence. For he does not doubt that he has been scorned, and this sentiment cannot fail to lower and depress him in his own estimation. But the sage is despised by no one. He knows his own greatness and is convinced that no one is in a position to despise him, and does not overcome all these—I shall not call them miseries of our minds but rather plagues, nay, he does not even feel them. There are other things, however, which do assail the sage, even if they do not overthrow him, as, for example, physical pain and debility, or the loss of friends and children, and the ruin of his country in the flames of war. I do not deny that the sage feels these misfortunes. For we are not attributing to him the hardness of stone or iron. There is no virtue in supporting misfortunes one does not feel. In what then does the virtue of the sage consist? He receives certain blows, but overcomes those received and heals and checks them. But these minor ills, namely insults, he does not even feel, nor does he employ against them that virtue with which he is accustomed to endure hardships, but he either does not notice them, or judges them worthy of a laugh merely."†

* *Ibid.*, IX.
† *Ibid.*, X.

"Moreover since most of our affronts are offered by proud and insolent men, who are unable to stand prosperity, the sage can repel such pride with that noblest of virtues, magnanimity. He passes over such trifles, regarding them merely as idle dreams and visions of the night without reality. . . . *Contumelia* [insult] comes from *contemptus* [contempt], since men insult only those for whom they have contempt. But no one really despises a greater and a better man, even if he comports himself in the same way as those who do despise. For children slap a parent's face, and the child disarranges and pulls the hair of the mother, and spits on her, or exposes in the sight of its parents what should remain covered, and uses obscene expressions. We do not call any one of these acts an insult. Why? Because he who has committed them is not in a position to despise. . . . But what folly it is at one moment to be pleased, and at another to be vexed by the same actions, and to call a remark made by a friend an affront, but if made by a young slave a droll bit of repartee?"*

"The same feeling that we have toward children the sage has toward all who even after youth and gray hairs still remain like children. Have those men secured any advantage, whose minds are evil and whose errors have grown greater, who differ from children merely in the size and shape of their bodies, but are not less inconstant and unreliable, men who are eager for pleasures without discrimination, restless beings and kept quiet not by their nature but by fear? No one would say therefore that there is any difference between such men and children, since the latter display avarice for knuckle-bones, nuts, and small change, while the former are greedy for gold and silver and cities. . . . Therefore children and those more advanced in years are equally in error, but with the difference that the latter fall into other and greater evils. Rightly therefore does the sage regard their affronts as mere pleasantries. And sometimes he admonishes and punishes them as though they were children, not because he has suffered an injury, but he corrects them because they have inflicted one, and with the idea that they will cease to act in this way. For so also are cattle mastered with the lash, nor do we become angry at them when

* *De Constantia,* XI.

they refuse to be ridden, but we curb them, in order that the pain may conquer their obstinacy. Therefore you will perceive that the objection has been removed . . . why, if the sage has not suffered an injury or insult, does he punish those who have inflicted them? For he is not avenging himself, but he is correcting them."*

"Does a physician become angry at an insane patient? . . . The sage has the same attitude of mind toward all men as the physician has toward the sick under his care. The sage knows that all these grave personages who pass before him clad in purple and whose visage proclaims good health are of unsound mind. He regards them in no other light than as sick men lacking self-control. Consequently he does not even become vexed if in their sickness they have ventured to illtreat him who is trying to cure them, and he shows the same good sense in reckoning as equally unimportant both their dignities and their depravities. As he will not be flattered at the attentions of a beggar, nor will he regard it as an insult if a man from the dregs of the people does not return his salutation, so will he feel no pride if many rich men pay him honor. For he knows that they differ in no respect from beggars, nay, that they are more wretched. For the former need little, while the needs of the latter are great. And again the sage will not be affected if the King of the Medes or Attalus King of Asia passes him in silence and with a haughty look as he bows. Am I to be vexed if one of those . . . whose shops are filled with a horde of the worst kind of slaves, has failed to greet me by name? No, without doubt. . . . Therefore the sage will not be affected by the insult of any one. For they all differ from one another, but the sage considers them on an equality owing to the equality of their folly. For if he should once lower himself to the point where he is affected by injury or insult, he can never be secure. But security is the sage's particular blessing, nor will he consent to pay honor to the man who has insulted him by feeling that an insult has been inflicted upon him. For one must necessarily value the esteem of the man whose contempt hurts."†

"But what is the sage to do if he is slapped in the face? He

* *Ibid.*, XII.
† *Ibid.*, XIII.

is to do what Cato did when he was insulted in this way; he did not fly into a passion, he did not seek vengeance, he did not even pardon the injury, but said that it had not been done. He displayed a greater elevation of soul in disavowing the injury than in pardoning it. For who is ignorant that the sage does not hold the ordinary opinion with respect to what is believed to be evil or good? . . . He pays no heed to what men in general regard as disgraceful or wretched. But as the stars hold their way in a direction opposite to that of our world, so the sage moves forward in opposition to popular opinion."*

"After you have calculated what you think you can endure, you assign a slightly further limit to the patience of the sage, but his virtue has placed him in another world where he has nothing in common with you. This being granted, the throng of hardships and difficulties hard to bear and of things revolting to the ear and the eye will not overwhelm the sage; he will offer the same resistance to all as to each in particular. He who pretends to determine that which the sage can or cannot endure, he who limits the grandeur of the sage's soul within certain bounds, is doing wrong: fortune vanquishes us unless she is completely vanquished. . . . The home of the sage is small, without luxury, without uproar, without sumptuous equipment, is not guarded by janitors; but over this threshold tended by no doorkeepers fortune does not pass. She knows that she has no place there where nothing is hers."†

"Epicurus said that injuries are supportable by the sage; we say that he suffers no injuries. Nor may you say that this is repugnant to nature. We do not deny that it is a disadvantage to be lashed and to be struck, and to lose one of our members; but we refuse to consider all those things injuries. We do not take from them a sense of pain, but we do remove the name of injury, which cannot be accepted without impairing virtue. . . . We are taught by both these examples to despise injuries and insults which I may call the semblances and suspicions of injuries. To disdain such one need not be a sage but merely a man of discernment. . . . If I have deserved that these things should befall me, I am justly punished. If I am not guilty, he

* *De Constantia,* XIV.
† *Ibid.,* XV.

should blush who commits an injustice. . . . The fruit of an insult consists in the sentiment of indignation which it excites in him who is subjected to it."*

"Let us take as our models those whose patience we praise. Let us imitate Socrates who took good-naturedly the sarcasms launched at him in the comedies, and laughed as merrily as he did on the occasion when he was doused with dirty water by his wife Xanthippe. When Antisthenes was reproached with the fact that his mother was a barbarian and a Thracian, he replied that the mother of the Gods was born on Mount Ida."†

"We must not engage in quarreling and contention. . . . Whatever is done by foolish people must be disregarded, and honors and injuries having their origin in the vulgar throng are to be viewed in the same class; we are not to grieve over the latter nor be elated at the former. . . . Moreover liberty does not consist in exemption from suffering. Liberty is a superiority of the mind to injuries."‡

Chapter XII

Seneca in his book addressed to his mother Helvia speaks about the remedies not only for grief and suffering, but also those for poverty, exile, insult, and many other misfortunes of this kind. Therefore he proposes the following remedy to her on the occasion of an affliction which she found hard to bear: "Accordingly I shall exhibit to that heart all its own griefs and bereavements. This will be effecting a cure not by gentle means, but by burning and cutting. What end have I in view? That the mind victorious over so many sorrows may be ashamed not to bear bravely a single wound on a body marked by the scars of so many. Let us leave therefore tears and lamentations to those weak minds, so enervated by a long period of prosperity, that the least shock of adversity overthrows them; but let those whose whole life has been spent in adversity, endure griefs even the most severe with a firm and unalterable con-

* *Ibid.*, XVII.
† *Ibid.*, XVIII.
‡ *Ibid.*, XIX.

stancy. Constant misfortune has the advantage of finally hardening those whom it is ever assailing."*

"As recruits cry out at trifling wounds and are more afraid of the hand of a physician than of a sword, but veterans although seriously wounded permit their wounds to be treated with patience and without a groan, as though their bodies belonged to other people." . . . and therefore he recounts to his mother all the misfortunes she has patiently endured, in order that he may remove her grief for her son.†

Then Seneca wishes to console her by his own example as follows: "But I shall overcome my grief, I believe, first if I shall show that I am suffering nothing that can render me an object of pity . . . I say that I am not unhappy. I shall add to relieve your anxiety that I cannot even be made unhappy." And he proves his statement as follows: "We are born under conditions which would be favorable if we do not abandon them. Nature's intention was that there should be no need of great magnificence for life to be happy. Every one can make himself happy. The power to turn the balance is slight in external things and it exerts little influence one way or the other; the sage is not carried away by prosperity nor cast down by adversity. For he has always striven to rely entirely upon himself, and to seek all his joy within himself. What then? Do I claim to be a sage? By no means. For if I were able to make such a declaration, I should not only deny that I am unhappy, but I should declare myself to be the most fortunate of men and almost the equal of God: as it is, I have done that which suffices to soften all asperities, I have put myself in the hands of wise men, and, too feeble for my own defense, I have fled to the camp of those who defend with ease themselves and their friends. They have bidden me stand constantly as though on guard and to foresee all attempts of fortune and all her assaults long before they happen. She is dangerous to those who do not expect her: her attack is easily sustained by him who is always on the lookout for it. For the arrival of the enemy dismays those only whom it has taken off their guard; but those who have made due preparation beforehand for war, calmly and easily sustain the first assault which is the most violent. I

* *Ad Helviam Matrem*, II.
† *Ibid.*, III.

have never trusted fortune even when she seemed to bring peace. All those things that her favor conferred upon me, money, honors, influence, I have placed where she could recall them without moving me. I have left a great interval between them and me. Therefore she has taken them from me, she has not torn them away. Adverse fortune never crushes a man unless good fortune beguiles him first. Those who have set their heart on her gifts as though they were their own permanent possessions, who have wished to be looked up to because of them are humbled and distressed, when their empty and childish minds, ignorant of all stable happiness, are deprived of deceitful and transient pleasures. But the man who has not inflated himself with prosperity also does not collapse when fortune changes; toward both conditions he possesses a mind of tested firmness: for in the midst of prosperity he has tested his own strength against adversity. For myself I have never believed that true happiness is to be found in those things which all men desire: besides I have found them empty . . . and smeared with a deceptive rouge, with nothing on the inside corresponding to their exterior."*

Later on he takes up the consideration of particular ills, namely, exile, poverty, insult, as follows: "Now in these things which are termed evils I find nothing so terrible and so hard to bear as the popular idea led me to apprehend. . . . But the decisions of the people in a great measure are repealed by the sages."

"Disregarding then the judgment of the majority whom the outward appearance in such matters without further examination leads astray, let us see what exile really is: it is to be sure a change of place. Let me add, that I may not seem to be narrowing its effect, and to be relieving it of its worst features, many disadvantages are attached to this change of place: poverty, ignominy, contempt. . . . I wish to consider in the first place what hardship mere change of place imposes."

"Consider, if you please, this throng for which the dwellings of an immense city (he means Rome) scarcely suffice: the greater part of this throng is deprived of their country. . . . Bid all these people be summoned and ask each where his home is: you will find that most of them have left their own

* *Ibid.*, IV, V.

abodes and have come to the greatest city in the world, but a city that is not theirs. Then leave this city which can be said in a sense to belong to all. Visit all other cities; there is not one of them that does not contain a large foreign population."*

His second reason is drawn from the nature of the soul. He says: "A restless and an unquiet mind has been given to man: it never remains at rest, it is ubiquitous, and directs its thoughts into all things known and unknown. The mind of man is always on the move, objects to inaction, and takes the utmost delight in constant novelty. You need not wonder at this, if you consider its origin; it is not formed from an earthly and sluggish body; its descent is from the pure celestial spirit. But perpetual motion is characteristic of the heavenly bodies which are borne along in their rapid course. Contemplate the stars that give light to the world; not one of them is stationary. . . . How idle then to suppose that the mind of man suffers with regret a transition and change of place, although nature either delights or preserves herself by a continual and very rapid change!"†

He draws his third reason from the experience of all nations. He says: "Turn now your thoughts from the heavenly bodies to the affairs of men: you will see that whole nations have changed their abodes. How can we account for Greek cities in the midst of barbarous lands? What of the speech of Macedonia among the Indians and the Persians? Scythia and that whole stretch of lands inhabited by savage and unconquerable races show Grecian cities planted on the shores of the Black Sea. The whole side of Italy that is washed by the Tyrrhene sea was greater Greece. Asia claims the Tuscans. The Tyrians dwell in Africa. The Carthaginians emigrated to Spain, the Greeks to Gaul, the Gauls to Greece. The Pyrenees offered no obstacle to the passage of the Germans. The wandering spirit of man has cut for itself roads through the unknown. Some after the trials of a long journey have selected an abode, yielding to their fatigue rather than making a deliberate choice. . . . This at least is manifest that nothing has remained in the same place in which it had its origin." He then returns to his

* *Ad Helviam Matrem,* VI.
† *Ibid.,* VI.

argument in the words, "But what else are all these migrations of nations but exiles on the part of peoples?"*

"Due allowance being made for all the other disadvantages that are inseparable from exile, Varro, the most learned of Romans, remarks as a sufficient consolation for change of place, that wherever we go we are bound to find the same nature. Marcus Brutus considers it sufficient that his own virtue accompanies the exile wherever he goes. If each of these methods of consolation, taken separately, does not suffice the exile, we can have no doubt of their efficacy when they are united. For how trifling is our loss? Two things that are most excellent will always accompany us, universal nature and personal virtue. But if he says that universal nature consists in whatever is best, this lies outside of the powers of man: it can neither be given nor taken away. I speak of this world, the grandest and most magnificent of the works of nature; of this mind made to contemplate and admire the world, of which it is the noblest part, ours as a lasting possession destined to remain with us as long as we ourselves shall last. Let us hasten then with alacrity and resolution wheresoever circumstances may direct. . . . From all places equally we lift our eyes to the heavens, all things divine are separated by equal intervals from all things human."†

"Narrow is the mind that earthly things delight," as quoted above from this book. "Brutus in his work on virtue says that he saw Marcellus in exile in Mitylene living as happily as human nature permits, and never more interested in the liberal arts than at that time. . . . Brutus adds that he felt when on the point of returning without Marcellus that it was he who was going into exile, and not Marcellus who was being left in exile. How much more fortunate was Marcellus when he merited the praise of Brutus because of his exile, than when he won the praise of the republic because of his consulship! . . . You so trained your mind, Marcellus, by methodical studies, that you knew that every place for the sage was his native land."‡

"Marcellus then supported exile well, nor did change of place produce any change in his mind, although poverty followed

* *Ibid.,* VII.
† *Ibid.,* VIII.
‡ *Ibid.,* IX.

upon it. No man considers poverty an evil, unless he has reached that point of madness which permits avarice and luxury to subvert all things. . . . The desires of the body are few: relief from cold, hunger, and thirst. He who desires more than these toils to serve, not his needs, but his vices. It is not necessary to ransack every sea, nor to burden the stomach by the slaughter of animals, nor to dig up shellfish from the unknown shore of a remote sea: may the gods and goddesses destroy those whose extravagance passes beyond the limits of an empire exposed to hatred. . . . From every land all things known to a pampered palate are brought to Rome. That which is admitted with difficulty by a stomach enfeebled by delicacies is transported from a remote ocean. They vomit that they may eat, and they eat that they may vomit, and do not deign even to digest feasts that have required a search of the whole world for their viands. What harm does poverty do the man who holds such luxuries in contempt? . . . Unhappy people"—as was noted above; and he continues; "I am disposed to say: Why do you launch ships? Why arm bands against wild beasts and against men? Why run hither and thither in such a commotion? Why pile treasures on treasures? Do you never stop to think how small your bodies are? Is it not the height of folly and madness, when you can hold so little, to desire a great deal? Therefore although you may increase your rating and extend your boundaries, you will never give your bodies a greater capacity. . . . Such is the lot of men when they measure wealth not by the standard of reason, which has fixed bounds, but by that of a debased habit of life, whose caprices are insatiable and incomprehensible. For cupidity nothing is sufficient, for nature even a little suffices."*

"Everything that nature has rendered necessary for man she has made easy for him to obtain. . . . That man is poor not through the fault of fortune but through his own. . . . He who accordingly keeps himself within the limits prescribed by nature, will not have a sense of poverty; he who disregards these limits will be pursued by poverty even in the midst of the greatest wealth." For "exile is" always "able to provide necessaries, but not even a kingdom suffices to supply things that are needless. It is the mind that makes men rich. This accompanies

* *Ad Helviam Matrem*, X.

the exile, and in the midst of the most cruel solitudes, after it has found enough to sustain the body, overflows with its own blessings and enjoys them; money has no more to do with the mind than with the immortal God. All these things . . . stones, gold, silver, and great circular tables are earthly burdens, which the unpolluted mind cannot love, remembering as it does its own nature, itself light, free from contamination, and ready to spring on high whenever released: meanwhile to the full extent permitted by hampering limbs and the burden that rests heavily upon us, the mind on the wings of thought traverses the realms of the gods. Therefore the mind can never be exiled, the mind that is free and related to God and equal to all space and all time. . . . This feeble body, the prison and the chain of the soul, is tossed hither and thither. It is against this that punishments, robberies, and maladies do their worst; the mind itself is sacred and eternal, and the hand of violence cannot be laid upon it."*

"Consider that the poor, who form the larger part of humanity, have not a more gloomy or anxious air than the rich; nay, I am inclined to think they are more joyous owing to the fact that their mind is distracted by fewer cares. . . . As for me, when I look back at instances in the past, I am ashamed to draw any consolation from poverty. Luxury has increased to such an extent in our day, that the provision made for exiles exceeds the patrimony of the chief men of the state in days gone by. We know that Homer had but one slave, Plato three, Zeno, founder of the unbending and virile philosophy of the Stoics, had none. Will any one say therefore that these philosophers lived in a wretched way, without seeming himself to be most wretched to all men on this account?"†

"The reply may be made: Why do you unnaturally separate these evils, which can be borne singly, but when united cannot be endured? Change of place is endurable if one change merely his dwelling-place. Poverty is endurable, if disgrace be not added, which even alone is wont to crush men's spirits. To him who seeks to terrify me with an aggregation of evils I must make this reply: The mind that is superior to any one phase of fortune will be superior to them all. The mind once hardened

* *Ibid.*, XI.
† *Ibid.*, XII.

by virtue is invulnerable to every assault. If avarice, a very deadly bane of the human race, has relaxed its grip on you, ambition will not cause you delay. If you do not regard your last day as a punishment, but as a law of nature, the fear of no other thing will venture to enter that breast from which you have driven the dread of death. If you consider that sexual desire was given man not for the sake of enjoyment but for the purpose of propagating the race, every other desire will pass by untouched him whom this ruinous passion deep seated in our very vitals has not injured. Reason does not triumph over the vices singly but over all of them together; her victory is general." And he continues in regard to disgrace: "Do you suppose the sage is disturbed by disgrace, who relies wholly on himself, and who is free from the opinions of the common herd? An ignominious death is more even than disgrace. Yet Socrates with the same look with which he had treated the thirty tyrants with disrespect on a certain occasion, entered the prison, destined to remove disgrace even from such a place. For that abode could not seem a prison in which Socrates was. . . . No man is scorned by another unless he has first been scorned by himself. A groveling and an abject mind is exposed to insult; but he who raises himself above the most cruel misfortunes and triumphs over evils by which other men are crushed, regards the very misfortunes as a badge of distinction, since," no doubt, "our disposition is such, that nothing challenges our admiration more than a man courageous in adversity. As Aristeides was being conducted to punishment in Athens, all who met him lowered their eyes and groaned at the fate, not of a just man, but of justice itself. One man, however, as he passed, spat in Aristeides' face . . . but Aristeides wiped his face off and with a laugh said to the magistrate who accompanied him: Warn that fellow not to yawn so offensively. . . . If a great man has fallen, he retains his greatness; he is no more an object of scorn than are the ruins of temples when trodden under foot. To such ruins the devout pay the same respect as to temples still standing."*

After giving his mother these remedies against adversity, he takes up again all the misfortunes that have befallen her, in order that he may teach her how one is victorious who has al-

* *Ad Helviam Matrem,* XIII.

ready vanquished so many ills by strength of character. He says accordingly: "But the harder these trials are, the greater the courage you must summon to your aid; it is an enemy known and often vanquished, against whom you must struggle with fresh ardor. Blood in this instance has flowed from a body that has already suffered wounds, through whose very scars you have been stabbed."*

Chapter XIII

Writing to Gallio on the remedies for misfortunes Seneca says: "You are going to die, death is natural to man and is not to be regarded as a punishment. I entered the world on the condition that I should leave it. It is foolish to fear what you cannot avoid. . . . You are going to die; I am not the first nor the last: many have preceded me, all will follow me. . . . Am I ignorant that I am a rational and a mortal animal?"†

"Men think evil of you. But they are evil men. Now to displease evil men is worthy of praise. An opinion can have no weight when he who condemns is himself worthy of condemnation. . . . Men are speaking ill of you. I should be disturbed, if they were acting with sound judgment: as the matter stands, their action is prompted by a diseased state of mind. They do not know how to speak well of a man. They act as they do, not because I deserve it but because such is their habit. . . ."‡

"You will suffer exile. You are mistaken: there is only one country for us all. I am not forbidden to dwell in my native land but in a certain locality. . . . No foreign land is a place of exile but simply another country. . . . A man's country is where he does well. But well-being is in the man himself, not in his location. . . . If he is a sage, he is simply dwelling abroad; if he is a fool, he is suffering exile."§

"Grief threatens. If it is slight, let us bear it: patience is a small matter. If our grief is severe, let us bear it, glory is not

* *Ibid.*, XV.
† *De Remediis Fortuitorum*, II.
‡ *Ibid.*, VII.
§ *Ibid.*, VIII.

a small matter. Grief is a hard thing. Nay, you are soft. Few have been able to endure grief. Let us be among the few."*

"Poverty is grievous to me. Nay, you are grievous to poverty. The fault is not in poverty but in the man suffering from it. Poverty is free from encumbrance, blithe, safe. . . . You are poor because you think you are. The birds lack nothing. The beasts of the field live for the day. . . . That man has received a great sum of money. Therefore pride also. . . . Do you consider him a man? He is a money-chest. Who is envious of a treasury or of full coffers? He is merely the coffer whom you consider the owner of the money. If he is prodigal, he will not have it; if he is a miser, he does not have it. He whom you reckon fortunate often grieves, often sighs. Many accompany him. Flies follow honey, wolves carrion, ants grain. That throng is after the booty not the man."† Death, exile, grief, pain, and the like are not the punishments but the tributes of life.

Chapter XIV

Consoling Marcia for the death of her son, Seneca writes as follows: "Grief renews and strengthens itself daily . . . and sorrow becomes the pleasure of an unhappy mind. Do not imagine it a great achievement to preserve a courageous bearing in the midst of prosperity when life moves forward propitiously. A calm sea and favoring wind do not display the skill of the pilot; something adverse must occur to test his courage. . . . The envy of fortune is aroused by nothing else to such a degree as by tranquillity of mind. The steersman of the ship is disgraced who permits the helm to be wrested from his grasp by the waves, who abandons the sails to the gale, and hands over the ship to the tempest. But we must praise him even in shipwreck whom the sea has overwhelmed while still retaining his ship and struggling to save it."‡

"Longing for one's own is natural. Who denies this, as long as it is within moderation? . . . But our feeling passes far

* *De Remediis Fortuitorum*, IX.
† *Ibid.*, X.
‡ *Ad Marciam*, I, V, VI.

beyond the requirements of nature. Consider how violent is the grief of animals and yet how brief. For one or two days the lowing of the cow is heard, and the frenzied wandering of the mare does not last longer. Wild beasts after following the tracks of their young, on their return to their plundered lairs allow their rage to subside within a short time. Birds with loud cries mourn over their empty nests, yet within a brief space of time they resume quietly their flight. Man is the only animal that suffers a prolonged grief for the loss of its young. . . . But to convince you that it is not natural to succumb to our griefs, consider that the same loss inflicts a deeper wound on women than on men, on barbarians than on cultured nations, on the ignorant than on the learned. But those things that have derived their force from nature retain the same. It is apparent that that which varies is not natural. Fire burns all ages, the citizens of all cities, men and women alike. Iron will display its power to cut in every body. Why? Because it has derived its powers from nature. . . . Each one in his own way feels poverty, grief, ambition, according to the impress of habit upon him: and according to a dreadful preconceived idea in regard to things that should not be feared, an idea that has rendered him feeble and incapable of endurance."*

"In the second place what is natural does not decrease with time: grief, however, is consumed by time. But you will say, 'I did not think that it would happen.' Do you think that something will not happen which you know can happen to many and which you see has actually happened to many? An excellent maxim and worthy of no common origin is the line,

That which can happen to anyone can happen to each.

That man has lost his children; you can also lose yours. This man has been condemned; and your innocent life is in imminent danger. This error deceives. . . . He robs present evils of their power who has foreseen that they were coming."†

"All this accidental splendor that surrounds us, Marcia, children, honors, riches, spacious halls, throng of clients, crowded vestibules . . . and all the rest depending on an uncertain and capricious fortune are the property of another and are merely

* *Ibid.*, VII.
† *Ibid.*, VIII, IX.

loaned to us. No one of these things is given us. They are like those borrowed decorations that embellish our theaters, which are to be returned to their owners, some on the first day, others on the second, while a few remain to the end of the play. Therefore there is no reason why we should admire these things as though we were located among our own possessions. The use and enjoyment of them is ours. It is God who gives these games, who determines the time of restitution. We must hold in readiness what has been given us for an indefinite time only, and when called upon must make restitution without complaint. It is only a very bad debtor who reviles his creditor. . . . The mind must often be admonished to love such objects as destined to leave us, nay, as now doing so. You are to possess the blessings of fortune without a permanent claim. . . . You have no promise for the coming night, none for the present hour. You must hasten; you are threatened from the rear. . . . All your possessions are subject to plunder; you are ignorant, poor wretches, that your life is only a flight."*

"Why should we weep over the details of life? It is deplorable as a whole. New misfortunes will press upon you, before you have finished with the old. . . . What is man? A fragile vase shattered by any jar. There is no need of a great tempest to shatter you. You will decompose under any shock. What is man? A weak and fragile body, naked, without natural defense, dependent on the aid of others, exposed to all the outrages of fortune . . . the prey and the victim of any wild beast . . . unable to endure cold, heat, toil. . . . An odor, a savor, insomnia . . . and food and the things without which man cannot live, prove deadly to him. . . . He is not capable of enduring every climate, change of water and the blast of an air to which he is not accustomed; in a word, the most trifling causes make him ill . . . meanwhile how great a commotion is stirred up by this animal so contemptible! In what great thoughts does he indulge, forgetful of his own condition! His projects are limitless, eternal, his plans include grandsons and great-grandsons. But in the midst of his great designs death overwhelms him. That which we call old age is merely the circuit of a very few years."†

* *Ad Marciam,* X.
† *Ibid.,* XI.

Moral Philosophy

"As a rule great and lasting blessings do not fall to the lot of anyone. Good fortune does not last nor continue to the end unless it be moderate."*

And he introduces examples of patience in bearing the loss of sons. "Greece is not the only nation to be proud of a father who in the midst of a sacrifice on learning of the death of a son merely bade the flute-player be silent, removed the chaplet from his head, and duly completed the rest of the ceremony. Pulvillus the pontiff acted in a similar manner when the death of his son was reported to him while he was consecrating the Capitol. He pretended that he did not hear what had been told him, and repeated the solemn words of the ritual, without suffering a groan to interrupt his prayer."†

"Cornelia, daughter of Scipio, mother of the Gracchi, recalled her twelve children by as many deaths. . . . The Gracchi, to whom one refuses the title of good citizens but not that of great men, the mother saw slain and deprived of sepulcher. To those who offered her consolation and called her unhappy she said, 'I shall never call myself unhappy, I who have borne the Gracchi.' Octavia and Livia,‡ one the sister of Augustus, the other his wife, lost sons both in the flower of their youth, and both regarded as a future emperor. Octavia refused all consolation. . . . Through the rest of her life she gave way to her grief as she had done at the funeral. She would have considered it a second bereavement had she ceased to weep; she wished for no portrait of her beloved son, she did not permit his name to be mentioned in her presence. . . . Livia displayed the sensibility of a mother and the firmness of the wife of an emperor. She did not cease to celebrate the name of her son, to picture him in private and in public, to speak of him and to hear him mentioned with the utmost pleasure."

"Human life is assailed by evils of every kind; they never accord us a long peace, scarcely a truce. . . . It is in fact the nature of mortals that nothing is more pleasing than that which they have lost."§

"It is then opinion that torments us; it is we ourselves who

* *Ibid.,* XII.
† *Ibid.,* XIII.
‡ See *Ibid.,* II and III, where this passage belongs.
§ *Ibid.,* XVI.

[737]

place the estimate on our misfortune. The remedy is in our hands."*

"All the works of man are perishable and of short duration; they do not occupy any place in the immensity of time . . . whose increment however great will be negligible. There is only one way to live for a long time, that is to live sufficiently. . . . You will find no difference between the longest life and the shortest if you compare the time one has lived with that which he has not lived."†

"Do you complain, Marcia, that your son did not live so long as he might have lived? How do you know if a longer life would have been to his advantage? If his own interest did not require his death? What man can you find today whose interests are on so sure a foundation, that he has nothing to fear as time goes on? Human affairs are always subject to change, are never stable . . . and for this reason death is to be desired by those who are most fortunate, because in such a state of instability and in such a disordered condition of affairs the past alone is certain. Nothing is so deceptive as the life of man, nothing so insidious; no one would have accepted it, had he known the nature of the gift."‡

"Besides this since everything in the future is uncertain and threatening, the pathway to the gods is easiest for the souls that have been set free betimes from human intercourse. For they have contracted very little defilement and sluggishness, since they are set free before an earthly character is too deeply impressed. They fly back on lighter wing to their origin . . . a lengthy sojourn in the body is never pleasing to great minds."§ There are other passages also as noted above.

Chapter XV

I HAVE treated this third part of Moral Philosophy at greater length than I purposed at the beginning. But the beauty of the moral sentiments delights us; and especially are these princi-

* *Ad Marciam*, XIX.
† *Ibid.*, XXI.
‡ *Ibid.*, XXII.
§ *Ibid.*, XXIII.

ples brought out with great clearness of thought by the efforts of philosophers. And we should accept them with greater eagerness since we Christian philosophers do not know how to reason on the subject of morals, nor can we make so eloquent an appeal. Would that we might approve by our conduct those principles which the philosophers so wisely propound. For although in regard to the virtues bestowing grace, namely, faith, hope, love, and the like, we are able to perceive truths of which even the philosophers are ignorant, yet in the virtues that in general are requisite for integrity of life and for the intercourse of human society, both in word are we no match for them, and in deed are we less efficient, as is clearly shown by a consideration of the wisdom taught by them. This is quite blameworthy in us and worthy of the scorn of all men. It should therefore be necessary for Christian philosophers to consider the unclouded glory exhibited by the philosophers. Moreover, we are encouraged thereto by the examples of the sacred writers. For they diligently applied to divine things the teaching of the philosophers, and especially those principles pertaining to morals and to the rules of correct living.

But there is a particular reason for my lingering on these works of Seneca, since although I have searched for books of this kind from my childhood, I have never succeeded in finding them until the present time. I refer to the De Ira, Ad Helviam, Cur bonis mala accidunt, An in sapientem cadunt contumelia et injuria, Ad Marciam, and the three following works. Since I do not know whether these books have been seen by your Excellency, I have attempted to quote them here somewhat freely.

Chapter XVI

Seneca begins his consolation addressed to Paulinus on the shortness of human life as follows:

"Most men complain of the injustice of nature, because our life is short. . . . We do not have too little time, we waste too much of it. Life would be long enough and would suffice to complete the greatest enterprises, if it were properly arranged as a whole. But when life has been dissipated in extravagance and in neglect of opportunity, when it is devoted to no useful occupation, at length under the prodding of the last grim necessity, we perceive that life has passed without our perception of its passage. The fact is, we have not been granted a short life, we have made it so. As riches falling into bad hands are dissipated in a moment; while a modest fortune if entrusted to a good guardian is increased by his care; even so our life if well employed extends over a long period.*

"Life is long if you know how to use it. But one is possessed by an insatiable avarice, another devotes himself constantly to superfluous efforts. Still another is steeped in wine. And yet another stagnates from sloth. . . . The whole period is not life but is time. Vices surround and press upon us from every side nor do they suffer us to rise or to lift our eyes to examine truth, but they press us down plunged and held fast in our lust. We are never permitted to recover ourselves; when perchance we have some moments of respite, our passions never permit us to be perfectly tranquil; we are like the sea whose waves continue in motion even after the wind has ceased. That man is attached to such a one, while this man is attached to someone else. No man belongs to himself."†

"Though all the geniuses that have enlightened the world by common consent express their wonder at this one thing, they will never express adequately their astonishment at this blindness of the human spirit. No man is found who is willing to distribute his money; among how many does each of us distribute his life! They are careful in guarding their patrimony; they are prodigal when it comes to wasting their time, the only thing in which avarice is laudable. . . . This is your hundredth year or more. Come, reckon up your life. Tell me how much of this time the creditor, how much the mistress, the patron, the client, have consumed; how much in the coercion of slaves, how much in running about to oblige your friends? Add the diseases we have brought upon ourselves. Add the time also of which we have made no use: you will see that you have fewer years than those you count. Recall how many times when you were firm in your resolution . . . when you made use of your own self, when your face remained serene and your spirit undaunted, . . . how many have pillaged your life without your

* *De Brevitate Vitae,* I.
† *Ibid.,* II.

perceiving what you were losing . . . you will perceive that your death is premature. What then is the reason? You live as though you expected to live always. Your frailty never occurs to you. Like mortals you fear all things, like immortals you desire all things. You will hear many say, 'At fifty I shall retire! My sixtieth year will free me from business.' . . . Who will permit those plans of yours to mature as you now arrange them? Are you not ashamed to reserve for yourself only the remnant of your life, and to destine for the good of your soul only that time which you can employ in no other way? How late it is to begin to live at a time when we must cease our existence . . . to postpone sane counsels, and to desire to begin life at a limit few have attained."*

"You will hear the most powerful and exalted personages say that they desire repose; you will find that they praise it and prefer it to all the blessings they enjoy. They wish meanwhile to descend from their lofty position if they can do so with safety. For fortune topples down upon herself although neither assailed nor shaken by an external force. The deified Augustus, on whom God bestowed more than upon any other prince, prayed without ceasing for repose and sought for relief from the affairs of state. All his conversation always returned to this one theme, his hope for rest. With this sweet yet deceptive solace he was wont to console his labors. . . . But those things can be accomplished with more glory than promised. . . . Repose seemed so desirable that, not being able to enjoy it in fact, he pictured it in imagination. He who saw all things dependent on himself alone, who regulated the destinies of men and of nations, regarded the day on which he should lay aside his greatness as the happiest in his life. For experience had taught him how much effort those benefactions cost which spread such luster throughout the world, how much disquietude they covered,"† but did not remove.

"Marcus Cicero . . . while driven hither and thither with the Republic and while endeavoring to keep it from going to ruin . . . how many times had he reason to curse that consulship of his, which he had praised not without cause but without end? How tearful the words he utters. . . . It is useless to recall

* *Ibid.*, III.
† *Ibid.*, IV.

here the examples of many who, reputed to be very happy, have borne true witness against themselves in their utter hatred of every act of their lives. . . . Though your life extend beyond a thousand years, it will be reduced to a very short span."*

"In the first place then I number those who have leisure for nothing except wine and lust. For none are occupied more disgracefully. As for the rest although they are possessed by a vain idea of glory . . . they err in a more manly way; it is a disgraceful wasting sickness that afflicts men given up to wantonness and lust. . . . Finally all are agreed that nothing can be handled properly by a man preoccupied with other matters; one cannot cultivate eloquence or the liberal arts, when his mind is distracted by other interests and is incapable of receiving any deeper impression, and rejects all that is forced upon it. Nothing is less in the possession of the preoccupied man than his own life; there is no science more difficult than that of life. All the other arts have many prepared to teach them. Mere boys seem to have mastered some of them to such a degree that they could even teach them: we require the whole of life to learn how to live; and what will perhaps surprise you still more, we require the whole of life to learn how to die. So many very great men, after freeing themselves from all hindrances, after renouncing riches, occupations, and pleasures, up to the very end of their lives have tried to learn how to live. Yet many of them departed this life confessing that they were still ignorant of this art. . . . It is the mark, believe me, of a great man who is raised far above human errors to permit none of his time to be wasted. His life therefore is a very long one, since whatever its span, it has been wholly at his service. No part of that time was unemployed or wasted in idleness, no part was under the control of another. A rigid economist of his time, he finds nothing worthy to be received in exchange for it. Therefore his allotted time sufficed him: but of necessity time failed those, from whose life the public took a large portion," and their vices robbed them of still more. . . . "Count up, I say, and examine closely the days of your life; you will see that very few of them remained at your own disposal. . . . But he who employs some of his time to his own advantage, who arranges all his days with a view to life itself, neither wishes for the mor-

* *De Brevitate Vitae,* V, VI.

row nor fears it: he actually directs fortune as he wills; his life is in safety. Nothing can be added to him, nothing taken away. Such an addition is like a portion of food given to a man already sated and filled; he receives that which he does not desire. You should not accordingly think that a man has lived a long time because of his gray hairs and wrinkles; he has not lived a long time, but he has existed a long time. What then! Are you to think that he has made a long voyage whom the savage gale caught on leaving the port and bore hither and thither? Or likewise he whom shifting and raging winds have driven around in a circle over the same spot? Such a man has not made a long voyage, but has been much buffeted."*

"I am constantly surprised to see people asking for the time of others; I am also surprised at those who grant requests of this kind with such readiness. Both regard the motive of the request, neither pays heed to the thing requested: as if nothing is asked for, as if nothing is given, the most precious thing in the world is made a jest of. It deceives them because it is incorporeal, because it does not come under their eyes." . . . But "no one puts a value on time. They employ it as a thing of no value. But behold these same men, when they are sick and believe themselves in danger of death, embracing the knees of their physicians; if they fear capital punishment, behold them ready to expend their all, in order that they may live; so great is the discord of their passions. But if each of us could know the number of his years in the future as he does the number in the past, how would those of us tremble who saw that they had few left, how sparing they would be of them? And yet it is an easy matter to regulate what is certain even though it be small: we should guard with greater care that which may fail us at any moment."†

"They arrange their life at the expense of life. They direct their thoughts far afield. Postponement is responsible for life's greatest loss . . . it robs us of our present while promising what is more remote. Life's greatest hindrance is the expectation which depends on tomorrow and loses today. You make disposition for that which has been placed in the hand of fortune; you lose that which has been placed in your own. Whither

* *Ibid.*, VII.
† *Ibid.*, VIII.

are you directing your gaze, to what point are you straining? All that is to come is uncertain: begin to live now. Behold, the greatest of bards warns us . . . *'The best day in the life of unhappy mortals is that which flees first.'* "*

"Why do you delay? Unless you seize it, it is gone. And when you have seized it, it will still be in flight. Therefore you must combat the swiftness of time with promptitude in making use of it. The poet seems to reproach us admirably for our endless planning for the future by saying not that it is the best age that flees first, but only that it is the best day. It is of the day the poet speaks to you, of this very day which is in flight. There is no doubt, then, that the best day is the first that takes flight for unhappy mortals, that is, for mortals burdened with the cares of life, whose minds, still those of mere children, are crushed by old age which they have reached unprepared and defenseless. For they have made no provision; old age assails them suddenly, at a moment when they did not expect it."†

"Fabianus, not one of your pedantic philosophers, but a true philosopher of the old type, used to say, 'We must combat the passions with force, not with subtlety; we must repulse their evil band not with light blows but with a vigorous assault.' . . . When we reproach men for their errors, we should teach them and not merely deplore their blindness. Time is divided into three parts, past, present, future. Of these what we are doing is short: what we are going to do, doubtful: what we have done, certain. Fortune has lost her rights over the last: it is no longer at the disposal of any one. It is the past that men lose who are wrapped up in their own affairs. For they have no leisure to review the past; and if they should have the leisure, the recalling of a thing to be repented of is not pleasant. It is therefore in spite of themselves that they recall times that have been misspent, nor do they venture to return to those subjects whose faults are evident on review. The man whose conscience, always an infallible judge, has censored all his actions, is the only one who will look back to the past with pleasure. But he whose ambition has been inordinate, whose pride has rendered him contemptuous, who has been insolent in his success, who has insidiously deceived, greedily stolen, prodigally squandered, of

* Vergil, *Georgics,* III, 66, 67.
† *De Brevitate Vitae,* IX.

necessity fears his own memory. Yet this is the portion of our time that is sacred and consecrated, beyond the reach of all human accidents, withdrawn from the realm of fortune, which neither want, nor fear, nor disease assails. This can be neither disturbed nor snatched away; the possession of it is lasting and unshaken. Each of our days is present only moment by moment, but the days that have passed will present themselves at our bidding, and will submit to inspection and detention in accordance with our will. . . . It is the untroubled and tranquil mind that can survey all the portions of its life; the minds of the preoccupied, as though under a yoke, are unable to turn and look back. The life of such men therefore passes away into obscurity . . . thus it matters not how much time is granted them . . . it passes through minds shattered and riddled with holes. The present is very brief; so much so, in fact, that some do not think that it has any existence. For time is always on the wing, it flows along and speeds ahead, it is over before it arrives. . . . The present, then, is the only time that concerns the preoccupied, but this so brief that it cannot be seized, and is lost so far as it affects them."*

"Do you wish then a proof of the shortness of their life? Consider how they wish to prolong their life. Decrepit old men beg in their prayers for a few additional years. They pretend that they are younger than they are. They delude themselves with the lie, and willingly deceive themselves, as though they were deceiving the fates at the same time. When at length some infirmity has warned them of their mortality, in what great fear do they die, not as if they are departing from life, but as though they are being dragged out of it. They cry out that they have been foolish not to have lived, and that if they may only recover from that illness they will live in repose. It is then that they realize how vain has been their preparation of things they were not to enjoy, how profitless all their labor has proved to be. On the other hand how ample is the life that is passed far from all distraction . . . no part of it is dissipated . . . nothing is subject to fortune . . . nothing is lost through negligence . . . nothing is superfluous. . . . Therefore no matter how short life may be it is amply sufficient, and when the last day

* *Ibid.*, X.

comes, the sage will not hesitate to advance to death with a firm step."*

And since Seneca has conceived of the sage as being in a state of repose, and the foolish and the vicious as preoccupied and not enjoying repose, he has divided them into three classes. For some men have minds busied with the cares that sins and vanities impose, although they do not commit such or at least only a few, possibly because they are not able. Of these men Seneca says: "Certain have an occupied leisure; in their country house, in their bed, in the midst of solitude. For although they have withdrawn from men, they are a burden to themselves, whose life must not be called one of leisure, but a slothful occupation." Those do not enjoy leisure whose desires embrace many projects. Of the man who is continually given over to sins and follies and plunged in vices Seneca says: "This man does not enjoy leisure. You should employ another term in his case. He is sick, nay, he is dead." Of those who are not addicted either in thought or deed to such sins of the flesh, yet find delight in curious trivial details of learning, Seneca says: "No one doubts that" when "you devote yourself to scholarship of a useless kind, your laborious efforts have no real value. . . . If you keep these results to yourself, your inner man is no better off; if you publish them, you appear not more learned but more of a bore. A useless zeal for such information has appealed to Romans also. . . . I heard recently a certain savant recount what each of our Roman generals had been the first to inaugurate: Curius Dentatus was the first to lead elephants in a triumph. . . . Who was the first to persuade the Romans to go aboard a ship? It was Claudius, surnamed Caudex for this reason, because by this word the ancients designated a framework of many planks. For the same reason the public registers are called codices, and boats which, following ancient usage, carry provisions on the Tiber are called *codicariae*. Such knowledge is not likely to profit us. . . . Will you suffer any one to give himself concern over the fact that Lucius Sulla was the first to put unbound lions in the circus to be slain by javelin-throwers sent by King Bocchus, while in general they were presented bound? . . . What benefit is it to know that Pompey was the first who showed in the circus a combat of

* *De Brevitate Vitae,* XI.

eighteen elephants with criminals? . . . He considered it a notable kind of spectacle to destroy men in a novel way. . . . It were better that such things as these be forgotten, lest some man in power should learn about them and be tempted to imitate their inhuman cruelty. . . . Then there are a host of other things which are either fictions or resemble lies. . . . For our Fabianus used to say he was in doubt whether it is better to apply oneself to no studies at all than to become entangled in these."

Seneca has cited these things to illustrate his meaning, and includes them as things to be avoided. But I have introduced them rather because of their value in explaining ancient words, in which we all make mistakes regarding their meaning not only in profane but also in sacred writings. For, omitting any consideration of the other words, we learn from this passage the meaning of the word *Circus,* from which is derived *ludi circenses* [contests in the Circus Maximus], of which Jerome makes mention in his Epistle to Paulinus which serves as a preface to the Bible. The contests are not called *circenses* because they are *circa enses* [having to do with swords], although Isidore gives this explanation in the eighteenth book of the Etymologies, nor is the true explanation found in any of the other ones suggested. But the contests are called *circenses* from *circus* [circle], which was a place circular in form, in which gladiators and javelin-throwers used to fight with wild beasts as a public spectacle, as is still the custom in many provinces where men gather in a circle around those who fight with wild beasts.

But we must return with Seneca to our topic. He says: "Alone of all men those enjoy repose who have leisure for wisdom; they alone live; for they not only conserve carefully their own time," but "they judge all the ages to be theirs. All the years that have preceded them are their possession. Unless we are most ungrateful, we shall recognize the fact that it is for us those very illustrious authors of thoughts regarded with reverence have been born and have prepared life. We are conducted through the labor of others to very beautiful things which have been drawn by them from darkness into the light. No age is forbidden us, we are admitted to all ages. And if we have sufficient greatness of spirit to advance out of the narrow confines of human weakness, we see open to us a vast stretch of time. We may, if we desire, dispute with Socrates, doubt with Carneades, . . . conquer human nature with the Stoics, escape from it with the Cynics, since nature permits us to enter the fellowship of all time. Why not whole-heartedly transfer ourselves from this narrow and fleeting passage of time to those boundless and eternal spaces which offer us fellowship with nobler men? . . . Those who wish to have daily Zeno, Pythagoras, Democritus, and the remaining masters of the liberal arts, and Aristotle and Theophrastus as their most intimate friends . . . will receive from them whatever they wish. Men will have their full permission to drink their fill. What happiness, what a noble old age awaits the man who has made himself their client! He will have counsellors with whom he may consult on matters of the least and of the greatest moment, whose advice he may ask daily concerning himself, from whom he may hear the truth without offense . . . in whose likeness he may mould himself. . . . These men will show you the road that leads to eternity, and will raise you to that place from which no one is cast down, this is the true way of extending your mortal life. . . . Honors, monuments, all that ambition has ordered by her decrees or reared by her efforts are quickly overthrown. . . . What wisdom has consecrated no age will destroy. . . . The life of the sage therefore has a wide range. His life is not closed by that same limit that bounds the life of other men. He alone is set free from human limitations. All ages render him service as though he were a god. The time that has passed he grasps with memory, that which is present he makes use of, that which is to come he anticipates"* and arranges. . . .

"The life of those is very short who forget the past, neglect the present, fear for the future. . . . Their joys also lack tranquillity; for they do not rest on solid foundations, but are troubled by that same insecurity from which they spring. . . . All their greatest blessings are sources of anxiety, and the highest good fortune is always least to be trusted. To safeguard good fortune additional good fortune is required, and prayers must be offered for the prayers that have just been answered. For all that comes as the gift of fortune is unstable. The higher

* *De Brevitate Vitae,* XIV, XV.

fortune rises the more liable it is to fall. That which threatens ruin cannot be a source of pleasure to any one. Most wretched, therefore, as well as very brief must be the life of those who secure with great labor what they retain with still greater effort. They laboriously acquire what they want, they retain with anxiety what they have acquired. . . . They substitute new occupations for old ones. Hope excites hope, ambition arouses still further ambition. No end of their woes is sought for, only the cause for them is changed. . . . There will never be lacking either unfortunate or harrowing causes of care, all repose will be gnawed away, so to speak, by the occupations of life. Repose will never be enjoyed. Life will always be desired."*

"Separate, then, yourself from the common throng, dear friend, and withdraw at length into a more peaceful haven, after your stormy voyage which has lasted longer than one of your years should reasonably expect. Consider how many waves you have breasted, how many storms you have endured, some of which you have encountered as a private citizen, while others in your public capacity you diverted from the state to yourself. You have given a sufficient proof of the quality of your virtue in labors and difficulties: now give it a trial under peaceful conditions. The greater part of your life, certainly the better part, has been devoted to the state: devote some of your time also to yourself. . . . You administer the affairs of the whole world as disinterestedly as those of others, as diligently as your own, as faithfully as those of the republic. In your public position in which it is difficult to avoid hatred you win affection. But, believe me, it is better to know the value of one's own life than that of the public grain supply."†

"We must press on to better things while our blood is warm and we are still in our prime. In this new kind of life you experience the enjoyment of all the liberal arts, the love and the exercise of virtue, forgetfulness of the passions, the art of living and of dying, a profound repose. The state of all men preoccupied with worldly affairs is indeed an unhappy one, but most wretched is the lot of those who toil without profit for themselves, whose sleep is subject to the sleep of others, whose step

* *Ibid.*, XVI, XVII.
† *Ibid.*, XVIII.

must be accommodated to the step of another. . . . If these men desire to know how short their life is, they should consider how small a part of it is their own."*

"At fifty years of age the law exempts the soldier from service, at sixty it does not summon the senator. Men obtain more easily from the law than from themselves an end to their labors."†

Chapter XVII

As a solace for a man's death and that of his loved ones Seneca eloquently says: "Who is so vain, so presumptuous, as to wish that he and his should be the only ones exempt from the laws of a necessity by which nature summons all things back to the same end? Who will pretend to shelter his family from a destruction that menaces the world itself? It is therefore the greatest consolation to think that nothing has befallen us except that which all before us have suffered and all are destined to suffer. And nature accordingly seems to have dealt her severest blow to all men alike, so that the equality of our fate might console us for its severity."‡

"We can accuse destiny over and over again, we cannot alter it. . . . But what is so abject and effeminate as to allow oneself to be consumed with grief?" And since the man was a great one to whom he is speaking, he says, "Many things are not permitted you which are permitted men in an humble and obscure position. High rank involves great slavery. He is happier, believe me, for whom fortune is unnecessary, than the man who has her at his command. All those blessings which delight us with their specious but deceptive pleasure, money, rank, power, and many other things which excite the admiration and cupidity of blind mortals, are retained with effort and viewed with envy, and crush those very same men whom they adorn. They threaten more evil than they bring good. They are hazardous and uncertain. We never are in secure possession, for supposing that we need not fear for the future, yet the mere

* *De Brevitate Vitae,* XIX.
† *Ibid.,* XXX.
‡ *Ad Polybium,* I.

guardianship of great wealth is filled with anxiety. If you wish to take the view of those with a deeper insight into truth, all life is a punishment: cast upon this deep and restless sea, with its change of ebb and flow, at one moment we are raised on the crest of the wave and at the next are precipitated into its trough; we are unceasingly buffeted and have no secure resting place. We are in suspense and float hither and thither, one colliding with another, and at some time or other we suffer the shipwreck of which we are in constant fear. For those embarked on this troubled sea, exposed as it is to every storm, there is no haven except death. . . . There is, believe me, great happiness in the mere happiness of dying. Nothing is certain for an entire day. Where the truth is so involved and hard to see, who can divine whether death has envied the dying one or has dealt kindly with him?"*

"He is unjust who does not leave to the donor the power to deal with his gift; miserly is the man who treats as gain that which he has received, and puts down as loss that which he has returned. Ungrateful is the man who calls the termination of a pleasure an injury, foolish he who finds profit only in present blessings. . . . Is not he to be regarded as an unjust man who is vexed at having paid back borrowed money, especially when it was borrowed without interest? Nature has given life and then, exercising her own right, takes it away. Nor is nature at fault whose terms were well known, but the greedy hope of the mortal mind, a hope that constantly loses sight of what nature is, and never remembers its own lot except when it is admonished. How much juster was he who, when his son's death was announced to him, expressed a sentiment worthy of a great man: 'When I brought him into the world I knew that he must die.' . . . Let us rejoice over that which shall be given us, and let us return it on demand. . . . I do not know whether it is more foolish to be ignorant of the law of mortality or more shameless to refuse to submit to it."†

"The deified Augustus lost his very dear sister Octavia . . . sons-in-law, children, grandsons; and during his whole life no one realized more than he that he was a mere mortal. Yet his heart, capable of confronting all things, mastered these

* *Ibid.*, IV, VI, IX.
† *Ibid.*, X, XI.

many bitter afflictions, and the deified Augustus became victor not only over foreign nations but over his own griefs also." "But to pass over all other instances . . . twice has fortune assailed me with grief for a brother, twice she perceived that I could be wounded, but that I could not be vanquished. . . . Thus, however, have I controlled my feelings, that I neither left undone anything that should be required of a loving brother, nor did I do anything that could be censured in a prince." "For not to preceive one's misfortunes is unworthy of a human being, and not to bear them is unworthy of a man."*

Chapter XVIII

WE must now consider Seneca's views on the blessed life and on peace of mind. For the statements in those books strengthen and fortify the mind against adversity, and render it careless of outward prosperity. Seneca, a master of moral precepts, begins his essay addressed to Gallio on the Blessed Life as follows :

"All men, brother Gallio, wish to live happily, but have no clear vision when they are called upon to determine what makes life happy. . . . So that if one has lost his way, his speed merely increases his distance from his destination, since he is on a road leading in the opposite direction. . . . But as long as we wander about with no other guide but the uproar and discordant shouting of those summoning us in different directions, life will pass away amid errors—life which is short, even if we labor night and day with excellent intentions . . . since the conditions in this case are not the same as those in our other travels. For in the latter there is some well-defined road, and natives of the locality on being asked do not suffer us to go astray. But in life all the most beaten and frequented paths lead us farthest astray. We must therefore exercise the utmost care not to follow like sheep the flock ahead of us, which is moving forward not in the required direction but along the trodden path. And yet there is nothing that involves us in greater ills than lending an ear to mere rumor, considering as we do those things best which have received general assent."

* *Ad Polybium*, XV, XVI.

Moral Philosophy

The other causes of error I have collected and noted in their proper place in the first part of this work. "For we are harmed by attaching ourselves to those advancing ahead of us, and as long as we prefer to trust others rather than to judge for ourselves, we form no judgment in regard to life. . . . Our cure depends on our separation from the crowd."*

"There is no occasion for your answering in the conventional way; 'This side seems to have the majority'; since for this very reason it is in the wrong. Human affairs are not so well ordered, that better counsels appeal to the majority;" and Seneca makes other statements as above. "Let us seek to discover what conduct is best, not what is most usual; and what will place us in possession of happiness, not what has won the approval of the multitude, the very worst judge of the truth. . . . I have a better and more certain light by which to distinguish the true from the false; let the soul discover the good qualities of the soul. If the soul ever has time to breathe and to withdraw into itself, how it will confess the truth to itself after self-examination and will say, 'All that I have done up to the present time I should prefer undone. . . . I am not yet a friend to myself. . . . Those things that attract attention, at which men pause, which one man points out to another with admiration, are bright and fair externally, but within are hideous.' "†

"Let us seek for some good possessing not mere appearance but solid and abiding worth, one that is more beautiful in that which is less visible to the eye . . . nor is such a boon remote from us; it will be found. It is only necessary to know in which direction to extend your hand; now we pass by as though in darkness what is near at hand. . . . But not to take you by too long a circuit . . . I assent to nature. Wisdom consists in keeping close to nature and forming oneself in accordance with her law and model. Happy then is the life that is in harmony with its own nature. Such a life cannot be realized unless the mind is sound and in constant possession of its sanity; it must also possess courage, strength, magnanimity, patience, resignation to circumstances. The care of the body and of what concerns it is not excluded, but must not be a source of anxiety. We can procure the commodities of life without being disturbed by

* *De Vita Beata*, I.
† *Ibid.*, II.

any of them; we can use the gifts of fortune but we must not be enslaved by them. You perceive, even if I do not add, that perpetual peace and liberty are the result when those things have been removed that irritate and terrify us. For in place of pleasures and in place of what is trivial and perishable . . . a great joy, constant and unalterable, succeeds, also peace and harmony of mind and greatness united with kindness."*

"We can also give other definitions of our good in different terms but with the same meaning. . . . The greatest good is a mind that despises all that depends on fortune, a mind that rejoices in virtue; or, it is an invincible force of mind, fortified by experience, calm in action, endowed with much benevolence and regard for one's fellow men. We may also define the happy man as one for whom there is no good and there is no evil except a good mind and an evil one. Such a man fosters what is honorable, is contented with virtue, and is neither exalted by fortune's favors nor broken by her rebuffs. He knows no higher good than that which he can bestow upon himself; his greatest pleasure is the contempt of pleasures. . . . For why should we not define the happy life as the possession of a mind free, upright, undismayed, firm, placed beyond fear, beyond desire, whose only good is integrity, whose only evil is shame. Such a mind regards as of no moment all other things, which neither take from the happy life nor add to it, which come and go without augmenting and decreasing the highest good. Constant happiness and profound joy must attend the man with such principles, since he finds his happiness in what he has, and does not crave more than he possesses in his own store. . . . Contempt of fortune alone can bestow this liberty; then will come into being a peace of mind based on security, an elevation of thought, a great and unalterable joy from the knowledge of the truth after fears have been banished, and an affability and serenity of mind, which will delight the sage not as mere blessings but as blessings arising from his own goodness."†

"The happy life then is based on a correct and certain judgment and is immutable. For then is the mind pure and free from all evils when it has escaped not only from lacerations but even from stings, resolved always to stand her ground and to

* *De Vita Beata,* III.
† *Ibid.,* IV.

maintain her position even against an angered and hostile fortune."*

And he shows that carnal pleasure is not the supreme good in the following statement: "Pleasure enters the worst life, but virtue does not admit an evil life. . . . Pleasure itself is a source of man's unhappiness, which could not be if virtue and pleasure could mingle, because virtue often lacks pleasure, but never needs it. Why put together dissimilars, nay, opposites? Virtue is something high, lofty, royal, invincible, indefatigable; pleasure is low, servile, weak, perishable, whose post and abode are brothels and cook-shops. You will find virtue in the temple, in the forum, in the senate house with hands hardened by labor; you will discover pleasure more frequently in hiding and eager for dark retreats around the public baths and sudatories . . . steeped in wine and perfume." Likewise he says, "The highest good is immortal . . . contains neither satiety nor regret. An upright mind never varies, nor does it become hateful to itself. . . . But pleasure vanishes at the very moment when it delights most. Pleasure has narrow borders and quickly fills them, then wearies, and languishes after the first impression is passed. Nor is that ever certain whose essential nature is movement. Thus it is not even possible that there should be any real substance to a thing that comes or passes with the utmost speed, destined to perish in its very use. For at the point where pleasure arrives it ceases, and even at its commencement is near its end."†

Likewise, "What of the fact that the evil enjoy pleasure as well as the good? The vicious find as much pleasure in their shame as the virtuous in their moral rectitude. It is for this reason that the sages of old have taught that men should lead the best life, not the most agreeable one, to the end that pleasure should not be the guide but the companion of good and honorable intentions. For it is nature that we must take as our guide: it is she that reason follows and consults. It is the same thing, then, to live happily and to live according to nature. I shall now explain my meaning. If we conserve with care but without fear our bodily gifts and such things as are fitting to nature, regarding them as given but for a day and likely to take flight,

* *Ibid.*, V.
† *Ibid.*, VII.

if we do not enslave ourselves to them, nor permit ourselves to covet the possessions of others, if we regard all that is pleasing to the body and all that comes to us from without as, so to speak, merely auxiliary and light-armed troops in the camp, we shall be living according to nature. Those things should serve, not master us; thus then they become useful to the mind. A man should be incorruptible and unconquerable as regards external things, and should admire himself alone, confident in mind and prepared for either of the two contingencies, the artificer of his own life. His confidence should not be without knowledge, his knowledge not without constancy; his decisions should stand, nor should there be any alteration in his decrees. It is evident, even if I do not state the fact, that such a man will be well constituted and properly regulated, and in all his conduct displays greatness combined with cheerfulness . . . let it return into itself. For this world also which embraces all things, this God who rules the universe extends outwardly, but yet wholly returns into himself from all directions. Our mind should do the same: When the mind following its senses has with their aid extended itself to external objects, it should be master of them and of itself. In this way a single force will be produced and a power in harmony with itself, and pure reason will come into being, certain in its conclusions and without inconsistency or vacillation in its ideas. . . . The mind that has arranged itself properly, that has coördinated its own parts, and brought them into tune, so to speak, has attained the highest good. For nothing base, nothing slippery remains on which it may stumble or fall. Such a mind will do all things at its own bidding, it will meet nothing unexpectedly, but easily, readily, without question will turn its every act into good. For inaction and irresolution indicate lack of harmony and inconstancy within. Wherefore you may declare with confidence that the highest good consists in peace of mind. For the virtues must be present where harmony and unity prevail: the vices are always at variance with one another."*

"But you yourself, they say, cultivate virtue for no other reason than your desire to derive some pleasure from it. . . . If virtue shall guarantee us pleasure, virtue is not sought after for this reason . . . but the effort of virtue, although directed

* *De Vita Beata*, VIII.

to another object, will secure for us pleasure also. As in a field that has been ploughed for a crop of grain, flowers spring up amid the grain, yet so much labor has not been expended on their behalf although they do please the eye. The sower had something else in view, the flowers came merely as an accessory. So also pleasure is not the recompense nor the cause of virtue, but the accessory. . . . The supreme good consists in the judgment alone and habit of a virtuous mind. When such a mind has rounded out its own goodness and has enclosed itself within its own boundaries, it has attained the supreme good and desires nothing more. For nothing exceeds the whole, nor extends beyond the end. Therefore you make a mistake when you inquire what ulterior motive I have in seeking virtue; for you are asking for something higher than the summit. Do you ask what I am seeking from virtue? I am seeking virtue itself. Virtue has nothing better to give me; virtue is its own recompense. . . . For when I tell you that the supreme good consists in the firmness, foresight, keenness, sanity, freedom, concord, and beauty of a strong mind; why speak to me of pleasure? I am seeking man's good."*

And since the objector would at once say that he is not speaking of carnal but of spiritual and mental pleasure, Seneca for this reason introduces a statement of the supposed objector excluding carnal pleasure in order to assign another pleasure to virtue. Because of this other pleasure, then, the objector says, "I am not seeking the pleasure of the belly, an organ which is larger in domestic animals and in wild beasts. You profess ignorance of my meaning, he says. For my assertion is that no one can live pleasantly unless at the same time he also lives virtuously. Such a life is not possible for dumb animals nor for men who measure their good in the terms of food. I aver clearly and openly, says he, that this life which I call pleasant is inseparable from virtue." But Seneca meets the objection with the statement that pleasure is found not only in gluttony and debauchery, but in other spiritual vices also, since men take pleasure in these other vices as well as those mentioned above. And therefore virtue cannot exist for the sake of mental pleasure, since pleasure accompanies sins as well as virtue, being in fact common to both virtue and sin, because

* *Ibid.*, IX.

men rejoice and find pleasure in evil as well as in good. This is his further statement: "Who does not know that all men with the least sense are the most sated with pleasures? And that wickedness is overflowing with pleasurable things? that the mind itself supplies many low kinds of pleasure? Chief among these are arrogance, too high an opinion of oneself, a fancied superiority to others, and a blind and heedless love for one's own possessions." Since then the reply might be made that the good man at least experiences pleasure and joy and therefore has pleasure of mind, he says, "Virtue judges pleasures before she admits them, nor does she place a high value on such as she approves, for she merely admits them, and does not rejoice in the use she makes of them but in the limits she prescribes." And he says to the objector, "You embrace pleasure, I restrain it. You enjoy it, I use it. You consider it the greatest good, I not even a good. You do all things for the sake of pleasure, I do nothing."*

"I do not call that man a sage to whom something is superior, and still less if this something be pleasure. For, dominated by pleasure, how shall he withstand labor, danger, and want . . . how shall he endure the sight of death, of pain? How shall he endure the convulsions of nature and such a host of bitter foes, he who has been vanquished by so feeble an adversary?" And because the objector might still press his point, Seneca continues his opposition, "Do you not see how many counsels pleasure is likely to give?" "She will be able to give no bad advice since she is joined to virtue," is the objector's reply. But Seneca thus refutes the statement: "Do you not see what would be the nature of a supreme good that requires a keeper, that it may be a good? But how shall virtue rule pleasure which it follows, since it is incumbent on one who obeys to follow, and on one who commands to rule. Do you place your general in the rear? The eminent function of virtue in your system is to test in advance the pleasures . . . and as happens to many they are mad with a jovial madness and laugh in their delirium. But the pleasures of the sage are mild and restrained and almost listless. They are kept under subjection and are scarcely noticeable, since they come unsought, and when they present themselves, they are not received with honor nor welcomed with

* *De Vita Beata,* X.

any joy on the part of those experiencing them. For they mingle them and intersperse them through life like play and jest in the midst of serious matters. Let them cease, then, to try to ally two things that are incompatible, namely, to combine pleasure with virtue, a fault by which they pay court to all the most corrupt. The corrupt man, absorbed in his pleasures, always overfed and drunken, believes that he is living virtuously since he is living pleasurably. For he is told that pleasure cannot be separated from virtue; he then gives to his vices the name of wisdom and makes a display of what he should conceal. Therefore steeped in vices they seek for some defense and cloak for their lusts, and they lose the only good thing they possessed among their evils, namely, their feeling of shame at wrongdoing. . . ."*

"That which suffices nature is insufficient for debauchery. Whosoever has given his assent to virtue has given the appearance of noble qualities. He who follows pleasure seems soft, without vigor, degenerate, a man destined to fall into evil ways, unless someone distinguish for him among the pleasures, in order that he may know which of them confine themselves within the limits of natural desire, which are uncontrolled and unrestrained and the more they are sated the more insatiable they become. . . . No good is burdened by its own greatness."†

"And if that union of virtue and pleasure pleases you, let virtue precede, let pleasure attend upon it, and be like the shadow to the body . . . we shall have pleasure, but we shall be its masters and controllers. Whatever pleasure secures from us will be won by entreaty not by compulsion. But those who have entrusted pleasure with the leadership have deprived themselves of both; they lose virtue, and they do not possess pleasure but pleasure possesses them, victims equally of its absence which torments them, and of its excess which suffocates them; wretched if they are deserted by it, still more wretched if they are overwhelmed. . . . The greater and the more numerous they are, the smaller is he whom the world calls happy, and the slave of many masters. . . . He who follows pleasure, renounces liberty first, and expends himself for the sake of his belly; he does not purchase pleasure for himself, but he sells

* *Ibid.,* XI, XII.
† *Ibid.,* XIII.

himself to his pleasures. Yet what prevents, he asks, virtue and pleasure being united into one, and the supreme good being formed in such a way that it becomes at the same time both honorable and pleasing? Because no part of the honorable can be dishonorable. Nor does the supreme good retain in itself its own purity, if it beholds in itself something inferior. . . . But he who associates virtue and pleasure weakens whatever vigor is found in the one good by the frailty in the second, and sends under the yoke that invincible liberty than which nothing is known to be more precious. For he begins to have need of fortune, which is the very worst slavery. . . . You do not, therefore, grant to virtue a solid and immovable base, but you bid virtue stand in a changing and uncertain position. For what are so uncertain as the expectation of what is fortuitous and the diversity of bodies and of things affecting the body? How can this man obey God and accept with a tranquil mind whatever happens? . . . How can he put a favorable construction on his own ills if he is sensitive to the least incitements of pleasure and pain? But not even of his country is such a man a good guardian and avenger, nor is he a defender of his friends if he is given over to pleasures. Let, then, the supreme good mount to a point from which no force can drag it down, to a point inaccessible to pain, fear, hope, and to all else that may impair the full rights of the supreme good. But virtue alone can mount to this height; that ascent can be mastered by her alone. She will stand firm and will endure whatever betides not only with patience but also with pleasure, and will realize that all difficulties are in accordance with nature's law. She is like the courageous soldier who endures his wounds, counts his scars, and pierced by darts dies still loving the commander for whom he falls. He will bear in mind that old precept, Follow God. Whosoever complains and laments and groans is none the less forced to obey, and, in spite of his resistance, to execute the orders imposed upon him. But what folly it is to be dragged along rather than to follow! It is both ignorance of one's condition and folly to grieve . . . to be astonished and indignant at those things that happen to the good as well as to the evil. Let us meet with high courage all the universal order requires us to endure. We have been caused to take this oath to bear the lot of mortals and not to be perturbed by those things which it is not in our power to avoid. . . . Obedience to God is liberty."*

"True happiness, then, rests in virtue. What advice will this virtue give you? Do not consider anything as either good or evil that does not proceed from virtue or vice. She will further counsel you to be firm and in opposition to evil to form God from the good, as far as you may do so in accordance with the divine will. What does she promise you for such an enterprise? Great blessings and equal to those possessed by the gods; you will suffer no compulsion, you will lack nothing, you will be free, safe protected from loss. You will never attempt anything in vain, you will never be arrested by any obstacle, all things will happen to you in accordance with your wish. Nothing adverse will happen, nothing contrary to your expectation. . . . What then? Virtue suffices for a happy life. Why should it not suffice? Nay, it is more than sufficient. For what can a man lack who is without desires? What need of external things can he have who has gathered all things into himself?"†

But since no men or at least very few attain such moral excellence, and since Seneca might be subjected to criticism for certain imperfections of his own, in not conforming as a teacher of virtue all his actions to the requirements of virtue, Seneca replies when criticism of this kind is directed against him as follows:

"Now I make this reply to you; I am not a sage, and, to add more fuel to your fiery criticism, I shall not become one. Exact of me, therefore, not that I equal the best, but that I be better than evil men: this suffices me daily to lessen somewhat my vices and to correct my errors. . . . I prepare palliatives rather than cures for my gout, content if it returns less frequently and is less painful: I am a weak runner compared with your powers."‡

"Your speech and your life do not correspond, you say. Plato and Zeno were subjected to this same reproach. All those teachers used to tell not how they themselves were living, but how they ought to live. I am speaking of virtue, not of myself, when I abuse the vices. . . . Nor shall that malevolence of

* *De Vita Beata*, XIV, XV.
† *Ibid.*, XVI.
‡ *Ibid.*, XVII.

yours, imbued as it is with much venom, deter me from what is best. Not even that poison with which you attack others, with which you kill yourselves, shall hinder me from continuing to praise the life, not that I am leading, but the one I know that I ought to be leading. Nor shall it hinder me from adoring virtue and from creeping after her at a great distance."*

"The philosophers are useful in their statements regarding virtue. . . . For if they acted in accordance with their teachings, what life could be happier than theirs? Meanwhile there is no reason why you should despise good words and hearts full of good thoughts. The pursuit of useful studies is to be commended apart from their result. Is it surprising that by routes so difficult men do not reach the summit? But recognize powers that are attempting great things even though they fail. It is a noble thing to attempt lofty things and to conceive in the mind projects too great even for a great soul to accomplish. Such a man has proposed to himself this line of conduct: I shall view death on its arrival with the same look that I have when I hear it mentioned; I shall resign myself to labors, however great they shall prove to be, supporting my body with my mind; I shall be equally contemptuous of riches whether I have them or lack them, neither sadder if I know that they are in the possession of others, nor prouder if I find them casting their luster about me: I shall look with indifference upon fortune whether she comes or goes: I shall view all hands as belonging to me, and mine as belonging to all other people: I shall so live persuaded of the fact that I have been born for others. . . . She has given me to everybody and everybody to me; whatever I possess I shall not guard in a niggardly way nor scatter abroad lavishly: I shall believe that I possess nothing more than what I have bestowed with discernment: I shall not count my benefits, I shall not weigh them, nor shall I value them except in accordance with the merit of him who receives them. If he is worthy of them, I shall not think that I have done much; I shall never take opinion, but my conscience, as the motive in all that I do; I shall believe that whatever I do, when I am the sole witness, is done in the sight of the whole world; my purpose in eating and drinking will be to satisfy the desires of nature, not to fill and empty my stomach; I shall be agreeable

* *De Vita Beata,* XVIII.

to my friends, mild and affable to my enemies; I shall be appeased before I am asked, I shall meet more than half-way reasonable requests; I shall know that the world is my country and God is its ruler; that he is above me and about me as the censor of my deeds and my words; and when either nature shall demand back my spirit or reason release it, I shall go hence after bearing witness that I loved a good conscience, honorable pursuits, that I impaired no man's liberty. . . . He who shall propose, wish, try to do these things, will be making his journey toward God; verily, such a man even if he does not keep to his course 'falls in a daring and a great enterprise.'* You indeed who hate virtue and him who practises it do nothing new. For weak eyes fear the sun and . . . nocturnal animals . . . are dazed at his rising and everywhere seek their lurking-places . . . groan, employ your wretched tongue in abusing the good . . . you will sooner break your teeth than sink them in."†

"Why does he who is devoted to philosophy live in opulence? Why does he say that riches should be despised and yet still hold on to them? Why does he think that life should be despised and yet still live? Why does he think that health should be despised and yet guard it with the greatest care? . . . And thinks and says that exile is only an empty name: what harm is there in changing countries: and yet . . . he is growing old in his native land?"

He answers this question by showing how the sage can be good who wishes to have riches and does not wish to be poor: by drawing a distinction between the use made of riches by the sage and by the foolish, he shows how the sage should regard riches. The sage as well as the man of evil habits requires the necessities of life: and so out of the abundance owing to the world's resources he wishes to have what is necessary for himself and for others, that he may aid the indigent, and handle the business of the state. And thus since he possesses his riches for an honorable and useful purpose, he will not lose his virtue, which the evil man will throw away because of his abuse of riches. He says therefore that "these things should be despised by the sage, not that he should not possess them, but that he should not possess them with uneasiness of mind. He does

* Ovid, *Metamorphoses*, II, 328.
† *De Vita Beata*, XX.

not drive them away from himself, but attends them on their departure without regret. Where indeed shall fortune deposit more safely her riches than with him, from whom she will receive them back again without complaint? . . . The sage does not love riches but prefers them. He receives them into his home, not into his heart. . . ."*

And he says to the foolish man "If riches forsake me, they will carry away nothing but themselves; you will be amazed and you will think you have been left without yourself, if they should depart from you. With me riches have a place, with you they hold the highest place. . . . Riches belong to me, you belong to riches."†

"The philosopher will have ample riches, not stolen from any one nor stained with another's blood, secured without injury to any one, free from sordid gain, riches which pass out as honorably as they enter, and are complained of by no one unless he be envious. . . . Such a man will neither boast of his patrimony gained by honest means nor will he blush because of it. He will have . . . reason for pride if, on opening his house and admitting the public to view his possessions, he shall be able to say, Let each one take what he recognizes as his own. O great man, rich in the most excellent way! . . . Let riches come, let them enjoy his hospitality. He will neither be prodigal with them nor will he hide them; the former is the act of a silly mind, the latter that of a timid and petty one. . . . He will possess his wealth but will regard it as fickle and likely to vanish: nor will he suffer his riches to weigh upon either himself or another. . . . He will give to the good . . . or to those whom he shall be able to render good. He will give with the greatest discretion choosing the most worthy. . . . He will give from upright and laudable motives. For a gift unworthily bestowed is to be classed among disgraceful losses. His purse will open easily, but will not have a hole in it, a purse from which much comes out and nothing falls out."‡

"And note this first; there is a difference between him who is interested in wisdom and the man who has actually acquired it. The former will say to you, 'I speak excellently, but I am

* *De Vita Beata,* XXI.
† *Ibid.,* XXII.
‡ *Ibid.,* XXIII.

still involved in very many evils. There is no reason why you should judge me in accordance with the rule I have laid down for myself. . . . I am still working on myself and fashioning myself and trying to attain to a high standard. If I advance as far as I propose, then require that my acts correspond to my words.' But the second man, having attained the height of human wisdom, will talk to you in a different way and will say to the foolish man: 'First, you should not permit yourself to pass judgment on your betters; I already possess a proof of rectitude in being displeasing to evil men. . . . I deny that riches are a good: for if they were, they would make men good. Now since they are found in the possession of evil men, riches cannot be called good: I refuse them this name. . . .' "*

"Place me in the most luxurious home with gold and silver at my command. . . . I shall not respect myself because of those things which, although they are in my possession, are yet not part of me. . . . Drive me away among the beggars: I shall not, however, despise myself on this account, because I am found among those who hold out the hand for alms. For what matters the lack of a morsel of bread when one has still the opportunity to die? . . . I shall not think myself a whit more happy because I have a soft cloak, and because my guests recline on purple. . . . I shall not be more unhappy if my wearied head finds repose on a bundle of straw. . . . No hour is without some complaint; I shall not for this reason call myself wretched in the midst of these adversities. . . . For I have provided that no day should be a sinister one for me. . . . Therefore," declares the sage, "my life is not at variance with my teaching. But you do not hear aright. The sound merely of my words reaches your ears, you do not seek their meaning."†

"What then is the difference between me with my folly and you with your wisdom, if we both desire to have riches? A very great difference. For riches in possession of the sage are in servitude, in the possession of the fool are in command. The sage intrusts nothing to riches; riches mean everything to you. You accustom yourselves to them and cling to them as though some one had promised to you their eternal possession: the sage never meditates so much on poverty as when he is in the midst

* *Ibid.*, XXIV.
† *Ibid.*, XXV.

of affluence. . . . You waste away in the midst of your own possessions nor do you think how many chances threaten every moment to carry off your precious spoils. He who deprives the sage of his wealth leaves him all things that are really his. For the sage lives pleased with the present and without anxiety for the future. Of nothing has Socrates so firmly convinced me as that I should not regulate the conduct of my life in accordance with your opinions. Marshal from all sides your usual array of words: I shall consider that you are not uttering insults but wailings like very unhappy children. . . . Your hallucinations I put up with as does Jupiter the absurdities of the poets, one of whom has attached wings to him, another horns, and still another has introduced him as an adulterer. . . ."*

"Lo! Socrates, from that prison which he cleansed by his entrance and rendered more august than any senate-house, proclaims, 'What madness is this of yours, what nature hostile to God and man that prompts you to decry the virtues and to violate all that is sacred by your wicked statements?' Praise the good if you can; if not go your way. But if you find pleasure in exercising that foul freedom of yours, direct your attacks on one another. For when you rave against heaven, I do not say you commit sacrilege, but you lose your pains. . . . It is an advantage for virtue to be brought forth and put to the test, nor do any perceive her greatness better than those who have felt her power from attacking her. It is only by striking a piece of flint that one realizes its hardness. I offer myself to their attacks like a solitary rock in a restless sea, which the waves lash unceasingly on every side, and yet they do not move it from its place or wear it away through so many ages by their incessant attack. Spring at me, make your assault. By my endurance I shall overcome you. All that rush upon what is firm and invincible expend their force to their own hurt. Therefore seek some soft yielding substance in which to drive your spears. But have you the time to examine the faults of others and pass judgments on any man? Why, you ask, does this philosopher live too well housed, why does that one dine too sumptuously? Are you observing the slight blemishes on others when you are yourself covered with many ulcers? Such conduct is like that of him who laughs at the moles or warts on the persons of

* *De Vita Beata,* XXVI.

the most beautiful when he himself is devoured by a terrible skin disease. Reproach Plato because he demanded money, Aristotle because he accepted it, Democritus because he neglected it, Epicurus because he expended it. Cast in my teeth my inheritance. How very happy you will be as soon as you are in a position to imitate our faults. Nay, regard rather your own vices, which riddle you everywhere, some raging externally while others burn in your vitals. What shall I say more? Is not a kind of whirlwind, even though you scarcely discern it, rotating and enveloping your minds as they flee from and pursue the same objects?"*

Chapter XIX

"For among our other ills the very worst is that we change our vices . . . and this also plagues us that our judgments are not only bad but also fickle. We move to and fro, we grasp at one thing after another, we abandon what we have been seeking, we seek again what we have abandoned. Our life is merely an alternative between our desires and our regrets. For we depend wholly on the judgments of others, and we consider that best which is praised and sought after by the multitude, not that which is praiseworthy and desirable in itself. We judge a road to be good or bad only by the number of footprints among which there are none of those returning."†

"Man is too mortal for the comprehension of things immortal." And since the pursuit of wisdom and virtue is still disapproved of by many on the ground that it involves the abandonment of civic duties, he therefore cites this charge against the leisure of the sage: he says, "Nature has destined me for two things, action and contemplation."‡

"Virtue banished to a leisure without action is an imperfect and languid good and never displays what it has learned. . . . He ought not only to think of what he should do but also take a hand sometimes in realizing his meditations. . . . The sage withdraws into seclusion, that he may be assured of the op-

---

* *Ibid.*, XXVII, XXVIII.
† *De Otio*, I.
‡ *Ibid.*, V.

portunity to do what will benefit posterity. We surely are ready
to admit that Zeno and Chrysippus accomplished greater results than if they had led armies, held offices, promulgated
laws; in effect they did promulgate laws, not for a single state,
but for the whole human race. Do you think, then, that such a
leisure is unworthy of a good man, a leisure in which he forms
the ages to come, and addresses not a small number of his fellows but the men of all nations present and future? . . . They
have found the means of rendering their leisure more useful
to men than the activity and sweat of others. Therefore they
accomplished much although they took no part in public affairs. . . ."*

"To what state shall the sage withdraw? To Athens in which
a Socrates is condemned, from which an Aristotle flees to escape condemnation? in which envy overwhelms the virtues?
Shall he go to Carthage where sedition is always rife and liberty is deadly to all good people? . . . If I should care to pass
in review all governments, I shall not find one which can endure
the sage or one which he can endure."†

CHAPTER XX

Now finally I shall introduce some quotations from Seneca's
work addressed to Serenus on peace of mind, because this accompanies the happy life; and it is certain that happiness cannot be possible in this life without peace of mind. Nor will the
life of true happiness in the future be complete without it. All
adversities can of necessity be easily borne if we possess this
peace of mind. But since we are just as prone to flatter ourselves
as others, and by palliating our vices measure our happiness of
mind by a false standard, Seneca says with excellent point, "We
look familiarly on the imperfections in our own household, and
our self-love blinds our judgment. I think that many could have
attained to wisdom if they had not believed that they were already sages, if they had not concealed certain vices in themselves, if they had not skipped over others with their eyes
closed. For there is no reason why you should think that we are

* *De Otio*, VI.
† *Ibid.*, VIII.

ruined more by flattery of others than by our own. Who has ventured to tell himself the truth? Who set in the midst of herds of flatterers and courtiers has not been his own most eager flatterer?"*

"What you wish for, Serenus, is to remain unshaken, a perfect state of mind resembling that of God himself. The Greeks call this stability of mind εὐθυμία, on which there is an excellent treatise by Democritus: I call it tranquillity. . . . We are seeking then to discover how the mind, enjoying always a perfect equality, may follow a uniform course, live at peace with itself, contemplate its lot with satisfaction, experience this joy without interruption, and maintain itself in a state of calm never suffering undue elevation or depression: this will be tranquillity." And first he touches upon the vices that destroy our peace of mind, in order that we may know how to avoid them and return to our former state of mind. He says accordingly: "Some men are plagued with a fickleness of mind and a feeling of irksomeness and habitual inconstancy of purpose, men who always prefer the plan they have rejected, . . . they are weak and indolent. Add those who resemble the victims of insomnia, tossing about and trying this position and that until fatigue finally brings them repose. Such men, constantly changing their manner of life, finally remain in that state in which not a dislike of change but old age too sluggish to make one finds them. Add also those whom the vice of sloth rather than reason preserves from inconstancy; they live not as they wish but as they have begun. Vice has innumerable forms but one general effect, namely, displeasure with oneself;" for which reason peace of mind departs. "This arises from lack of mental balance and from desires that are timid or from such as are crowned with little success, where either their daring is not commensurate with their wishes, or they do not obtain what they wish, and live entirely upon hope. Such men are always in a state of agitation and suspense, the inevitable result of being dependent on their own wishes. . . . Those men are possessed by regret for what they have begun and by fear of making a new start; and that agitation of a mind which finds no egress creeps upon them, since they are able neither to control their wishes nor to gratify them. Thus their life arrested so

* *De Tranquillitate Animi*, I.

to speak in its course drags along slowly and painfully, and the mind languishes in the midst of its disappointed hopes. All these ills are aggravated, when in their resentment at an ill fortune that is so burdensome they have taken refuge in leisure and private studies, which cannot be endured by the mind that is interested in public affairs, eager for action, restless by nature, and that possesses in itself few sources of solace. For this reason, when the delights are withdrawn which their occupations furnish, they cannot endure home and solitude and confining walls. The mind left to itself does not care to view its own image. This is the cause of weariness and self-disgust, of the agitation of a mind never at rest, and of the pain and bitterness with which it endures its own inaction. . . . Desires pent up without egress stifle themselves: then come grief and langor and the thousand fluctuations of an inconstant mind held in a gloomy and deplorable state of suspense by the hopes it has entertained. Then follows the condition of mind of the man who detests his own leisure and complains that he has nothing to do, and who views with an envious eye the success of another. For sloth causing unhappiness breeds envy, and men desire the fall of others, because they have not been able to advance themselves. . . . For the mind of man is naturally active and prone to movement. Every occasion of exciting and diverting itself is pleasing to the mind; still more pleasing to the worst characters who waste away voluntarily in their pursuits. As certain ulcers crave the harmful touch of the hand and find pleasure therein, and whatever irritates gives pleasure to a foul itch of the body, just so I may say that these minds in which desires like malignant ulcers have broken out find their pleasure in labor and vexation of spirit. For there are certain things that give pleasure to our bodies also, as for instance turning about in bed and changing a side that is not yet tired, and exposing ourselves to the air in first one position and then in another. . . . It is characteristic of a sick man not to endure anything for a long time and to employ changes as a means of relief. . . . We are weak in our endurance, we cannot stand either labor or pleasure for any length of time, and grow weary of our own and of all other interests. Some have been driven to suicide when they realized that by frequent change they had arrived again at the point of departure and had deprived themselves of

Moral Philosophy

the possibility of further change. Life and the world itself became a source of disgust to them."*

Seneca then introduces remedies for these vices. And he first touches upon them, quoting the opinion of another writer. He says, "You inquire what remedy in my judgment should be used against this feeling of disgust. The best would be, as Athenodorus says, to keep oneself always on the alert in the management of affairs, in the administration of the state, and in civic duties. For as some spend the day in the sunshine in the exercise and care of the body, and as athletes find it most serviceable to spend most of their time in exercising their arms and nursing their strength, to which alone they have devoted themselves; so is it most fitting for us in preparing our mind for the arena of public life to be always at work. For since he has determined to render himself useful to his fellow citizens and to mankind, he is occupied and of service at the same time when he has placed himself in the midst of affairs and administers public and private matters to the best of his ability."

Seneca, however, does not agree with him in this, but recommends the pursuit of wisdom. He says therefore: "But since in this mad race of ambition, with so many detractors putting the wrong construction on upright conduct, integrity has insufficient protection, and since there will always be more to hinder than to promote success, we should withdraw from the forum and from public affairs. But a great mind has an opportunity to develop itself freely in private life. The power of lions and of other animals is held in check by the cages that restrain them; not so with man, whose greatest actions are performed in retirement. Let the sage conceal himself indeed, but with the intention of serving in his solitude both public and private interests with his talents, his voice, and his counsel. For he who defends the accused and votes on questions of peace and war is not the only one that benefits his country. The man who instructs the youth, who in so great a dearth of good teachers instills virtue in the youthful mind, who draws back those who are eagerly pursuing money and pleasure, and retards at least for a time their ruin, such a man, I say, even in his private position is working for the public. Is the magistrate who judges between citizens and strangers, or the city praetor who pro-

* De Tranquillitate Animi, II.

nounces on litigants the sentences dictated to him by his assessor, more useful than he who teaches what justice is, what loyalty is, patience, fortitude, contempt of death, knowledge of God, and the great benefit of a good conscience? Therefore if you should devote to study the time you take from active employments, you will not have deserted your post nor failed in your duty. For he is not the only one performing military service who stands in the line of battle and defends the right or the left wing, but he also serves who guards the gates, and fills a less perilous post, but not, however, an idle one, by standing guard and supervising the armory. These duties, although they are performed without risk to life, are classed as military services. By devoting yourself to study you will escape all the tedium of life, nor will you desire the return of night because of the irksomeness of the day. You will be neither burdensome to yourself nor useless to others. You will win the friendship of many, and all good men will be attracted to you. For virtue although obscured never remains hidden, but sends forth indications of its existence. Whosoever is worthy will find her by her footsteps. For if we break off all relationship and renounce the human race, and live occupied with ourselves alone, this solitary life deprived of every kind of liberal study will be followed by a total lack of occupation. We shall begin to erect buildings in one place and tear them down in another . . . and to make a bad use of our time, . . . a very serious fault. Often an aged man has no other proof to offer in establishing the fact that he has lived for a long time except his age."*

"Let him be in private, in public, at table, a good companion, faithful friend, temperate table companion. If he no longer performs the duties of a citizen, let him fulfill those of a man. We have not shut up our minds within the walls of a single city, but have sent them forth to have intercourse with all lands and we have claimed the world as our country, so that we may give our virtue a wider field. . . . The work of a good citizen is never useless. He has been heard, he has been seen; his look, his nod . . . even his step are of use. As certain medicines are efficacious by their odor apart from their taste and contact, so virtue though at a distance and unperceived spreads abroad an atmosphere of helpfulness; whether virtue walks abroad at

* *De Tranquillitate Animi,* III.

will . . . or enjoys only a precarious freedom in this respect
. . . or inactive, silent, narrowly circumscribed . . . in whatever guise she makes her appearance, she is beneficial. What
of this? Do you consider of little moment the example of a man
who knows how to rest? It is a very excellent thing, then, to
mingle leisure with action whenever a life of action is prevented either by adverse fortune or by the state of the republic.
For never have all avenues of approach been so closed, that
honorable effort found its passage completely barred."*

"Can you find a city more wretched than was that of the
Athenians when it was distracted by the thirty tyrants? The
thirty had slain thirteen hundred citizens, nor had they reached
by any means the end of their atrocities, but their barbarity was
increasing under its own stimulus. . . . Socrates, however,
continued to live in their midst, consoling bereaved parents,
encouraging those who were despairing of the state, reproach-
ing the rich who were trembling for their wealth . . . and
exhibiting a lofty example to those who were willing to imitate
him by boldly entering the presence of the thirty. Yet Athens
herself executed this man in prison, and even liberty did not
endure the man who as a free citizen had defied a throng of
tyrants."†

"But we must now consider in the first place ourselves; then
the matters on which we are engaged; finally the persons for
whom or with whom we must act. Before all else it is necessary
to form an estimate of ourselves, because frequently we over-
estimate our powers. One man will fail because of overconfi-
dence in his own eloquence, another has drained too heavily his
patrimony, still another has taxed his weak body with too
strenuous work. Some have a timidity rendering them unfit for
civic affairs which require resolution. The inflexibility of others
does not meet with success at court. Some do not keep their
anger under control, and under any provocation are indiscreet
in their language. Others do not know how to restrain their
raillery," in their reprimands, "and do not refrain from dangerous witticisms. For all these classes of people a quiet life is
better than one of action. . . . We must then estimate the matters themselves which we are undertaking, and we must com-

* *Ibid.*, IV.
† *Ibid.*, V.

pare our powers with the projects we propose to attempt. For the power must always be greater than the resistance. Of necessity he must be crushed who carries a burden too great for his strength. There are, moreover, certain matters which are not so important in themselves, but which carry the seed of many others. We must shun activities from which spring still other occupations of a new and complex nature. We must not travel to a point from which we may not return at will; let us charge ourselves with matters which we can terminate or at least hope to do so. Let us abandon projects that go too far afield and do not terminate at the point we have set."*

"In our choice, then, of individuals we must examine whether those are worthy on whom we are bestowing a portion of our life; whether the expenditure of our time has any good effect on them. For some people go so far as to charge against us the favors we render them. Athenodorus says that he would not even dine with a man who would not feel under obligation to him for this favor. . . . You must consider whether your nature is better fitted for a life of action or for a leisure devoted to study and contemplation; and you should follow your natural bent. . . . For natures that are forced make a poor response. . . . But nothing so delights the heart as a sweet and faithful friendship. How great a blessing it is when there are ready hearts to which every secret can be intrusted with safety, whose conscience you fear less than your own, whose conversation relieves your solicitude, whose opinion aids your judgment, whose gaiety dispels your sadness, the mere sight of whom is a pleasure! We shall choose, to be sure, those who are free as far as possible from passions. For vices creep along and pass to all that are exposed to them and harm by contact. Therefore as we are careful in times of pestilence not to sit near persons already infected and inflamed with the disease, because we shall incur danger and shall suffer even from their breath, so in our choice of friends we shall make every effort to select such as are least corrupt. Association of healthy people with sick folk is the beginning of disease. Nor should I give you this advice not to follow or attract any one but the sage. For where will you find him for whom we have been searching so many ages? The best is the least bad. . . . Now indeed in such a dearth of

* *De Tranquillitate Animi,* VI.

good men our choice should be less exacting. Avoid, however, in particular those gloomy and mournful individuals whose delight is in complaining of all things in general. Although he may be of a kind and loyal heart, a gloomy companion with a perpetual sigh on his lips is an enemy to your peace of mind."*

"Let us pass to riches, the greatest source of human anxieties. For if you compare all our other worries, such as death, sickness, fear, desire, endurance of pain and labor, with those ills caused by our money, you will find that the latter press far more heavily upon us. Therefore we must consider how much less painful it is not to have than to lose what we have had; and we shall perceive that the less we have to lose the less is poverty able to torment us. For you are in error if you think that the rich support losses with greater fortitude: the largest and the smallest bodies suffer equal pain from a wound. Bion cleverly says, 'Plucking out hair is just as painful to heads that are bald as to those covered with hair.' . . . It is more endurable . . . not to acquire than to lose; and for this reason you will see those more happy on whom fortune has never smiled than those whom she has deserted. Diogenes, a man of lofty spirit, perceived this truth, and was careful to have nothing which could be taken away from him. Call this condition poverty, need, indigence, give to this state of security any opprobrious name you wish; I shall cease to believe in his happiness only when you find me some one else guaranteed against loss. Either I am deceived, or it is a mark of kingship, that there is one man who cannot be harmed among the covetous, robbers. . . . He who is doubtful regarding the happiness of Diogenes may well be in doubt whether the condition of the immortal God is not deficient in happiness, since he has neither estates, nor gardens, nor farms enriched by the labor of slaves, nor a large income from money in bank. Are you not ashamed, you who are enraptured with riches? Just look at the world; will you not see God giving all, retaining nothing? Do you consider the man who has divested himself of all fortuitous things poor or like the immortal God? Is it your idea that a rich man is happier? Diogenes' only slave ran away from him, nor did Diogenes consider it worth while to have him brought back when he was informed of his whereabouts. 'It is disgraceful,' said he, 'that

* *Ibid.,* VII.

Manes can live without Diogenes, but Diogenes cannot live without Manes.' He seems to me to have said, 'Attend to your own business, Fortune; you have no longer any claim on Diogenes. Has my slave run off? Nay, it is a free man that has departed.' . . . But since we do not possess such strength of character, we should at least curtail our wealth, so that we may be less exposed to injury at the hands of fortune. Those are better fitted for warfare whose bodies can be contained within their armor, than those of too great bulk, whose size exposes them to wounds. The best measure of wealth is to be neither too near to poverty nor too far removed from it."*

"We shall be pleased with this measure, if we begin by taking pleasure in frugality, without which no riches suffice, . . . especially since the remedy is at hand, and poverty itself can be converted into riches by means of frugality. Let us accustom ourselves to do without pomp and to estimate things in accordance with their usefulness and not in accordance with their embellishment. Our food and drink should suffice to remove hunger and thirst; . . . let us learn to go about on our own legs, and not regulate our dress and mode of living after new fashions; . . . let us learn to increase our continence, restrain our luxury, temper our pride, soften our anger, look upon poverty in the proper light, cultivate frugality, even if the majority is ashamed to apply to natural longings relief secured at a small cost, let us learn to restrain as it were in fetters unbridled hopes and thoughts soaring into the future, and to exert ourselves in seeking riches from ourselves rather than from fortune. . . . Let us accustom ourselves, then, to dine without a number of guests, to require the service of fewer slaves, to get our garments for the purpose for which they were intended, and to dwell in narrower confines."

Seneca speaks of the aid we derive from study as follows: "Our expenditure on studies is most praiseworthy so long as it is kept within reasonable limits. To what end such numberless books and libraries, whose owner in the course of his whole life scarcely reads through the titles? A multitude of books burdens, does not instruct, the learner; and it is much better to devote yourself to a few authors than to lose your way in a host of them. Forty thousand of the books in Alexandria were

* *De Tranquillitate Animi,* VIII.

destroyed by fire. The vaunting of this superb monument of royal magnificence I leave to another, as Livy, for example, who says that it was a masterpiece of taste and care on the part of sovereign power. As a matter of fact it was not an example of taste and care, but of the extravagance of study, nay, not even of study, since they did not have study in view but merely ostentation. . . . In all excess there is vice. Why should you pardon the man who eagerly acquires bookcases laden with the works of either unknown or discredited authors and yawns in the midst of so many thousands of books, a man whose chief pleasure is derived from their titles and frontispieces? . . . I could certainly pardon this madness if it had its origin in an excessive zeal for study. As a matter of fact, they search with such care for the works and busts of revered men of genius in order that they may use them as mural decorations."*

"You have fallen into a difficult sort of life, and either public fortune or your own particular fortune has fastened a noose upon you without your knowledge, which you can neither loosen nor break. Consider how prisoners at first endure with difficulty the chains and shackles on their legs; then when they have made up their minds not to worry over but to endure them, they are taught by necessity to bear their shackles with fortitude and by familiarity with ease. You will find in every kind of life delights, relaxations, and pleasures, if you wish. . . . On no other count has nature deserved more gratitude from us than for her discovery of habit as an alleviation of woes, familiarizing us quickly with the severest evils, fully aware as she is of our heritage of cares. No one could hold out if adversity oft repeated had the same impact as its first blow. We have all been linked with fortune: of some the chain is golden, of others lax, of still others tight and foul. But what difference does it make? We are all prisoners together, and those who have bound others are bound themselves also . . . one is bound by honors, another by wealth. Some are the slaves of their high birth, others of their obscurity. Some are subject to a strange yoke, others are subject to a yoke of their own. These are kept in one place by exile, those by their priestly office. Every life is servitude. One must accustom himself, therefore, to his lot and complain of it as little as possible. . . . There is nothing so

* *Ibid.*, IX.

bitter that a tranquil mind does not find some comfort in it.
. . . Apply reason to difficulties; hard things can be softened
and narrow places broadened. . . . Moreover, we should not
permit our desires to go far afield, but should limit their excur-
sions to the immediate neighborhood. . . . Renouncing objects
that we cannot obtain, at least without difficulty, let us seek for
those things that are at hand and offer encouragement to our
hopes; and let us realize that all things are equally worthless,
outwardly differing in appearance, but inwardly alike vain.
And let us not envy those above us. This seeming elevation is
but the edge of a precipice. . . . There are many . . . on a
lofty pinnacle from which they can descend only by falling; but
this very fact is evidence that their burden is a very great one,
because they are compelled to be burdensome to others, and
that they have not merely been raised to their high position but
have been pilloried there. Let justice, human kindness, liberality, prepare resources for the lot which awaits them, in the
hope of which they may hang on the edge of the abyss with
greater security. Nothing, however, will serve better to emanci-
pate these men from these mental upheavals than always to fix
some limit to the increase of their greatness, and not to leave
the decision of their retirement to fortune, but to halt far this
side of the boundary set. In this way the mind will feel the
goad of desires, and will not be carried on into a limitless un-
certainty, since its desires are limited."*

"This discourse of mine is not addressed to the sage, but to
those who are imperfect and whose health is not assured. The
sage must advance neither timidly nor step by step. For so
great is his confidence in himself that he never hesitates to meet
Fortune and will never give ground to her, . . . since not only
his slaves and possessions and rank but his body also and eyes
and hands, and whatever renders life dearer to him, nay, his
very self he reckons among things committed merely to his
care, and he lives as though lent to himself and is prepared to
return them on demand without regret. Nor is he cheap in his
own eyes because he knows that he does not belong to himself;
on the contrary, he will do all things with all the care and caution with which a scrupulously honest man guards all that is
intrusted to his keeping. But whenever he is bidden return the

* *De Tranquillitate Animi*, X.

loan, he utters no complaint to Fortune, but says, 'I thank you for what I have possessed and had. It is true that I have cared for your property at great expense, but at your demand I give, I yield it up gratefully and willingly. . . . My treasures, my home, my family I give back, I restore.' If it is Nature who has summoned us to restore what she previously intrusted to us, we shall say to her also, 'Take back a better soul than you gave. I do not refuse nor do I seek to flee. I restore to you voluntarily that which you gave me without my knowledge.' . . . He will have a bad life of it who does not know how to die properly. Therefore the first value set upon life must be revised and the spirit must be reckoned among things of little value. . . . The fear of dying is often the cause of death. Fortune, who stages shows for her own amusement, says, 'Why should I reserve you, evil and cowardly creature? You shall be wounded and stabbed the more, because you do not know how to present your throat; but you shall live longer and die more easily who do not draw back your neck from the iron nor resist with your hands but receive it with courage.' . . . But if we know that from the instant even of our conception the verdict has been passed upon us, we shall live following the order of nature; and the same strength of mind will prevent our regarding any event as unexpected. For by foreseeing the possibilities the future has in store for us we shall lighten the force of all evils which bring no surprise to those who are prepared and ready for them. Misfortunes come to those who believe themselves secure and are concerned with their own happiness alone. For sickness, captivity, ruin, fire, are by no means unexpected. I knew that Nature had shut me in a troubled lodging. I have heard so often the funeral lamentations in my neighborhood, I have seen pass so often before my door the torches and wax tapers attending the funeral processions of those who died young. Often the crash of a falling building has met my ear. A single night has carried off many of those with whom the forum, the senate-house, conversation had brought me in contact, and severed hands joined in friendship; ought I to be surprised that the dangers have at last reached me which have always been roving about in my vicinity? . . . Publius, a more forceful writer than the authors of tragedy and comedy, has said:

'That which can happen to an individual man can happen to all.'

Opus Majus

If any one has grasped the full meaning of this maxim, and has viewed all the numberless and daily mishaps of others with a realization that he himself is equally exposed to their assaults, he will arm himself long before he is attacked. Too late is the mind trained to endure dangers after it has been exposed to them. I did not think that this would happen. . . . What riches are there which are not followed by indigence, hunger, and beggary? . . . What kingdom is there for which overthrow and ruin do not lie in wait? . . . Nor are such changes separated by long intervals, but the short space of an hour reduces a monarch to a suppliant. Know then that every condition is subject to change, and whatever can happen to another can happen to you also. You are rich; not richer than Ptolemaeus, I suppose? . . . He begged for the rain drops: he perished of hunger and thirst. . . . On the same day on which the senate escorted Sejanus, the populace tore his body in pieces. . . . Therefore in such constant vicissitudes of rising and falling fortune, if you do not regard the possibilities the future holds in store for you, you are lending force to your own adversity, a force which he has already broken who has foreseen it."*

"We must curtail restless activity, such as engages most men as they wander about their homes and the theaters and the forums. They busy themselves in the affairs of others always with an assiduous air. If you ask one of these men as he leaves his house, 'Where are you going? What have you in mind?' He will answer you, 'I do not know; but I shall see some people, I shall do something or other.' Without any definite aim they go to and fro seeking for things to do; . . . their inconsiderate and useless course is like that of ants crawling on trees which mount to the top and then descend without carrying anything. . . . Therefore every labor should have some definite purpose, some definite end in view. . . . Not real diligence but false views of life actuate these restless madmen. . . . In the same way each one of those whom vain and trifling motives lead hither and thither through the city and who sally forth to swell the crowd . . . some run as to a fire or to salute some one who will not return their greeting, or to escort the dead body of a man unknown to them. . . .† On this evil hangs that heedless

* *De Tranquillitate Animi*, XI.
† Bacon has altered this sentence greatly.

vice of prying into secrets of state and of learning many things which are neither told nor heard with safety."*

"It is this consideration, I suppose, that led Democritus to begin as follows, 'To live in tranquillity one must abstain from many public and private matters.' He had reference to superfluous things. . . . For he who engages in many enterprises frequently gives Fortune a hold upon him, with whom it is the safest course not to have any dealings, but always to keep her in mind and to put no confidence in her loyalty. . . . This is why we say that nothing can happen unexpectedly to the sage. We are not exempting him from the accidents to humanity, but from humanity's errors: nor do all things turn out for him as he wished, but as he thought. But first of all he perceived that his projects might meet obstacles. But lack of success in a cherished plan is necessarily less painful when one has not promised himself its realization."†

"We ought to cultivate a complaisant disposition, that we may not indulge too far our fixed ideas and projects, and may accommodate ourselves to changed conditions, accepting without fear such as are dictated by our position or by wisdom, without, however, becoming the victims of inconstancy, a vice most hostile to tranquillity of mind. For obstinacy, of necessity, is an anxious and wretched condition of mind; . . . inconstancy is much worse, since it in no way sets a curb on itself. There are two excesses equally deadly to tranquillity, the impossibility of changing and the impossibility of enduring anything. Undoubtedly the mind must retire into itself from all external interests; the mind should trust itself, be pleasing to itself, have regard for its own interests, withdraw as far as possible from the concerns of others, and cling to itself; it should not feel losses, and should put a kindly interpretation even upon adversity. Zeno the philosopher on learning of a shipwreck in which he lost everything merely said, 'Fortune bids me take up philosophy with fewer encumbrances.' A tyrant was holding out the threat of death and loss of sepulcher to the philosopher Theodorus. 'You can please yourself,' the philosopher said, 'I have a measure of blood at your disposal; as regards my burial you are indeed a fool if you think that it mat-

* *Ibid.*, XII.
† *Ibid.*, XIII.

ters to me whether I rot above ground or beneath it.' Canus Julius, a man . . . of true greatness, . . . on being condemned to death after a long dispute with Caius Caesar said, 'I thank thee, excellent prince.' . . . He was playing chess when the centurion who was leading to execution a band of other victims bade him be summoned also. At this order he counted his pieces and said to his companion, 'See that you do not after my death state falsely that you won.' Then nodding to the centurion he said, 'You will be my witness that I am one point ahead of him.' . . . His friends were sad at the thought of losing such a man. 'Why are you down-hearted?' he said. 'You ask whether the soul is immortal: I shall soon know.' He did not cease to search for truth even at the very end, and to make his own death a subject of investigation. . . . And at length the eminence was close at hand on which a daily sacrifice was offered to Caesar. A friend said to him, 'Of what are you now thinking, Canus? Or what idea is in your mind?' 'I have determined,' said Canus, to observe in that fleeting moment of death whether the soul is conscious of its own departure.' He promised that, if he discovered anything, he would go about and make known the state of the departed. Lo! a calm in the midst of a storm. Lo! a soul worthy of eternity, a soul that summons its own condition to bear witness to the truth, and at the very end of life makes an inquiry regarding its own departure, continuing to learn not only up to the moment of death, but even from death itself gaining information."*

"But it is vain to have rid ourselves of the causes of personal unhappiness" unless we overcome those that are general. "For sometimes a hatred of the human race takes possession of us, and the throng of so many wrongs that prosper passes in review; . . . Honesty is rare . . . and innocence unknown. . . . We must accustom ourselves, therefore, to look upon the vices of the multitude not as hateful but as ridiculous, and to imitate Democritus rather than Heraclitus. For the latter used to weep, the former to laugh, whenever they appeared in public. All our actions seemed tragic to the one and comic to the other. . . . There is the added fact that he is more serviceable to the human race who laughs at it than he who mourns over it; the former leaves something at least to kindly hope, while the latter fool-

* *De Tranquillitate Animi*, XIV.

ishly weeps over what he regards as without hope of correction. And after a general survey he is possessed of a greater mind who does not restrain his laughter than he who does not refrain from tears. . . . Let each one of us represent to himself all those things that render him sad or joyous, and he will perceive the truth of what Bion has said, 'All the actions of men are like mere beginnings, and their life is neither a more revered nor a more serious matter than their conception.' But it is better to view without emotion public morals and human vices and to refrain from both laughter and tears. For to torture oneself with the evils of others is a never-ending misery, and to take delight in their ills is an inhuman pleasure."*

"We shall pass to the case that habitually and rightly depresses us; . . . I mean the unhappy end of some good men. Socrates, for example, is forced to die in prison, . . . Cicero to offer his neck to his own clients, Cato, . . . the living image of the virtues, by falling on his sword to put an end to his own life and the republic as well. . . . Consider how each of them bore his fate, and wish for the courage of those who showed themselves brave. If they perished like weaklings and poltroons, no loss was suffered. . . . I shall weep over no man who rejoices" in meeting dangers, "I shall weep over no man who weeps when confronted with peril: the former has himself wiped away my tears, the latter by his tears has rendered himself unworthy of any."†

Chapter XXI

Since according to Scripture the body which is corrupted burdens the soul, and our earthly habitation is depressing to the sense that is cognizant of many things, for peace of mind, therefore, human frailty must necessarily relax the mind at times through the comforts and recreations necessary for the body. For otherwise the spirit becomes anxious, dull, fitful, and gloomier than it should be, languid with the tedium of goodness, complaining, and prone to frequent fits of impatience and anger. For this reason the most godly men would seek relief

* *Ibid.*, XV.
† *Ibid.*, XVI.

sometimes from their spiritual cares, soften at times the rigor of their abstinence, and moderate their excessive vigils. The most blessed John the Evangelist as a relief to his human frailty used to amuse himself with a partridge, as we learn from the Collations of Cassianus; and the blessed Benedict, when he was rebuked by a passing traveler for diverting his monks with physical pleasure, replied by asking the stranger to stretch a bow more and more. On the stranger's replying, "I will not do so, because I should break the cord," Benedict drew the parallel that he could force his monks to the rigor of penitence to such a degree that they could not endure it, but would break under the strain. And for this reason the Patriarch Jacob excused himself from accompanying Esau, fearing lest, if he tried to keep pace with him, his sons and his wives and his cattle would die.

Hence it is that Seneca wisest of men, who was granted a revelation accorded by God to few, as the Apostle says, realizing the weight of human frailty, took up the question of relaxation and recreation for the body at the end of his essay on Peace of Mind, in order that by introducing remedies of this kind our vigor may be more strongly restored. For even Cato says, "Intersperse sometimes joys with your cares," so that we may say to God with the Psalmist, "My strength will I ascribe unto thee." Seneca accordingly touching upon solaces of this kind speaks as follows: "The world and the retreat are two things that should intermingle and one succeed the other. The latter will cause us to long for our fellow men, the former for ourselves, and the one will be a remedy for the other. Solitude will relieve the irksomeness of the throng, and the throng that of solitude. The mind should not be kept at the same tension, but should be relieved by witticisms" and recreations for the body besides. "Socrates did not think it beneath his dignity to play with children. Cato used to refresh his mind with wine when he was wearied with affairs of state. Scipio, after so many triumphs, did not disdain to move his martial body to the rhythm of the dance, not affecting, as is the custom today, those soft attitudes and wanton movements which give to our dancing an effeminate air, but dancing in that manly fashion which characterized the heroes of old on festive days, and which would not provoke unfavorable criticism even if they were seen

by the enemies of their country. We must give our minds relaxation; they are better and more active after a rest. Just as
we must not constantly force fertile fields, since an uninter-
rupted productiveness will soon exhaust them, so unremitting
toil will break our mental vigor. Repose for a short period and
relaxation will restore our powers of mind. A certain dullness
and languidness are produced by incessant mental effort. If
play and jest did not possess some natural attraction, men would
not be so strongly drawn to them. Frequent indulgence in them,
however, will rob the mind of its force and gravity. For sleep
is necessary to refresh the body, but if it continues day and
night it will become death. There is a great difference between
relaxing a thing and decomposing it. Our legislators appointed
feast days, in order that men, assembled for public amusements,
might find some intervals of relaxation necessary for their
work; and illustrious men were in the habit of observing each
month certain holidays. Some of them in fact would divide each
day between leisure and business, whom no matter of business
detained beyond the tenth hour. They would not even read a
letter after this hour for fear that it might prove to be the
source of fresh worry, but during the two remaining hours they
would refresh themselves from the fatigue of the whole day.
. . . Our ancestors forbade any new motion in the senate after
the tenth hour. The mind requires indulgence and rest from
time to time to serve in the nature of nourishment and renewal
of its powers. It is also essential to take walks in the open
country; a free and abundant air gives the spirit a new tone.
Sometimes a ride, a journey, a change of scene, a banquet and
a somewhat great indulgence in drink will give us renewed
vigor; . . . for wine drowns cares, lifts the soul out of its depression, and is a cure for sadness as well as for certain ills of
the body. Liber, who is Bacchus, has been called the inventor
of wine, not owing to the freedom of speech he imparts, but because he frees the mind from the servitude to care and makes
it more daring in all its efforts. . . . It is generally believed
that Solon, one of the seven wise men, and the philosopher
Arcesilaus were fond of wine. Cato has been charged with
drunkenness. He who casts this reproach will find it easier to
prove the vice of drunkenness honorable than to prove Cato
base. But moderation in both liberty and wine is beneficial; we

must not repeat the remedy too often, lest the mind acquire a bad habit. And yet there are times when the mind should be aroused to a state of exultation and freedom and permitted to throw off for a season its gravity and sobriety. For if we are to believe a Greek poet, 'It is sometimes pleasant even to lose one's reason,' or Plato, 'In vain has a man in his senses knocked at the door of the Muses,' or Aristotle, 'There has never been a great genius without a strain of madness.' The mind unless stirred cannot utter anything sublime, surpassing the speech of others. It is only when it has spurned all that is common and ordinary and has mounted aloft with divine inspiration that it has uttered something too sublime for human lips. The mind cannot reach the realms of the sublime while it remains sane. It must leave the beaten track, dash forth, take the bit in its teeth, and carry its rider where he would have feared to mount himself."*

Seneca† ends his discourse at this point, maintaining that he strengthened the vigor of his mind by proper relaxation at times, and that he would make greater efforts than if he devoted himself constantly to spiritual and mental activities. The prophet Elijah bade the lute be brought, in order that his soul, stirred by the delight of physical harmony, might be caught up to contemplate divine things.

* *De Tranquillitate Animi,* XVII.

† Bridges has the following note: "The foregoing extracts from Seneca contain many variations from the text now usually adopted. Some of these are evidently due to Bacon himself, occurring naturally as the result of condensation. Some may be due to the imperfection of the text used by him. Other errors are doubtless due to the incompetence of Bacon's transcribers. Some of the more obvious mistakes have been corrected. But no attempt has been made to elevate this series of extracts to the standard of a critical edition."

FOURTH PART OF MORAL PHILOSOPHY

CHAPTER I

I HAVE dwelt upon this third part of Moral Philosophy at greater length than I was required to do, owing to the beauty and helpfulness of moral sentiments, and because the books are rare ones from which I have gathered these roots, as it were, flowers, and fruits of morals. I now wish to take up the fourth part of this science, which although not so rich and abounding in material as the third part, is, however, more wonderful and more exalted than not only this third part, but also than all the other divisions of the subject, since it consists of a plea for belief in the religion which the human race should accept, for loyalty to it, and for confirmation of it by our deeds. There is nothing else within the range of philosophy more necessary for man or of such great utility and worth. For because of this part of the subject is it especially true that all the other sciences are subordinate to Moral Philosophy. For all wisdom is constituted with a view to the discovery of salvation for the human race; and this salvation consists in the perception of those things that guide man to the felicity of the other life. Avicenna says that this felicity is such as eye hath not seen nor ear heard, as I stated above. And since this fourth part of philosophy has as its object the investigation of this salvation and the attracting of mankind to it, all the sciences, arts, and activities are attached to this most noble part of civil science; and this is the end of all human consideration.

For this reason it is most profitable to consider the purpose of this part of the subject; and it is fitting that every Christian should do so for the confirmation of his own profession, and to the end that he may have the means of correcting those in error. Verily, God can never deny to the human race a knowledge of the way of salvation, since he wishes that all men should be saved, according to the Apostle. And his goodness is infinite, wherefore he has always left men the means by which they might be enlightened to gain a knowledge of the ways of truth. Aristotle in his Politics takes up the different kinds of sects, and says that he wishes to consider out of the sects and laws of states four or five of the simple ones, and see which laws corrupt states and kingdoms and which do not. He says also that the four or five simple ones are corrupt sects, meaning that a sect or law is called simple because it has only one end in view, and is called complex when the end in view is complex, since every sect varies according to the end it has in view, as Alpharabius teaches us in his book On the Sciences, expounding the view of Aristotle regarding the sects. According to Alpharabius, and still more clearly according to Boetius in the third book of the Consolation of Philosophy, these simple aims are pleasure, riches, honor, power, fame, or glory of name.

I shall now state the principal nations in which the various sects are found that are now existing throughout the world, namely, Saracens, Tartars, Pagans, Idolaters [Buddhists], Jews, Christians. For the principal sects do not exceed this number nor can they do so until the sect of Antichrist appears. There are, moreover, sects formed from all of these, or from four, three, or two of them, according to various combinations.

But besides these aims there is another, namely, the felicity of the other life, which is sought and striven after in different ways. Because some believe that it consists in the delights of the body, some in the delights of the soul, and still others in the delights of both. In addition there are sects that include this felicity and all the others aims, or at least many of them, and that too in various ways. For although they all have in view a future felicity, yet many men abandon themselves to pleasures, and others are eager for riches, and certain aspire after honors, while others desire sovereign power, and still others crave glory and fame. I shall touch first upon the three divisions of the sects, that the end in view may be made clear. Then I shall deal with the choice of the sect of the faithful, which is the only one that should be spread throughout the world.

Some desire to confine those aims to the present life, without considering that they are losing future felicity, abusing temporal blessing, and yielding themselves up to the allurements of pleasures, as, for example, the Saracens, who, in accordance with their law, take as many wives as they wish.

Some are inflamed with the lust for dominion, as the Tartars, whose emperor says that there should be only one ruler on earth just as there is only one God in heaven, and that he himself ought to be constituted that ruler, as we see in the letter he sent to the Lord Louis, King of France, in which he demands tribute from him. This is recorded in the book of Friar William on the Manners of the Tartars, which he wrote to the King of France just mentioned. From their actions it is clear in what way they have already gained possession of the kingdoms of the East. They care nothing about the refinements of life but are quite barbarous in this respect. They use the milk of mares for drink, and make a practice of eating unclean foods, as we learn from the book just mentioned and from that of Friar John on the Life of the Tartars, and also from the Cosmography of the philosopher Ethicus. For that philosopher and those books on the manners of the Tartars describe this very foul and wicked race, as we stated in the section on Mathematics describing the races and localities of this world.

Real Pagans, like the Praceni and the nations bordering on them, live according to custom and not according to laws based on reason. Their interests are centered in the delights, riches, and honor of this life, and they believe that the life to come is similar in every way to this. Hence at death they have themselves burned publicly, together with their precious stones, gold, silver, equipment, family, friends, and all their wealth and goods, hoping to enjoy all these things after death.

Similarly the Idolaters expect to possess a future in the enjoyment of all the blessings they had in this world. Their priests, however, take a vow of chastity, and rejoice in abstinence from the delights of luxury, as we learned in regard to the regions of the East lying toward the north in the section of this work dealing with the localities of the world. All these expect corporeal blessings in the life to come, and have no discernment regarding spiritual blessings. It is not contrary to their laws to seek for this world's goods in any way possible, nor do they believe that in any event are they deprived of the life to come.

But the Jews hoped for blessings both temporal and eternal; in a different way, however, since with spiritual discernment by virtue of their law they aspired after blessings not only of the body, but also of the soul. But interpreting their law in its literal sense they believed the blessings of the law only corporeal. Similarly according to their law they seek temporal possessions not as a matter of right and wrong, but on the authority of God and in accordance with his laws. For although they plundered many nations and subjugated them, they had a just right to do this. For the Promised Land was due them by hereditary right, because they were descended from a son of Noah; and the sons of Cham invaded those lands without any right, since they did not fall to their lot at the beginning. For Egypt, Africa, and Ethiopia were given to the sons of Cham, as we learn from Scripture, the sacred writers, and the histories. We have touched upon this topic also in a previous section.

The Christians, securing spiritual blessings by spiritual means, according to their law are able to have temporal blessings, owing to their human frailty, in order that they may practice the things of the spirit in this life, to the end that they may at length reach the life eternal both in body and in spirit. And yet in that life they will live without the extrinsic things men employ in this present life. For the animal body will become spiritual, and the whole man will be glorified, and will live with God and the angels.

These then are the principal sects. The first is that of the Pagans, who have less knowledge about God and are without a priesthood, but each man fashions a god to his own liking and worships whatever he pleases and sacrifices at will. Then come the Idolaters, who have priests and synagogues and huge bells like those of the Christians, with which they are summoned to their office and to certain prayers and regular sacrifices; and they maintain that there are many gods, but that no one of them is omnipotent. The Tartars are third, who adore and worship one God as omnipotent. But they nevertheless venerate fire and the threshold of the home. For they cause all things to pass through fire; for this reason they cause the effects of the dead and gifts and messengers to pass through flames and other things, that they may be purified. For their law declares that all things are purified by fire. Moreover, he who treads on the threshold of the house is condemned to death. Both in these two matters and in certain others they are quite barbarous. In the fourth class are the Jews, who should have had a better knowledge of God in accordance with their law, and should have truly desired the Messiah, who is Christ. And those have actually done so who knew the law spiritually, as the holy Patriarchs and Prophets. In the fifth place are the Christians, who accept the law of the Jews spiritually and complete it by adding the faith of Christ. Last of all will come the law of Antichrist, who shall subvert the other laws for a time, except that the elect in the Christian faith shall remain firm, although with difficulty, owing to the fury of the persecution. There are, then, six laws according to this division, and six according to the former one, each with its special aim, pleasure, wealth, honor, power, fame, and felicity of the life to come apart from these temporal blessings.

In the relationship of Mathematics to the Church discussed in a preceding section the sects were considered with reference to planetary influences and were found to be six, namely, the law of Saturn, the law of Mars, the law of the Sun, the law of Venus, the law of Mercury, the law of the Moon. In whatever way, then, we may distinguish the sects, we shall find that they are always six in number. For the first and principal distinction is this one in regard to the planets; upon that the other distinctions follow, since the celestial influence inclines a man to receive the laws, either as a controlling influence, or as an important one, or as one that renders the reception easier. For although the rational soul is not forced to anything, yet, as we proved above, a man's habit of thought is much altered with regard to the sciences, morals, and laws. By these changes the soul is stimulated as far as the action of the body is concerned, and is influenced to acts both public and private, with complete freedom of the will, however, in all matters. And hence it comes to pass that, in accordance with the conjunctions of Jupiter with the other planets, six changes appear in the laws and habits in men's hearts, as we noted above. There cannot be more than the six sects; and at times the followers of one sect incline to another, owing to the strong influence of the constellation, and sometimes they change their own sect entirely, or in great part, or modify it with the tenets of another sect in accordance with the occurrence of the several constellations. It is in this way that sects become composed of the parts of several others. For the Saracens, although they follow in the main the law of Venus, yet derive much from the Jewish law and from the Christian law, since they employ various baptisms and sacrifices quite similar in part. They say, moreover, that Christ is the Son of the Virgin and the greatest of the prophets, and they retain many words of the Evangelists in their law, and they all wish to die the death of Christians. They made this declaration in the disputation they held with Christians and Idolaters in the presence of the great emperor of the Tartars, as we learn in the book on the Manners of the Tartars. But the Tartars profess chiefly the law of Mars. For they venerate fire, are eager for war, and devote their leisure to the principles of philosophy, like the ancient Chaldeans, to whom the law of Mars is attributed. They, however, are modified by the law of Mercury. For they permit their sons to be instructed in the Gospel and in the lives of the Fathers. When they become sick they ask for Christian priests and the cross and holy water, as we learn in the book of Friar William, and as the experience of men worthy of our belief renders us certain in this matter. The law of the Jews is that of Saturn; and the law of the Christians is called that of Mercury by the astronomers for certain reasons noted above. The sects of the Pagans and Idolaters are reduced to the sect of Mars and that of the Egyptians, a sect worshiping the sun, which is the leader of the heavenly host. For these two sects worship the creature instead of the creator, since the Idolaters worship images made by hand and the heavenly bodies. And therefore in as far as they worship the celestial natures they agree with the Egyptians. In as far as they worship these objects here below they are in accord with the law of Mars. But the Pagans worship both terrestrial and celestial things. For whatever they meet with of a useful character, as the sun, moon, an animal, a grove, water, fire, or anything else they worship from affection. But whatever they find terrible they worship from fear.

After the statement of these principal sects as regards the following they have among the nations, the influence of the planets upon them, and the diversity of their aims, the consideration follows of the necessary means to be employed in persuading men of the truth of a sect. I said above, in the section on Mathematics, in regard to the conversion of unbelievers, that persuasion of the truth as alone contained in the Christian religion is a twofold matter, since we may appeal to miracles which are beyond us and beyond unbelievers, a method in regard to which no man can presume; or we may employ a method familiar to them and to us, which lies within our power and which they cannot deny, because the approach is along the paths of human reason and along those of philosophy. Philosophy belongs in an especial sense to unbelievers, since we have derived all of our philosophy from them, and not without the most weighty reason, to the end that we may have on our own behalf a confirmation of our faith, and that we may be able to speak convincingly on behalf of the salvation of unbelievers. Nor should the statement of Gregory be urged as an objection that faith has no place where reason furnishes the proof. For this statement is to be understood of the Christian who relies only or mainly on human reason. But this should not be: nay, we must put our faith chiefly in Church and Scripture and the Sacred Writers and Catholic doctors.

But as a solace for human frailty, to the end that it may avoid the attacks of error, it is useful for the Christian to have effective reasons for those things which he believes, and he should have a reason for his faith for every case requiring it, as the blessed Peter in his first Epistle teaches us, saying, "But sanctify in your hearts Christ as Lord; and be ready always to give an answer to every man that asketh you a reason of the faith and hope that are in you." But we are not able to argue in this matter by quoting our law nor the authorities of the Sacred Writers, because unbelievers deny Christ the Lord and his law and the Sacred Writers. Wherefore we must seek for reasons in another way which is common to us and to unbelievers, namely, philosophy. But the power of philosophy in this particular is in perfect accord with the divine wisdom, nay, is a vestige of the divine wisdom given by God to man, that by this vestige man might be stimulated to comprehend divine truths. Nor do these things belong exclusively to philosophy, but are common to theology and philosophy, to believers and unbelievers, given by God and revealed to philosophers, to the end that the human race might be prepared for particular divine truths. And the reasons of which I speak are not alien to the faith or outside of its principles, but are drawn from its roots, as will appear from what is to be said.

I might indeed be able to present these methods in a simple

and crude manner within the grasp of the unlettered multitude
of unbelievers, but this is not expedient. For the multitude is
too imperfect, and for this reason a plea for the faith that is
within its grasp is crude, undigested, and unworthy of the
learned. I wish, therefore, to proceed on higher ground and to
present a plea concerning which the learned can judge. For in
every nation there are some active individuals who are fitted to
receive wisdom who can be persuaded by force of reason; so
that when these men become enlightened, the persuasion
through them of the multitude is much easier.

I assume in the first place that there are three kinds of knowledge; one comes from study of our own devising along the
pathway of experience. The second is that which is learned
from others. The third precedes these and is the pathway to
them, and is called natural knowledge, being so named because
common to all. For that is natural which is shared by all members of the same species, as, for example, burning is natural
to fire, as Aristotle explains in the fifth book of the Ethics; and
Cicero makes this same statement in the first book of the Tusculan Disputations, and we see it exemplified in numberless
ways. For we say the cries of animals have a natural signification because they are common to the individuals of their
species; and things of this kind are naturally known by us in
which we all agree, as, for example, that every whole is greater
than its part, and the like, both simple and complex. For we
know that the rational soul is formed to learn the truth and to
love it, and the proof of this love is shown in our deeds, according to Gregory and all the sacred writers and philosophers.
Certain, however, think that there are two distinct divisions in
the rational soul, or two faculties; that by one of these the soul
learns the truth, and by the other desires to hear the truth when
learned. But certain believe that there is one substance of the
soul that performs both functions, because these acts are related to each other, since the knowledge of the truth is owing
to the love of it; for it is one and the same faculty. According
to these thinkers the mind first perceives truth, and then loves
it when known and carries it into practice. Hence Aristotle
maintains in the third book on the Soul* that the speculative
intellect through the extension of truth to the love of it becomes

* *De Anima,* III, 7.

the active intellect. Nor does he ever make a specific difference between the speculative and the active intellects, as he does between the intellect and the sense and the vegetative soul. For he proves in the second book on the Soul that these three are different in species, because their actions are different in species, namely, intelligence, feeling, and growth; nor are they related to one another. But the knowledge of the truth is related to the love of it and is because of it; and for this reason there is one faculty, or nature, or substance of the rational soul that learns the truth and loves it. Hence in the third book on the Soul Aristotle thus begins: "Concerning the part of the soul with which it learns and understands I must now speak;"* maintaining that it is the same part that has both functions; just as it is in the sensitive soul; because it is the same faculty that perceives and desires, as is evident in every sense. For touch perceives warmth and seeks for it, and so taste with savor, and the same is true of the other senses.

But as regards these matters it is not of great moment how we define the faculty. For we know that the rational soul is formed to learn the truth and to love it. But the truth of a religion is perceived only so far as the knowledge of God abounds in the individual, because every religion is referred to God; and therefore he who wishes to arrive at a definite knowledge of a religion must begin with God. But the knowledge of God, so far as the question of his existence is concerned, is known to all naturally, as Cicero shows in his book on the Immortality of the Soul. And he proves it with this statement,† "No nation is so savage and barbarous as not to have some conception of God, nor is there any nation without some form of divine worship." But should Avicenna say in the first book of the Metaphysics‡ that this science seeks to prove the existence of God, we must reply that this is true as regards full certitude. For the natural knowledge possessed by the individual in regard to God is feeble, and is weakened by sins which are numerous in every one. For sin darkens the soul, and especially is this true with regard to divine things.

Therefore this knowledge needs the support of argument and

* *Ibid.*, III, 4.
† *De Natura Deorum*, I, 16, 23.
‡ *Metaphysics*, I, 1.

faith. But the knowledge of God's unity and of his other attributes is not known by nature. For in these particulars men were never in agreement, some maintaining that there are many gods, others believing that the stars are gods, and still others that things here below are deities, as, for example, the pagans and the idolaters. And therefore they must err in their religion. All others who say that there is only one God do not understand other truths regarding him. And therefore the advocate of a religion in the first place must know how to answer the questions that are asked about God in general. He must not, however, enter into a discussion of all the particular truths at once, but should proceed gradually and begin with the easier topics in this way. For as the geometer gives his definitions in order, that the symbols and terms he employs may be known, so should we proceed in religious instruction; for unless we know the meaning of the terms used, we shall arrive at no proof.

God, then, is the first cause antecedent to which there is no other, a cause that did not emerge into being nor will it be possible for it to cease to be, of infinite power, wisdom, and goodness: the Creator of everything and the director of every man according to the susceptibility of individuals to such guidance. And in this definition Tartars, Saracens, Jews, and Christians agree. The learned also among the Idolaters and Pagans cannot contradict when the reason for this has been grasped, nor can the multitude as a consequence whom the learned direct as rulers and guides. For there will be a double method of proof on this point: one is the consent of all other nations and religions and of the rest of the human race. But the minority must conform itself to the majority; and the part is disgraced that is not in accord with the whole. It is generally agreed that the wiser men are found among the other sects, and the Pagans and Idolaters are not ignorant of this fact. For when we meet them they are easily convinced and clearly perceive their own ignorance; as was shown by the emperor of the Tartars, who summoned before him Christians, Saracens, and Idolaters to confer on the truth of their religions; and forthwith the Idolaters were confounded and convinced. This fact is stated in the book on the Manners of the Tartars addressed to the present Lord King of France. And when Christians confer with Pagans, like the Praceni and the other adjoining nations, the latter are easily convinced and perceive that they are in error. The proof of this is found in the fact that they would become Christians very gladly if the Church were willing to permit them to retain their liberty and enjoy their possessions in peace. But the Christian princes who labor for their conversion, and especially the brothers of the Teutonic order, desire to reduce them to slavery, as the Dominicans and Franciscans and other good men throughout all Germany and Poland are aware. For this reason they offer opposition: hence they are resisting oppression, not the arguments of a superior religion.

Then the advocate of the religion of the faithful has on the part of Metaphysics and this Moral Science another method of procedure in giving his proofs, which I merely wish to hint at, until the treatise is finished which your Highness has requested. And in fact we can present to the assiduous man who is amenable to the force of reason the following as an acceptable proposition. Causes do not go back endlessly, since they cannot be infinite in number nor can they be so conceived of. For all things that exist and that are perceived are included within some number, as Aristotle says in the third book of the Physics. There is not therefore a cause preceding a cause endlessly. Therefore we must stop at some first cause, which does not have a cause antecedent to it, and the whole number is reduced to a single one. And in every class one must be first to which all the rest are reduced. But if this should be the first cause without any other cause antecedent to it, it is evident that it did not come forth in being through some cause; nor is anything else the cause of its being, nor does it cause itself to exist after non-existence, since in that case, while it was non-existent, it would have existence, so as to cause itself to be. For everything that causes something else to be after non-existence, has being while it is performing this act; therefore nothing is the cause of its own being. Wherefore this first cause never had non-existence, and therefore has always existed. But if this is granted, then it will always exist, since there are many things that will always exist, and yet have not always existed, as angels, souls, the heavens, earth, and the like; and for this reason that which never had non-existence will far more easily preserve its existence eternally. Moreover, that which never had non-existence is infinitely removed from non-existence, and therefore it is impossible that it should pass into non-existence. For some things that have come forth into being can cease to exist, because they are not infinitely removed from non-existence. For at one time they did not exist: therefore since non-existence is infinitely removed from that which has always existed, there is no comparative relationship between them. And therefore such a thing will not be able to cease to be; and this statement is more readily accepted than any of the other statements here made, and for this reason is rather a matter of perception than one in need of proof.

But it is evident that the thing that has always existed and shall exist is of infinite power. Because if it is of finite power, then is its power imperfect, since in every finite thing something can be added, and every imperfect thing is naturally subject to change; but it is not possible to assume some change unless a first one be assumed. For what is first naturally precedes what comes after. And therefore since the first change is in regard to existence and non-existence, this change must be possible in that which has finite power. But this change does not happen in that which has always been and always shall be: wherefore there is no limit to its power.

Likewise Philosophy argues in the third book on Consolation* in this fashion. In every class where the imperfect is found it is natural that the perfect be found. And therefore in the genus of power we must find a perfect power, since we find an imperfect one. But that is perfect from which nothing is lacking nor can something be added, according to Aristotle in the third book of the Physics and the fifth of the Metaphysics. And that to which nothing can be added is infinite; because to everything finite in so much as it is such, an addition can be made, and something else can be understood beyond it. Therefore perfect power must be infinite. But in things apart from this cause which we are seeking there is not a power that is perfect and infinite, therefore in this cause there will be such power. But if its power is infinite, then is its essence infinite, since power does not exceed essence. For essence is either equal to power or greater. Already the proofs on this point have been stated in the discussion of matter. It is manifest, therefore, that the essence of the first cause is infinite.

* *Consol. Philosophiae,* Bk. III, Prosa X.

And surely if its essence and power are infinite, its goodness must be infinite, since a thing whose essence is finite has finite goodness. Therefore infinite essence will have infinite goodness; and otherwise there is no comparative relation of goodness to essence in this cause; which cannot be in so great a majesty. And if its goodness were finite, it would be imperfect, and something could be added to it, and it could be lessened, and it could thus be subject to change; and for this reason it is natural for it to have non-existence, just as we proved above with regard to power. But that which has infinite majesty in essence and power and goodness cannot possibly lack knowledge, since a thing which is of such a nature has usefulness, nor can it be referred to the infinite majesty like the elements and stones and vegetation.

Then we see that things lacking infinite power, as animals and men and angels, have knowledge, owing to the nobility of their nature: therefore since the nature of the cause now sought for is infinitely nobler than anything of this kind, it will have the power of knowledge. But since all the other things that are in it are found to be infinite, this cause has infinite wisdom. Moreover, if it were finite it would be imperfect and subject naturally to increase and diminution, as we see in the case of other intelligent beings, and as is true in all imperfection. And therefore the first change which is with regard to existence and non-existence could be found here, as we argued above. Therefore the wisdom in this cause must be infinite; but if its power is infinite it can create this world, and its infinite wisdom knows how to make the best possible arrangement in regard to it, because it is characteristic of the best to do the best, and to communicate its goodness to others, as far as it is possible for them to receive it. Therefore this cause has necessarily produced the world.

Unless an objector might say that the world never came forth into being, and did not have a non-existence. But in that case it would be of infinite power, just like this cause, and therefore would be equal to it and would be God, a conclusion that no one deems worthy of a hearing, and which no religion maintains. For if the world has always been, and never had non-existence before existence, then it did not come forth into existence after non-existence. Nor at the same time did it have existence and non-existence, because contradictories are not true either at the same time or by nature. Therefore the world was brought into being, but by no agency except this first cause. Unless you say that there are more causes than one of this kind, which cannot be true, since no one of them would be of infinite power. Because if one is of infinite power it can do whatever it wishes, and therefore can act contrary to the will of another; therefore this other is not of infinite power since its will can be thwarted. And at any rate in one world there will be one God. For one God suffices for one world. And Aristotle in the eighth book of the Physics says that it is better to assume that there is one than more, since one suffices; but more worlds cannot coexist, as we showed in the chapter on Unity of the World. It is manifest, therefore, that there is only one God. Likewise if there were more worlds, one God would still suffice, because he is of infinite power, therefore he would be able to produce and rule all those worlds, since all of them, no matter how many in number, would not make something infinite.

But Aristotle* in the eighth book of the Physics and in the eleventh of the Metaphysics concludes that there is one prime motor, or one first cause, since there is one prime motion, namely, the daily one, and one world. And that there cannot be more worlds he himself proves in the first book of the Heavens and the World,† because the earth of this world would be similar in nature and species to the earth of another world. But things of the same nature have a natural motion to the same place, just as all heavy bodies naturally tend to move to the same point below. Therefore the earth of another world would tend to move to the same place to which the earth of this world naturally moves, since it is of the same specific nature. But the earth of another world could not move to the center of this world unless it passed through the circumference of the other world so as to penetrate it and at length fall to the center of this world. Since therefore this is impossible, it is not possible that there should be two earths or two worlds. There is therefore one God, who is the first cause of all causes, who has always existed and always will exist, possessing infinite majesty, power, wisdom, and goodness, the Creator and Ruler of all

* *Nat. Auscult.,* Bk. VIII.
† *De Coelo,* I, 8, 9.

things. Nor can there be more than the one God blessed for ever and ever, Amen.

After the Christian advocate has sufficiently verified this fundamental principle of religion, he should then argue further that man is bound to do God's will and to serve him with all reverence. For his majesty is infinite, as we have shown. Therefore boundless reverence is due him. But the blessing of creation is a boundless one in this, that it cannot be brought to pass except by infinite power. For no finite power is able to create, because there is an infinite distance between non-existence and existence. Therefore the transition from non-existence to existence must be through the infinite power of an agent. Wherefore the creature owes the Creator boundless reverence. Hence Avicenna says in the Elements of Morals that it is God's right that we should obey his precepts. For the creature must obey the commands of its Creator.

But a third reason is found in the infinite felicity he will bestow on those who obey him and the endless punishment he will inflict on those who are disobedient to him. Hence Avicenna expresses these reasons why we must serve God in the statement that he has prepared a promised felicity which eye has not seen nor ear heard for those who obey him, and for those who are disobedient he has prepared a terrible future punishment. This is also made apparent by Metaphysics and the first part of this Moral Science. For the soul is immortal, as Aristotle, Avicenna, and all the noble philosophers say; and Cicero has composed a book on this immortality. Seneca, moreover, avows this truth everywhere, and all sects aspire to this other life. Even the simple Pagans believe that they will live after death in body and soul, as I explained before; and therefore they hold that there is a resurrection of the dead. Hence the Saracens hold this belief also. But they have in mind only the physical enjoyments of this present life. For Avicenna says in the Elements of Morals that Mahomet offered only a glorification of our bodies, not of our souls, except in so far as the soul shares in the enjoyment of the body. The Jews also hold that there is a resurrection, and the Christians as well. And if the first and the last, that is, Pagans and Christians, agree in this belief, all the intermediate sects must necessarily believe in it; and for this reason the Idolaters like the others must avow it.

And the philosophers in particular teach this tenet, as I showed above in the first part of this Moral Science.

But it cannot be that a man pleasing to God in this life will have after the resurrection a life such as we have now, because this life is full of all miseries, and is not in accordance with the goodness of human nature. And therefore when the resurrection shall grant us an immortal state, we must of necessity be free from these miseries. Nor shall those who serve God meet with any misery, because it is just that they be given a reward according to the bounty of the divine goodness. And in the second place, the good as a rule have more misfortunes here than the evil. Therefore if God is a just judge he does not assign in this present life his rewards to the good, nor consequently will they be similar in the other life to the blessings in this. Therefore of necessity the just must be free from all misery; and since that state is perfect, there must be a glory of both body and soul. But the desire of the rational soul transcends all finite good. And therefore its desire cannot be satisfied except by an infinite good, and this is God; and therefore our human glory will participate in the goodness of the Deity; and from this the noblest corollary of philosophy follows, found in the third book of the Consolations,* namely, that by participation in the Deity men will become gods, although God is one by nature.

Similarly since the evil here offend the divine Goodness, which is infinite, and fall into the crime of treason against God, their punishment of necessity in the other life must be inexpressible and of infinite duration. Since these are the facts, a man should desire to please God by doing his will, to the end that he may so serve God that he shall escape intolerable punishment, and obtain infinite beatitude.

But if it behooves a man to do the will of God for the reasons given, namely, the dignity of an infinite majesty, and because of the benefit of creation into the existence of nature and of preservation therein, and because of the retribution to come, he should learn the divine will, and the things that belong to God, and the state of future felicity and misery. But man cannot of himself know these things, as is evident because of the errors and heresies and differences, nay, the contradictions of the principal sects, and not only of these, but because of the

* _Consol. Philosophiae,_ Bk. III, Prosa X.

articles of the same principal sect. For among Christians we
see so many differences: since some are heretics, some schis-
matics, some true Christians. The difference among heretics
has no limits. Similarly among the Jews; for some were Phari-
sees, some Sadducees, and others differing from both, as the
Gospels teach us, and Josephus makes clear in his books of
Antiquities. Similarly the Saracens, for Avicenna and other
philosophers contradict the rank and file and the priests. For
they show that not only does glory belong to our bodies, but
also, and in greater measure, to our souls; and they decide that
that sect will soon be destroyed. So too the Idolaters have different sects. For those called Ingures, whose literature is possessed by the Tartars, hold that there is but one God, a belief
not shared by many other Idolaters, as we learn in the book on
the Manners of the Tartars. But the Tartars likewise are in
serious disagreement. For some of them lean to the Christian
rite, some to that of the Saracens, and others to that of the
Idolaters, although they are members of the same principal
sect. Among the Pagans there are still greater diversity and
error, because the individual fashions a god according to his
liking and worships what is pleasing to him.

But the power of knowledge in man does not suffice for the
material things of this world and objects of sense, as is obvious
to all. For no man knows with certainty and sufficiency the nature of the smallest thing, as, for example, a small plant, or
fly, or anything else. And we see the utmost disagreement on
the part of the learned in regard to the natures of material
things. Much more then will man err in regard to things im-
material, as spiritual substances, and the state of the other life,
and especially as regards those things which pertain to God and
to God's will. Wherefore man must have revelation.

This is in accordance with Aristotle's statement in the second book of the Metaphysics, that the human intellect is so related to the most manifest things of this kind in its own nature
as the eye of the bat and of the owl to the light of the sun. And
Avicenna says in the first book of the Metaphysics that man's
relation to those things that belong to the Lord of the ages in
his kingdom is like that of a man deaf from his birth to the
delight of musical harmony or of a paralytic to the delights of
food. Wherefore man will not be able to attain certainty in

these matters to a greater degree than the bat, owl, deaf man, or paralytic in the subjects mentioned. Moreover, Alpharabius says on this topic in his Morals that the untaught child bears the same relation to the man most learned in human wisdom as such a learned man to the divine verities: and therefore he will not be able to advance except through instruction and revelation. And he adds that if man could attain to the verities of sacred religion the world would not require revelation and prophecy. But both these, as he says, have been granted to the world and are necessary. Therefore man cannot unaided know verities of this kind. Avicenna makes this clear in his Elements of Moral Philosophy in his statement that religion requires a revelation from God; and that mortal man cannot pass to these immortal things. This accords with Seneca's statement in his book on Peace of Mind, that man is too mortal for immortal things.

Then, as man cannot unaided attain to these things, so should he not presume of himself to decide on these questions without revelation and instruction, for two reasons. One reason is found in the fact that those things that pertain to the other world, and in particular the will of God and matters pertaining to God, are of infinite greatness. Therefore they transcend our wretched humanity; nor is man worthy to try to discover and understand these matters of his own powers; wherefore it suffices for him to believe the one instructing him. Nor is he also worthy to believe those verities because of his sins and his wretched state. Let him rejoice, then, that he is taught by another, but not unless he be taught by God or by angels on God's authority. For it is obvious, therefore, that man should not attempt to inquire regarding these divine verities before he is taught and believes. Moreover, God himself has infinitely better and more certain knowledge of all that concerns him than the creature can have. The authority and wisdom of God are infinite, with respect to which no human authority has comparison or wisdom, and especially with respect to those things that are divine.

It remains, then, that the authority of God should alone be sought, since his goodness is infinite which wishes to reveal to the human race what is necessary for salvation. And without doubt we clearly see in the sects that all believe that their religions possess a revelation. For this is evident in the case of Christians and Jews. The Saracens also believe that Mahomet had a revelation, and he himself makes such a claim; otherwise he would not have been believed. Moreover, if he did not have a revelation from God, he had one from demons. The Tartars similarly say that God revealed their religion, as we find written in the book mentioned and as we are assured. The Idolaters and Pagans in like manner believe that God reveals all pertaining to religions of this kind: because man would not believe man otherwise in this matter. For every one who establishes a sect ascribes the authority to God that he may gain greater credence.

Since then these sects are so constituted we should be more fully persuaded that revelation should be made to only one perfect lawgiver, and that one perfect law should be given by God. And this is apparent because of divisions and heresies. For if there were more heads, the human race could not be united, since each man strives to defend his own view. Moreover, since there is one God and there is one human race to be regulated in accordance with God's wisdom, of necessity this wisdom must choose unity from the twofold unity just mentioned, or otherwise it would not conform to either one God or one human race. For if there were more gods and more worlds, and, so to speak, more human races, then there could be more than one divine wisdom. But the existence of many gods and many worlds is not possible. Therefore God's wisdom cannot be plural. Moreover, since the perfect religion should show man what he ought to know about God and all that is useful for the individual, another religion will be either superfluous if it treats of the same subjects, or erroneous if it promulgates opposing doctrines. Wherefore there can be only one perfect sect of the faithful, and likewise only one lawgiver who receives this revelation from God; because if there is only one religion, there is also only one lawgiver; and the contrary would also be true. This is also the teaching of Avicenna in the Elements of Morals, and of Alpharabius in the Morals. For, as Avicenna says, there must be one mediator of God and men, and a vicar of God on earth to receive the law from God and to promulgate it. Of this lawgiver Alpharabius says, "When it has been proved that he comes to us by inspiration from God he cannot possibly be false. And when we have established a truth of this kind, his word must remain unquestioned. Nor is further scrutiny of his statements permissible, nor must there be further consideration if we are to put implicit faith in him."

This point settled, we must then inquire who should be proclaimed as lawgiver and which sect should be spread throughout the world. The principal rites are first that of the Pagans, who live according to custom alone, and have no priests, but each man is his own teacher. The second rite is that of the Idolaters, who have a priesthood, agree in certain regulations, and assemble in one place at required hours to celebrate their rites. For they have large bells like those of the Christians, as I stated above. The Idolaters also differ from the Pagans. For the Idolaters worship images, while the Pagans worship natural objects like woods, waters, and the like in endless number. The third rite is that of the Tartars, who pursue eagerly philosophy and the arts of magic. The fourth is that of the Saracens. The fifth is that of the Jews. The sixth is that of the Christians. For there are no more principal sects in this world, nor will there be until the sect of Antichrist appear.

Since the Pagans and the Idolaters maintain that the creature is God and avow that there is a multitude of gods, and since both of these tenets are impossible for the reasons given, it is evident that their rites are erroneous. Hence the Emperor of the Tartars, who is named Mangu Khan, of whom mention was made above in what was said about Places in the World, assembled together Friar William with his Christians, and Saracens and Idolaters, in order that they might dispute in regard to their religions. Both the Christians and the Saracens at once proved the Idolaters in the wrong and the latter ceased to defend their religion, as Friar William states in his book mentioned above, addressed to the Lord Louis, illustrious King of France. And since the foul state of the Pagans and the Idolaters is evident, we shall not consider them further at present.

Although the Tartars worship the one true God, yet they nevertheless incline to idolatry. For they adore fire, believing that all things are purged and expiated through it. Hence they cause their sons and messengers and gifts to pass through fire. Similarly they honor the threshold of the house; for he who steps on the threshold is condemned to death. Hence likewise the Azotii did not step on the threshold of the temple of Dagon, as recorded in the fifth chapter of the first book of Kings. Moreover, they do not have any priests except philosophers who also lean to magic arts and employ the responses of demons, as we learn in the book on their manners and as we know for a fact. Hence they do not pass beyond philosophy either true or magical. But I showed above that philosophy is related to religion. For he who is perfect in the wisdom of philosophy bears the same relation to revealed religion as the untaught child to the aforesaid sage, as I explained above. It is evident, then, that the religion of the Tartars is not that which we are seeking, and the Tartars themselves acknowledge this. For the Emperor of the Tartars mentioned above acknowledges that the religion of the Christians is given by God to man and is the best. Moreover, the Tartars have their sons instructed in the Gospel and in the lives of the Fathers, and they accept holy water and the cross and Christian priests when they are sick and have recourse to them as to a last refuge, as we learn in the book on their manners, and as we ascertain through experience. For the empress wife of that emperor summoned Friar William and Christian priests, along with their holy water and cross, seeking their counsel, when she had become ill. It is an easy matter, therefore, for one who considers the facts to perceive that these religions should be eliminated. But the three others are more rational, namely, the religion of the Jews, of the Saracens, and of the Christians.

But that the Christian religion alone should be preferred we can decide in the following ways: first, from the views of the philosophers noted above in the relationship of mathematics to the Church, and in the first part of the Moral Philosophy. For in that section are presented their noble testimonies regarding the articles of the Christian faith, namely, regarding the blessed Trinity, Christ, and the Blessed Virgin, creation of the world, angels, souls, judgment to come, life eternal, resurrection of the body, punishment in purgatory, punishment in hell, and the like, which are contained in the religion of the Christians.

Philosophy is not, however, in such conformity with the religion of the Jews and with that of the Saracens; nor do the philosophers bear witness in their favor. It is evident then that, since philosophy is the forerunner of religion and disposes men to it, the Christian religion is the only one that should be adhered to. Moreover, the philosophers not only give way to the Christian religion, but they destroy the other two. Since Seneca, in the book which he composed against the religion of the Jews,* shows in many ways that it is most irrational and erroneous, so far as the carnal Jews are bound to the letter alone, according to their belief that it suffices for salvation.

The Saracen philosophers, moreover, find fault with their own law and decide that it will soon come to an end. For Avicenna in the ninth book of his Metaphysics proves Mahomet in error because he has set forth only physical delights and not spiritual ones. Albumazar, also, in the first book of the Conjunctions teaches that that sect will not last for more than 693 years, and already 665 have passed, and he holds that it can cease in less time, as I noted above in the section on Mathematics. And it is evident that the Tartars have destroyed nearly the whole dominion of the Saracens on the north, east, and south as far as Egypt and Africa. Thus it happens that their Caliph, who holds the position of a pope among them, was destroyed thirteen years ago, and Baldach, a city belonging to that Caliph, was captured with a great number of Saracens. But we can see this same thing in another way through the testimony of the Sibyls. For, as shown above, they proclaimed that Christ is God, and made known all the principal articles of the Christian faith. But they do not bear witness to the other religions: nay, they have said that this religion alone possesses salvation.

But there is also another way of considering these matters by reviewing the peculiar characteristics of the lawgiver and of the religions. The religion of the Jews does not in truth end with Moses, but looks forward to a Messiah who is Christ; although the Jews do not expect the Christ who is the head of the Christian Church, but another, who, they imagine, is still to come. Therefore it is evident that their law does not suffice, since they expect a more perfect lawgiver than Moses. But that this is Christ the Lord of the Christian can be proved by their law and by their authorities. For the prophecy of Daniel by a com-

* Quoted by St. Augustine, *De Civitate Dei,* VI, 11.

putation of years evidently extends up to Christ; for he came after that time. Moreover, at the advent of Christ the priesthood of the Jews ceased and also royal power among them, as they themselves cannot deny. But this was fulfilled at the time of Christ. For the kingdom of the Jews passed first to Herod and then to the Roman empire, as the histories of the Jews teach us. This information is contained in the books of Josephus, a Jew who narrated the destruction of the Jews by Titus and Vespasian. But Josephus says in the same work that in his time "Jesus Christ, a most holy man, appeared, if it is right to call him a man, concerning whom all things were fulfilled which our prophets said regarding him, as he himself gloriously bears witness." Likewise he himself says that, when the Lord was crucified, the voice of the heavenly powers was heard to say in Jerusalem, "Let us abandon our abode." Since Josephus is the chief authority on history among Jews, Greeks, and Latins, as all learned men and the sacred writers acknowledge, the fact is established by him that the Messiah promised by the Jewish law is the Lord Jesus Christ whom the Christians worship. We see this clearly from the fourth book of Esdras. For he states that God the Father thus spoke, "For my son Jesus shall be revealed with those that shall rejoice with him and that remain four hundred years: and after four hundred years my son Christ shall die, and the world shall be changed."* But so many years passed from Esdras to Christ. Likewise in the book of the twelve Patriarchs there is teaching of the clearest nature regarding Christ. For each Patriarch gave his tribe definite proof in regard to Christ, and there was corresponding fulfillment.

And if it be said that these books belong to the Apocrypha, that is, of unknown authorship, this fact does not destroy their veracity, since these books are accepted by Greeks, Latins, and Jews. For the blessed Ambrose in his homily on the Gospel of Luke quotes the authority of Esdras. And the Church in its office employs many other passages from that book. For there are many books current among Latins, Hebrews, and Greeks, the authorship of which is uncertain: nay, we Latins are certain of the authorship of only a few books, and in many cases we are in error. For when we think that Avicenna composed the book on the Heavens and the World which is commonly

---

* 2 *Esdras*, VII, 28, 29.

attributed to him, we are in error. And many commentaries are thought to be the work of Averroës, but are to be considered rather those of Alpharabius, as, for example, the commentary on the Physics of Aristotle. And in theology the authors of Ecclesiasticus and of Wisdom are unknown, some regarding them as works of Solomon, others of Philo, while still others believe them the works of some one else. Hence we cannot urge as an objection that a book is of unknown authorship, provided that the book has the sanction of the majority of learned men.

Moreover, if we consider the Jewish religion literally as it is presented, it is abominable, irrational, and intolerable. It is abominable because the slaughter of those rams, calves, bulls, and goats by the priests in the temple is horrible and most unclean; and it is wholly irrational because it contains abuses without end, as is apparent to every one; and it is intolerable because the burden of it is without limit; nor were the Jews able to carry out fully the ceremonials of that law; as the blessed Peter says, "Neither we nor our fathers." And this is evident from the series of Scripture bearing on the law; since owing to the intolerable burdens they turned to idolatry and to strange gods from age to age. And God himself bears witness that ceremonies of this kind did not please him, as we learn from many Psalms, where the Psalmist says, "Sacrifice and oblation thou hast not desired, but mine ears hast thou opened." And in another Psalm, "I shall not accept from your house calves nor he-goats from your flocks." And in the first chapter of Isaiah and elsewhere the same fact is made clear. Hence lest they should become wholly Idolaters, God kept them busy in ceremonies of this kind. In the second place, the law promises only temporal and physical blessings; but the perfect religion promises eternal and spiritual blessings, as is evident from what precedes.

In the same way we may consider the religion of the Saracens and their lawgiver. In fact, Mahomet himself in the Koran, which is the book of his law, says that Christ was born of the Virgin Mary by the influence of the Holy Spirit without a human father, and that he is the greatest prophet of God. Hence Christ takes precedence of Mahomet, and for this reason the law of Christ must take precedence. Since, therefore, there should be only one law in the world, as we have proved, it will be that one which is better and more worthy; and this is the religion of Christ. Moreover, the philosophers of the Saracens find fault with their own religion. But the religion of truth, although it is above philosophy, is not, however, contrary to it, nor is it called in question by philosophy but is approved by it, as I have shown in regard to the religion of Christ in the section on Mathematics and in the first part of the Moral Philosophy. Likewise they point out that this sect will be destroyed and the time for its destruction is made known. But the religion of life eternal will always continue, even up to life eternal, because it leads to eternal life; therefore this religion is not that of Mahomet. Moreover, the lawgiver of this sect was most depraved in his life; for he was a very wicked adulterer, as we find recorded in the Koran. For every beautiful woman he took forcibly from her husband and violated her. But adultery is contrary to every law and religion, for this it is that introduces discord among citizens; and likewise causes false heirs to appear, and therefore destroys the laws of the state.

But if we examine more closely these three sects, we can see more clearly which of them should be preserved. We must assume as a fundamental principle in this consideration that the histories of all nations are to be accepted on an equal footing when we take up the form in which the disputation is to proceed. For if Christians should refuse to accept the histories of the Saracens and of the Jews, they with equal right will reject the histories of the Christians. Let us uphold for the sake of argument the histories of these sects, in order that we may see which sect should prevail in this matter. It is said then in Gospel history that among those born of women none has arisen greater than John the Baptist; but this same John says that he is not worthy to unloose the latchet of the shoe of Jesus Christ: and therefore neither Mahomet nor Moses is worthy, since there is no comparison of them with Christ, nor are their laws comparable with his. Moreover, Alpharabius in his book on Sciences shows the ways in which religions are proved, and he presents two of these as more noteworthy than the others. One test is that there should be a perfect lawgiver to whom prophets preceding and following bear witness. But prophets preceding and following do not bear witness to Moses nor to Mahomet. Therefore Christ alone is the legislator whom we are seeking.

That the earlier prophets bear witness to Christ, he himself testifies, saying in the last chapter of Luke, "As is written in the law of Moses and in the Prophets and in the Psalms concerning me." Also in the second chapter of John, "For Moses wrote of me"; and we have further evidence in the prophecy of Daniel mentioned previously; also in Isaiah who says, "Lo a virgin shall conceive and bring forth a son"; and Mahomet is in accord with Isaiah when he says that Christ is the son of the Virgin. Josephus also testifies that all things were fulfilled in Christ that were said of him by the prophets. But the fact is made apparent not only in this way, but also through the prophets that followed him, namely, the numerous Sacred Writers, who not only gave testimony to Christ, but also testify that the earlier prophets spoke all things concerning him.

But these later holy prophets are to be believed for six reasons. The first and weightiest reason for believing them is their perfect sanctity, since Cicero in the Topics, in which he considers the question of authority, rightly assigns this first and *per se* to virtue; because a good and holy man does not wish to lie. The second condition is an ineffable wisdom by which they have known how to avoid all error. For they have knowledge not only of things present in their sight, but also of things that are absent; and not only of things physical, but also of things spiritual as affecting the consciences of men. Filled with the prophetic spirit these men had knowledge of the present, past, and future, as the histories of the Christians inform us in numberless instances. The third condition was the indescribable power of miracles with which these sacred writers were endowed. But Alpharabius says that men should believe because of miracles. For this is the second method offered by Alpharabius of proving a religion, namely, by means of miracles. The fourth condition found in these sacred writers was their steadfastness even unto death in defense of their doctrine, a quality they would not have exhibited had they not known that there was supreme truth in their teaching. The fifth condition is found in the fact that, while living in different parts of the world, they promulgated the same sentiment, although no one of them received the doctrine from another. Therefore they must have spoken by the inspiration of God, and hence without error. The sixth ground is found in the fact that they were private citizens and laymen, such as Peter and others, and poor, humble, downtrodden men: and yet their view prevailed over their emperors, philosophers, and pontiffs. It is evident, therefore, for these reasons, that those men are worthy of belief. But those men say that the earlier prophets bear witness to Christ: therefore this is true. Moreover, they themselves bear witness to Christ in numberless instances: nay, their whole life, not only their doctrine, was a confirmation of the Christian law. Since, therefore, the earlier and the later prophets in countless numbers have borne witness to Christ, as have also Moses and Mahomet, while lacking such witness themselves, as is evident from the histories of the Jews and the Saracens, Christ must, therefore, be the perfect lawgiver.

This same fact is proved by the second method of Alpharabius in regard to proving religions, namely, by miracles. For although Moses did great wonders in fact, and Mahomet in appearance only and by fraud, yet they are not to be compared with the miracles of Christ. For conceding all their miracles and all the histories, we shall find in the Gospel history of John in the last chapter this statement: "But there are many other things which Jesus did, the which, if they should be written every one, I suppose that even the world itself could not contain the books that should be written;" owing to the number and greatness of the miracles, a statement that cannot be accepted with regard to the histories of Moses and Mahomet. He likewise says, "But that ye may know that the Son of man hath power to forgive sins (he saith to the sick of the palsy), I say unto thee, arise." But to forgive sins and heal the soul is a miracle boundless in its nature, and greater than the performance of an infinite number of physical miracles. And on this fact rests a very strong argument in favor of Christ. For no one can forgive sin unless he be God; therefore Christ was God. Moreover, all histories confess that he is God, and these histories were given to the world by sacred writers whose sixfold qualification was stated above, who could not lie. Therefore the fact stated must be true. The earlier prophets moreover confess that he is God. Hence Isaiah says, "He shall be called Emanuel, that is, God with us." And David says, "Thy seat, O God, is for ever and ever." And there are very many other passages of similar import according to the exposition of the prophecies made by the later Sacred Writers who cannot err. Since then Christ is God, which is not true of Mahomet and Moses according to the testimony of even Jews and Saracens, it is evident that he and he alone is the perfect lawgiver, and that there should be no comparison of Moses and Mahomet or of any one else with him.

Moreover, this same fact is obvious from a comparison of the laws. For all sanctity and perfection of life are taught in the Christian law, and the impurity of sin is not permitted. But with Mahomet many sins are allowed, as is evident in the Koran, and no perfection of life is observed, since they are absorbed in sensual pleasures because of their polygamy. Similarly the Jews above all else were eager for offspring. For the barren woman lay under the curse of the law, and virginity was not commended by them, nor voluntary poverty, nor the submission of one's will to that of another, three things indicative of the utmost perfection. For no one can doubt that virginity is a most pure and holy state, and voluntary poverty is approved by all philosophers, as we learn above quite clearly from the third part of the Moral Philosophy. But to submit oneself entirely to the will of another is the supreme and the most difficult test of all, as every one knows. And therefore since these virtues are taught in the law of Christ, and not in the law of Mahomet nor in that of Moses, it is evident that the law of Christ is altogether superior. Moreover, by the law of Christ we are assured with reference to God and the future life of the good and of the evil, and likewise with reference to the blessed Trinity and other spiritual truths. But these verities are not presented in the law of Moses nor in that of Mahomet, as is evident. Therefore the law of Christ should be preferred to the others. But it is such a law that should be published throughout the world, as we have shown above. Therefore this law must be the Christian law.

Since we have proved that the Christian faith is to be accepted, all its articles must evidently be accepted also. For if the whole is approved, each part of it also must be conceded. Since, however, a certain article seems burdensome to human frailty, for this reason some deny it, others are doubtful in regard to it, still others accept it with difficulty, some look upon it as hard, others imperfectly understand it, a few grasp it easily with full peace and sweetness of mind. I refer to the Sacrament of the Altar, as regards which, according to the Apostle, many are weak and sickly among you and many sleep. Therefore in regard to it I have thought it proper to undertake to show that this sacrament is a most true and certain one, which ought to be most ardently desired and most earnestly sought for, which we should most fervently await, with all reverence worship, with joy and devotion retain, with most certain faith contemplate. If this sacrament did not exist, we should seek to obtain it from God with the utmost diligence, and to purchase it not with corruptible gold and silver but with life and death. If it should exist and be unknown, it should be received as soon as it is offered, nay, it should be snatched from the mouth of him who proffers it, nay, without a teacher it ought to be known and loved above all things, so that he that is faithful should rejoice in knowing and possessing nothing else; since this being known, all things are known that pertain to salvation; this being unknown, all things are unknown; this being possessed, all things are possessed, and he who lacks this is proved to possess nothing. Since, therefore, it is necessary for every one to understand this, although notwithstanding many are ignorant of this sacrament, while others on being converted to the faith are more disturbed by this particular doctrine than by any other, and many Christians, who strive to judge with their human sense in regard to divine things, waver or are imperfect; it is best to consider how both unbelievers and Christians can be most surely convinced in regard to this verity. I shall therefore give the main points of this persuasive reasoning according to the grace given me.

Therefore that this fact is most certain, namely, that the Lord Jesus is present in this sacrament as true God and true man, is shown first by the assent of the whole Christian Church; and since that Chuch has been proved to be the true one, and since this sacrament is one that this Church professes, it is evident that it will contain the truth. Moreover, in addition to the general proofs applicable to the whole religion, this blessed truth possesses its own particular modes of proof just like the whole religion. For this sacrament is clearly taught by holy Scripture in the Gospels and by the Apostle; "Your fathers did eat manna and are dead; he that eateth me liveth because of me; and, I am the living bread which came down from heaven;

if any man eat of this bread, he shall live for ever." And in the sixteenth chapter of the book of Wisdom, "Thou feedest thy people with angel's food"; and below, "For thy substance and the love thou hast for thy sons thou showest." This is the bread on which the angels desire to look, according to the Apostle Peter. And therefore it is not that manna of the ancient people, since that is not the food of angels; when he says, "Thy substance, etc.," we are evidently not to understand this of the ancient manna. And the Apostle who first persecuted the truth of Christ later confesses that he received this sacrifice from the Lord. Moreover, this truth is made manifest not only by Holy Scripture, but by all the Sacred Writers, who bear witness in regard to this article, who could not lie because of the conditions I have enumerated above regarding them. But this is evident by common agreement and definition of all Catholic doctors, masters, and readers in the law of God. For all agree in their testimony that Christ is present in this sacrament.

In the next place, there are an innumerable number of miracles which are found in the Sacred Writers and in the histories. But I shall here record two, which have not yet been chronicled, of undoubted authenticity and subject to no doubt. For a certain devout matron desiring to have offspring had her hopes excited by a heretical bishop, who promised her a son. Summoning a necromancer who knew how to evoke demons, the woman, the bishop, and the necromancer met at a secret place. After the necromancer had gone through all the rites to his satisfaction in the matter of circles and incantations, a demon appeared in the guise of a boy wearing a crown, who asked them what they wanted. Both the necromancer and the bishop asked the woman what she desired. But while she terrified and seized with the fear of God made no reply, the demon retired to a certain wall near by, and taking the crown from his head worshiped and bent the knee. After doing this he returned to them and again asked what they wanted. And when the evil men kept asking the woman, and she did not venture to speak from fear, the devil returned to the place where he had first adored, and bent his head, but did not lay aside his crown nor genuflect. On his return to them they inquired why he had acted as he had on the first and on the second occasion. He replied that a man lay sick in a house beyond the wall, and a priest brought the body of Christ to him; and "I was compelled," said the demon, "to lay aside the crown from my head and worship and genuflect, because it is written, At the name of Jesus every knee should bow of things in heaven, and things in earth, and things under the earth. And when I returned the second time, the priest had given the body of Christ to the sick man, and was carrying the empty vessel, and therefore I did not lay aside my crown nor genuflect, but I merely bent my head and adored out of respect for the priest who carries the body of Christ and for the sacred vessel." Then the heretical bishop became a true Christian, and immediately began to preach the faith of Christ, and to confound heretical evil. Oh, how true a proof and how noble a one this is, adequate praise of which cannot be expressed! Moreover, many are alive who know for a certainty the truth of this miracle.

It came to pass, moreover, that in the Franciscan order there was a brother who for many years was unable to partake of this sacrament, nor would he have stood before the altar with his brothers when they received the sacrament, had any one offered him the whole world; and yet he himself was ignorant of the reason of his own inability to receive the sacrament. And as it pleased God, a certain wise and holy brother said to him that he was either in cruel mortal sin, or that he was not baptized. The man himself, since after careful self-examination he had no consciousness of mortal sin, began to have doubts regarding his baptism. Inquiring of his parents in regard to the manner of his baptism, he learned that he and another boy were presented to the priest at the same time, who baptized the other child and innocently neglected to baptize him. After learning this fact he had himself properly baptized, and afterwards received the Sacrament of the Altar like any other man. From this it is evident that the truth of this sacrament is proved by baptism, and the truth of baptism by this sacrament. And therefore, since the Church holds that baptism must first be performed in order that the rest may follow, it is quite evident by this miracle that what the Church believes in regard to this most noble sacrament is true.

But besides these methods of proof there are reasons of the following nature. For just as the Creator is related to the creature and as far as he is related to the being of nature, so is the

Redeemer related to the redeemed or to those who are in the state of grace, and more abundantly so. For it is more to re-create than to create; but it is in accordance with the law of the Creator's majesty that he be omnipresent to the creature, nor is there any creature that does not share his presence. There-fore it will be in accordance with the power of the infinite Re-creator that he be present to every one who has been re-created and is in the state of grace. But his presence is not granted to us except in this sacrament. Therefore of necessity this sacra-ment must exist.

Likewise the boundless need of the creature requires the presence of the Creator. For the creature otherwise would fail, because it would tend to a state of non-existence, unless it is supported by the presence of majesty; as philosophy and the-ology agree. But so great, nay, greater, is the need of the re-created for the Redeemer; therefore the Re-creator must be in the re-created and be present to him, if he is to remain in the state of re-creation, that is, in the state of grace. For as the state of nature is related to the Creator, so is the state of grace to the Re-creator. And, therefore, just as the creature would fall into a natural state of non-existence without the presence of the Creator, so would the re-created fall into a state opposed to grace unless he be supported by the presence of the Re-deemer.

Moreover, the power of Christ is infinite, since he is God, and his wisdom is infinite, and his goodness likewise. Wherefore if from the infinity of his power he is able to do this, and from the infinity of his wisdom he knows how to do this, therefore from the infinity of his goodness he wishes to do this; because it is characteristic of the best to do what is best. And therefore since he possesses infinite goodness he must do infinite good, and as far as possible this must be received from him. But this good can be received by the re-created, that is, one in the state of grace; therefore it must necessarily happen to him.

And yet again this is evident by a comparison. For any crea-ture in the state of nature receives from the Creator as much as he can receive in his condition: as Cicero says in his book on the Nature of the Gods,* "All parts of the world are so consti-tuted, that they cannot be excelled in their utility, nor can they

* *De Natura Deorum,* II, 34.

be more beautiful in appearance." Therefore similarly whatever is re-created, being in the state of grace, will receive from the goodness of the Re-creator all that it is capable of receiving. But it can receive the blessing of his substance; therefore it will receive this blessing, as the book of Wisdom says, "Thy substance hast thou given them." And therefore every man in the state of grace must receive his Savior as the Church has appointed.

For the rest original sin cannot be removed without offering this sacrifice to God. But mortal sins are multiplied daily. Therefore it is necessary that this sacrifice make satisfaction to God the Father for the sins of the world. Likewise God assumed this humanity so as to permit his blood to be shed by dying for us, and thus he redeemed us. But this is more than feeding us with this flesh and this blood. Therefore if he has wished of his goodness to do what is more, much rather will he wish to do what is less, since it is useful, convenient, and necessary for us.

These arguments and the like can give conclusive proof that this sacrament is true, so that no one can nor should gainsay it. But mere assent is not the sole requirement; we should accept this truth with the greatest ease, nay, we should accept it more easily, more willingly, more devotedly than any other truth that can be submitted to us in this life; nay, we should so accept it that in this life we may be at peace just as in the sweetness of life eternal; that we should wish for nothing except this; and if we were without it, we should consider that we neither knew nor possessed anything with regard to this glorious truth by which we are deified and taken into life eternal.

As regards the ease with which we may accept it there are several modes of approach. The first method is the consideration of what is contained in this sacrament; the second is the mode of existence; the third is the manner in which it is made available; and there are certain other modes, as I shall note. In this sacrament are contained the culmination of majesty and glory and fullness of salvation and perfection of beauty; truths that are evident since God and Man, glorified and one, are here existent in one person. For God in accordance with his own nature possesses infinite majesty and goodness and beauty, as we see from the topics discussed above. For whatever is in him is infinite. Similarly man, received into the glory, goodness, and the beauty of God, shares the threefold infinitude by reason of the union of an indivisible person. Therefore there is full infinitude of glory, salvation, and beauty in the content of this sacrament.

The same is true in the mode of its existence. For since this Person in his divine and human nature of the same majesty is similarly present here and in heaven, so in every church, and in every one in the state of grace is he received similarly and at the same time. This is a mark of infinite power, because he is not limited to this nor to that, and this attests his infinite majesty. Similarly the fact that Christ as a whole is present in every part of the Host is a mark of infinite power; because he is not limited to a part, nor are his parts divided in the parts of the Host. There is therefore a threefold reason for his majesty in the mode of his existence. Moreover there is a fourth reason for his majesty evident in this sacrament. For his humanity, although in itself it is a creature, yet it there transcends the laws governing the creature, nor has it the mode of existence required of the creature, namely, that it confine itself within the limits of space and physical locality, but it is free in these respects like Deity; and therefore so far as its mode of existence is concerned it is raised to the divine mode of existence, so as to transcend every law of existence that trammels the creature. And this can be effected by the infinite power of God, just as the assumption of humanity into a union of persons was effected by this same power.

In like manner there is in this sacrament the infinitude of our salvation proceeding from the infinite goodness. For in conferring upon us the power at will through our ministry of causing the Savior to be present in a miraculous manner in this sacrament, God concedes more to us than if he granted any one of us the power to make a universe of himself, nay, more than if he granted him the power to make an infinite number of universes. For the advantage of an infinite number of universes to us is nothing in comparison with that of this sacrament. We need not say, therefore, with the Prophet, "If he delay, await him." Nor with that other prophet, "Would that thou wert breaking through the clouds and descending"; because God has placed in our hands the power to cause him to be present among us when we so desire, according to the dispensation of his divine goodness by which we say, "Do this in remembrance of me." For he commanded the clouds, and opened the doors of heaven, and rains upon us the manna of eternal life when we wish to utter five words. Wonderful goodness of God! which, since nothing is easier for us than to form a word, has granted us the power by merely a word to cause the Lord our Savior to be with us at our will. For we are not required to ascend into heaven, to pass over seas, nor to plow nor reap for this bread, nor to plant vineyards nor tread out the wine for this drink, but we are required to utter with ease five words, in order that our God and Lord may be with us, who is blessed for ever more. For this reason it is said in the thirtieth chapter of Deuteronomy, "For this commandment which I command thee this day, it is not hidden from thee, neither is it far off. It is not in heaven, that thou shouldest say, Who shall go up for us to heaven, and bring it unto us, that we may hear it, and do it? Neither is it beyond the sea, that thou shouldest say, Who shall go over the sea for us, and bring it unto us, that we may hear it, and do it? But the word is very nigh unto thee, in thy mouth, and in thy heart, that thou mayest do it." Therefore, in order that we may have eternal life, we need only believe in our heart, and utter a brief sentence compressed into the number of five words. For this number in its distinct comprehension of various things is better than all other numbers, according to Aristotle in his book of Secrets.

Moreover, that this is veiled from our sense is due to our inability to comprehend him. For we would not be able to sustain with our senses the majesty of God, but we should fail completely, owing to our reverence and devotion and wonder; just as the Apostles after the resurrection were not able to endure the sensible presence of the Lord. Even the blessed Dionysius the Areopagite was unable to bear the presence of the Virgin Mary after the ascension of the Lord. Nay, when he crossed from Greece to the Holy Land, that he might see the mother of the Lord, on entering the place where the blessed and glorious Virgin prayed, he fell as though dead, crying out that he should be led forth, freely confessing that no believer ought to look upon the glorious Virgin out of reverence for her. Therefore far less able would any one be to bear the sensible presence of the Lord; and this we prove by experience. For those who exercise themselves diligently in faith and in love of this sacrament are unable to sustain the devotion which springs from pure faith, but give way to a flood of tears and the mind is dissolved wholly in the sweetness of devotion, raised above itself, not knowing where it is or its own condition. Wherefore it would be impossible for a believer to sustain the sensible presence, and therefore God has arranged with the utmost goodness for us that the sensible vision should be veiled from us.

Moreover, we could not sustain it from horror and loathing. For the human heart could not endure to masticate and devour raw and living flesh and to drink fresh blood. And therefore the infinite goodness of God is shown in veiling this sacrament. But its advantage in other respects is very great, so that we may learn to aspire to real blessings. For all our principal blessings and evils are invisible; namely, God, the angels and the saints, eternal life, virtue and grace, demons, purgatory, and hell. And this could not belong to the class of our principal blessings unless it were veiled from our senses, for which reason the Lord says, "Unless I go away, the Comforter will not come to you": to the end that we should know that we should cleave to invisible blessings which do not appear; according to the Apostle, "Those things that exist, that is, are apparent, let us reckon as non-existent, and those things that do not appear let us reckon as existent and as good." It was necessary also for us for our infinite advantage, that this infinite good should be veiled from our senses, and that we should know this means of salvation by the intuition of our mind alone.

In the third place, we gain facility in believing by the use of this sacrament. For if the mode of its existence possesses an infinitude of salvation, majesty, and beauty, much more does the use itself of this sacrament in which we are united to God. Three things are here to be considered. For we are nourished by the glorious body and we are permitted to drink of his glorified blood, nay, we are renewed by the whole Christ, God and Man. But this is eternal life and infinite salvation as far as this mortality can sustain it. For God is not satisfied to feed us sensibly with his creatures and to give us drink, but he cherishes us spiritually with himself and with his flesh and blood. Then from participation in God and Christ we become one with him and one with Christ and are gods, as Philosophy in the third book of the Consolations concludes, because from participation in the Deity many become gods, although he is one by nature. And therefore by participation in Christ we become Christ's. And for this reason the Scripture says, "I have said, ye are gods"; and elsewhere, "Do not touch my Christs." And what more can a man seek in this life?

Here the manuscript breaks off abruptly.

INDEX

Aaron, his vestments, 233.

Abraham, instructed Egyptians, 53, 196.

Accentuation, errors in, 105; connection with music, 259.

Adversity, value of, ii, 712-716.

Aethiopia, 330-332, 337.

Africa, 334-337.

Air, gravity of, 152.

Albategnius, on motions of Mercury, 279.

Albumazar, astronomy taught by Shem, 196; prediction of Antichrist, 208; height of clouds, 252; prophecy of the Virgin, 280; his astrology, 404; on Incarnation, ii, 643; on Antichrist, ii, 644; on Creation, ii, 645.

Alchemy, improvements in, ii, 626.

Alchimus, ii, 655.

Alcuin, praises Augustine's translation of Categories, 30.

Alexander, correspondence with Aristotle, 312, 405, 408; self-mastery, ii, 705.

Alexandria, 333.

Alfraganus, earth relatively small, 201; on beginning of day, 216; diameter of earth, 248; on motions of Mercury, 279.

Algazel, faculties obscured by vice, ii, 671.

Alhazen, referred to in Part V, *passim:* spoken of as auctor perspectivae, ii, 434, 436; color ineffective without light, ii, 473; analysis of visual perception, ii, 497-499; of binocular vision, ii, 511; of double vision, ii, 512, 516; quotations from, ii, 442, 453, 464, 486, 495, 497, 498, 530; vision not by rays issuing from the eye, ii, 469; apparent size of stars near horizon, ii, 532.

Alkindi, theory of vision, ii, 468; transit of light instantaneous, ii, 486, 489.

Alleluia, explanation of, 105.

Almagest, size of heavenly bodies, 201.

Aloes, ii, 623.

Alphabet, Hebrew, 83; Greek, 85.

Alpharabius, commentary on Aristotle's Rhetoric, 34; separation of intellect from other psychical faculties, 44; practical side of logic, 81; connection of grammar and logic with mathematics, 118; inspiration of law-giver, ii, 805.

Altavicus, on astrological houses, 277.

Amazons, 378.

Ambergris, ii, 623.

Ambrose, 31, 36; admits astrological prediction, 269; on southern hemisphere, 326; description of Brahmins, 371; examples of virginal conception, ii, 644.

Amen, derivation of, 98.

Anacharsis, simplicity of life, ii, 684.

Anaxagoras on inundations of Nile, 341.

Anger, ii, 685-711; outward symptoms, ii, 686-688; destructive of reason, ii, 688-690; incompatible with clemency, ii, 690-693; with magnanimity, ii, 693-696; with mercy, ii, 696-698; with peace of mind, ii, 698; examples of, ii, 698, 699; comparison with other vices, ii, 700, 701; examples of self-restraint, ii, 702-706; remedies against, ii, 706-711.

Angles of incidence and reflection, ii, 547.

Animals possess judgment, ii, 424; also a faculty akin to reason, ii, 426; recognition of universals, ii, 543; unconscious of their mental

Index

processes, ii, 544; teach rules of health, ii, 620.

Antichrist, advent of, may be predicted, 289; will employ science, ii, 633; advent of, ii, 644, 788.

Antigonus, example of self-restraint, ii, 704.

Apocryphal works, value of, 68.

Apollo, more than one so called, 56, 57; tradition of, obscured, 64.

Apuleius (of Mandara) on Angels, ii, 646, 647; virtue spiritual health, ii, 669; vanity of worldly prosperity, ii, 677.

Aqueous humor (albugineus), ii, 435.

Aquila, translation of Bible, 77.

Arabia, 343-351.

Araxes, 379, 380.

Arcesilaus, enjoyment of wine, ii, 785.

Archytas, successor of Pythagoras, 60; visited by Plato, 61; intellect weakened by lust, ii, 679; self-restraint, ii, 703.

Aristides, calmness under insults, ii, 732.

Aristotle, great but not perfect, 10; attention to predecessors, 15; appreciation by Avicenna, 22; condemnation of works, ib.; his life, 62; entitled the philosopher, 63; translations of, not possessed by fathers, 63; Physics and Metaphysics introduced by Michael Scot, 63; disregard of wealth, ii, 675; translations of, defective and confusing, 77, 79; ii, 427, 475, 608.

Analyt. Post., 125; knowledge attained by study of cause, 190.

Categories, connection of mathematics with, 120.

De Anima, separation of Intellect, 44; Sensus Communis, ii, 421, 422; passivity of sensation, ii, 470; distance needed for sensation, ii, 55; taste and touch, ib.; effect of vacuum on vision, ii, 485; instantaneous transit of light, ii, 486.

Aristotle (*continued*):

De Coelo, geometrical figures filling space, 46; gravity of air, 152; form of universe, 174; disputes, relation of elements to regular solids, 183; opposed to plurality of worlds, 185; extent of sea between India and Spain, 311; on southern pole, 326; imperfect account of lunar phases, ii, 525; illusions caused by motion, ii, 535; scintillation, ii, 536; trinity in nature, ii, 611.

De Generatione, influence of heavens compared with elements, 394; moisture and dryness, ii, 423; passivity of matter, ii, 495; variety in eyes of animals, ii, 502.

De Insomniis, 164; shifting impressions of color, ii, 520.

De Memoria, 10, 125.

De Natural. Auscult., material and other causes not coincident in same object, 46; eight modes *essendi in actu,* 47; on vacuum, 166; controverts Parmenides, 169; influence of sun on generation, 394; transit of light, ii, 487.

De Plantis (apocr.), 394.

De Sensu, on Sensus Communis, ii, 422; on colors, ii, 197.

De Somno et Vigilia, ii, 422.

Ethics, 8, 10, 15; capacity of youth for mathematics, 123; principles of, ii, 664-667; difficulty of moral reformation, ii, 669; training of young, 674.

Metaphysics, 2, 6, 14, 120, 123; connection of dancing with music, 260; visual sense reveals differences, ii, 419; private and public good compared, ii, 663.

Meteorologica, lunar rainbow, 46; source of stellar light, 148; occultation of stars, ib.; formation of clouds, 252; Milky Way, ii, 517.

Poetic, 119.

Index

Aristotle (*continued*) :

Problemata (spurious), ii, 475, 680.

Soph. Elench., 14 ; ii, 668.

Topica, 12 ; remark on vision, ii, 469.

Arithmetic, theological applications of, 242 et seq.

Ark, 232.

Armenia, 379, 380.

Armenia (major), 379 ; destruction of churches, 380.

Armenia (minor), identical with Cilicia, 373.

Artephius on longevity, ii, 621.

Article, use of, in Greek, 87.

Arym, 319, 329.

Arzachel, his tables, 213, 297 ; on motions of Mercury, 279.

Asia Minor, 373.

Aspiration, note of, 92.

Astrolabe, 247 ; described by Ptolemy, ii, 616 ; movable in accordance with motion of heavens, ii, 616.

Astrology, 261-290, 391-418 ; predictions of, admitted by the fathers, 268, condemnation of, by recent theologians, 270 ; predictions not absolute, 270 ; applicable to states more than to individuals, 273-275 ; connection with religious changes, 254-280 ; effect of heavens on things of earth, 392 ; best understood by Hebrews, 395 ; special parts of the body affected, 396 ; relation of, to medicine, 397, 401, 406 ; lunar mansions, 399 ; legitimate use of, 403-411 ; studied by Tartars, 415.

Astronomy, appreciated by Cassiodorus and Augustine, 199, 200 ; reveals man's insignificance, 201 ; verifies Biblical geography, 203-208 ; governs construction of calendars, 208, 209 ; indicates date of creation, 210-213 ; of deluge, 215 ; of exit from ark, 220 ; of delivery of the law, 222, 223 ; of Nativity and Passion, 224-232 ; enables us to measure the earth, 246-249 ; the heavenly spheres, 249-251 ; height of clouds, 251-252 ; diameters apparent and real of planets, 253-257 ; the fixed stars, 257-259.

Athenodorus, ii, 771, 774.

Atlas, contemporary with Moses, grandfather of Hermes, 55.

Atoms, 172.

Attica, 389.

Augustine, St., 13 ; retraction of errors, 16 ; freedom of criticism, 17, 18 ; translated Aristotle's Categories, 29 ; scientific works, 196 ; value of science, 198-200 ; *De Doctrina Christ.*, 36, 39 ; *Soliloquia,* 47 ; on Biblical text, 88 ; admits astrological prediction, 269 ; views on propagation of rays, ii, 468 ; citations from Porphyry, ii, 641.

Authority, errors due to, 4-10, 13-19.

Aux, explanation of, 137.

Avarice, ii, 675-679.

Ave, derivation of, 100.

Averroes, 6 ; criticized Avicenna, 16 ; attacks upon, 22 ; Bacon's estimate of, 64 ; on transparency of planetary orbs, 149 ; continuity of points, 170 ; few solids can fill space, 184 ; generative force of sun, 308 ; influence of heavens, 394 ; his theory of vision, ii, 469 ; vision affected by cold, ii, 506 ; on transparency of heavens, ii, 483 ; scintillation results from density and motion of medium, ii, 540.

Avicenna on intellect, 44 ; principal expositor of Aristotle, 63 ; most of his work still untranslated, 64 ; celestial things nobler than terrestrial, 201 ; correction of Aristotle, ii, 428 ; an authority on optics, ii, 430, 433 ; theory of vision, ii, 469 ; *De Anima,* ii, 427, 473 ; *De Animalibus,* ii, 427, 445, 474 ; disturbances of vision, ii, 507 ; views of Creation, ii, 646 ; on spiritual blindness, ii, 651-653 ; future reward and punishment, ii, 655 ; cere-

Index

monial, ii, 657; legislation, principles of, ii, 661; mediator between God and man, ii, 805.

Bagdad, capture of, by Tartars, 287; ii, 808; position of, 351.

Baltic, countries bordering on, 376.

Basil, qualified approval of astrology, 268.

Bede, lawful to use pagan knowledge, 43; on Noah's exit from the ark, 220; date of law-giving from Sinai, 222; date of Passion, 225; relation of miracle indicating time of Easter, 303, 304.

Bee, operation of, ii, 544; a type of royal government, ii, 691, 692.

Bells rejected by Greeks because used by Buddhists, 388; ii, 806.

Bible, corrupt text of, 87, 243.

Binocular vision, ii, 511.

Black Sea, 374.

Boetius on authority in belief, 16; translated logical works of Aristotle, 30; knowledge of language, 76; precise comprehension of terms, 97; translated Greek mathematicians, 117; symbolic meaning of proportions, 118; *De Consolatione* quoted, ii, 484, 654, 672, 788.

Brahmins, 371.

Brain, organs and functions of, ii, 421, 428; is not sensitive, ii, 428; relation of, to heart, ii, 428; organs of vision and smell, ii, 452; larger in man than in other animals, ib.

Brevitas Vitae, Seneca's dialogue on, ii, 739-750.

Buddhists (idololatrae) description of their worship, 388; chastity of their priesthood, ii, 789; different sects of, ii, 803; are polytheists, ii, 806.

Bulgaria (major), 378, 383.

Cadmus, contemporary with Othniel, 56.

Caesar (Augustus), example of self-restraint, ii, 706; wish for retirement, ii, 741; endurance of bereavement, ii, 751.

Caesar (Caius), ii, 782.

Caesar (Julius) reported use of mirrors when invading Britain, ii, 581; friends more dangerous than foes, ii, 708.

Calendar, reduction of, to Christian standard, 209; correction of, 290-306.

Canus, ii, 782.

Cara-Cathaia, 384.

Carneades, ii, 748.

Carpini, mission to Tartary, 386.

Carthage, 335.

Caspian gates, 289, 372, 381; ii, 645.

Caspian Sea, rightly described by Franciscan missionaries, 372, 382; ii, 645.

Cassianus, ii, 702, 784.

Cassiodorus, theological value of science, 40; praise of mathematics, 197; on time in music, 260.

Cat, fact proving intelligence of, ii, 544.

Cathaia Magna (China), 387.

Cato, example of self-restraint of, ii, 706, 724; type of perfection, ii, 719; relaxation, ii, 784; enjoyment of wine, ii, 784.

Caucasian gates, 372.

Caucasus, variously defined, 369.

Censorinus, on accents, 260.

Centilogium, see *Ptolemy.*

Ceremonial of Pagans, worthless, ii, 658.

Chaldaean language used by Daniel and Jeremiah, 82.

China (Cathaia Magna), 387.

Choroid, see *Uvea.*

Christianity, supreme object of philosophy, ii, 787; comparison with other religions, ii, 790, 806-814; philosophical proofs of, ii, 792-804.

Chronology, dependence on Mathematics, 208-216; reduction of, to Christian standard, 208, 209.

Chrysostom, 7, 10.

Index

Cicero, Hortensius, 3; *Tuscul. Disp.*, 6, 13; philosophy a gift of God, 48; intuitive knowledge of geometry, 121; *Acad. Prior.*, 6; *Deorum Natura*, 7; on immortality, ii, 649; on future state of misery, ii, 655; divine worship, ii, 656; public spirit, ii, 663; virtue the sole good, ii, 667; consistency of character, ii, 668; sin, ii, 671, 672; endurance of ancient philosophers, ii, 676; disregard of wealth, ii, 678; lust, ii, 679-681; self-restraint, ii, 703; discontent with office, ii, 741.

Citizens, form organic whole, ii, 710.

Claudius, on Plato's teaching of Trinity, ii, 640.

Climate, conditions of, 153-158; influence on character, 159, 272.

Cloud, made visible by distance, ii, 482; height of, how estimated, ii, 523, 524.

Clouds, height of, 251.

Coelum, derivation of, 99.

Cognition, three modes of, ii, 497-500; examples of, by sense only, ii, 517-521; by *scientia*, ii, 521-523; by *syllogism*, ii, 523-525.

Color of eye, 11, 444; concerned in vision, ii, 449, 473, 495; mixture of, ii, 438-461; color of deep water and sky, ii, 482; apprehended by sensation, ii, 517; modified by passage through colored substance, ii, 522; dependence of, on angle of incidence, ii, 557; of rainbow, ii, 605, 610-612; of ocular structures, ii, 612.

Colure (equinoctial), definition of, 309.

Comestor (Peter), 215.

Comet, of 1264, 400.

Commissure (optic), ii, 431.

Conceit of knowledge, 20-26.

Confession (Bacon's) of imperfect knowledge, 231, 232, 290, 293; ii, 615.

Conjunctions, planetary, 278, 279, 284, 285, 401.

Consecration, formulae used in, 106, 107.

Constantia (de), Seneca's treatise, ii, 716-725.

Constantinus (Africanus), ii, 430.

Contact, point of, 169-172.

Contract, laws of, ii, 661.

Conversion of heathen promoted by Science, ii, 632.

Corinth, 390.

Cornea, described, ii, 433; functions of, ii, 444.

Cornelia, ii, 737.

Creation, date of, 210.

Cube, 181; related by Platonists with earth, 183.

Cumanians, destruction of, by Tartars, 375.

Custom, errors due to, 5-10.

Cycle, lunar, 216-220; its defects, 296-300; Arabian cycle preferable, 300.

Cyprian, 13.

Cyrene, 336.

Cyril, studied astronomy, 31.

Dacia (for Dania), 375.

Damiata, on site of Memphis, 333.

Dawn, due to accidental rays, ii, 519, 520; see *Twilight*.

Day, beginning of, 216.

Dead Sea, 356.

Degeneration, hereditary, ii, 618.

Degree, terrestrial arc corresponding to, 247.

Delos, Apollo worshiped in, 57.

Deluge, 215.

Demetrius (Poliorcetes), ii, 718.

Democritus, 173; on vacuum, ii, 485; on quiet life, ii, 781; the laughing philosopher, ii, 782.

Dialects, 75, 82.

Diameter, of earth, 248; of planets (apparent), 253, 254; (real), 254-256.

Index

Index

Eye, structure and functions of, ii, 430-448; spherical shape of, ii, 447; emanation of rays from, ii, 470-472; morbid states of, ii, 492; when deep-set sees further, ii, 501, 502; intrinsic light in, 505; compression of globe, effect of, ii, 508; allegorical significance of parts of, ii, 576-578.

Eye-lash, ii, 447.

Eyelids, ii, 447; their effect on sight, ii, 503.

Fabianus, ii, 744.

Facies (astrological), 282.

Falling bodies, strain of all parts except center, 189.

Fascination, 164, 413, 414; examples of, in Bacon's time, 416, 417.

Fire, sphere of, distinct from that of air, 153.

Force, propagated in straight lines, 131; distinction of vertical and oblique action, 139, 140. See *Species*.

Fortunatianus, letter of St. Augustine to, 18.

Fractions, reduction to common denominator, 242.

Franciscans, corrections of Biblical text, 88; their mission to the Tartars, 289, 324.

Freewill, interfered with by magic, 262; not so by astrology, 270, 406.

Future, knowledge of, necessary, 306.

Galaxy, ii, 517, 518.

Galen, on prognosis, 273; *De Dynamidiis*, 398; on critical days, 401.

Galilee, 366, 367.

Ganges, 371.

Gellius, A., *Noctes Atticae*, 11.

Gender, differences in Latin from Greek, 102.

Gennesareth, lake of, 360, 361.

Geography, 306 et seq.; general principles of, 308-319; its political and religious importance, 320-323;

mathematics needed for, 203; spiritual meaning of Biblical geography, 204-208.

Geometry, connection with theology, 232-242.

Georgia, 378.

Gerlandus, on date of Passion, 227.

Gluttony, ii, 682

Gnomon, addition of, to rectangle illustrates growth, 121.

Government, laws respecting, ii, 660-662.

Graecia Magna, 59, 61.

Grammar, Part III, *passim*.

Gratian, ignorant of science, 33, 34.

Gravity, of particle, affected by position, 191-194.

Greek fire, ii, 629.

Greek language, Part III, *passim*.

Greeks, received elements of science from patriarchs and prophets, 53.

Gregory, Pope, writings attacked after death, 21.

Grosseteste, scientific knowledge, 76, 126; translations from Greek fathers, 78, 82.

Gunpowder, ii, 629.

Habitable region, 310-313.

Halcyons, described, ii, 632.

Haloes, ii, 612-614; further experimental research needed, ii, 615.

Haly, distinguishes astrology from magic, 264; connection of astrology with medicine, 397, 399, 402, 407, 409; ii, 620; work *De Regimine Senum*, ii, 622, 625.

Health, rules of, ii, 617-619.

Heart, relation to brain, ii, 428, 429.

Heat, generated by motion, 189; solar effect of, 308, 314.

Heaven, influence of, on Earth, 307, 308.

Heavens, their transparency, ii, 482; optical illusion as to their shape, ii, 529.

Hebrew, affinity of, with Chaldaean, 82; correspondence of letters with

Index

those of Latin, 96; astronomers, excellence of, 301.

Hegesippus, 359, 365.

Heliopolis, 333.

Helvia, Seneca's discourse to, ii, 725-733.

Heraclitus, the weeping philosopher, ii, 782.

Hercules, 56.

Hermann, 82; difficulty of rendering Aristotle's Poetic Argument from Arabic into Latin, 119.

Hermes (Mercurius), nephew of Atlas, 55; on creation, ii, 646; future rewards and punishments, ii, 655; on divine worship, ii, 658.

Hesiod, 58.

Hexagons, will not fill a surface, 182; form of bee's cell and of certain crystals, 185.

Hipparchus (Abrachis), 57.

Hippocrates, 294.

Hippocrates, on prognosis, 273.

Homer, 58, 76.

Horace, 80.

Houses (astrological), division of heaven into, 277; two distinct meanings of, 280.

Hungary, 376; Asiatic origin of people, 383.

Hygiene, rules of, insufficiently observed, ii, 617-619.

Hyperboreans, 327, 376, 377.

Iconium, seat of Turkish power, 373.

Icosahedron, 181; related by Platonists with sphere of water, 183.

Illusions (optical), ii, 506-516, 520, 521, 523-525, 529, 532-535.

Illyria, 390.

Imaginatio, contrasted with Sensus Communis, ii, 422; their contiguous position in brain, ib.

Incommensurables, 173.

Inconsistency, ii, 761-765.

India, vast extent of, 327; southern boundary, 328; other boundaries, 370, 371.

Indus, 371.

Inheritance, laws of, ii, 661.

Injury and insult not felt by wise man, ii, 716-725.

Innate, disposition how determined, 159.

Ionic school of philosophy, 60.

Isaac (physician), on astrological prediction, 267.

Isidorus, 13; his Etymologica, 69; on time in music, 260; a geographical authority, 323; derivation of *circenses,* ii, 747.

Isis brought learning to Egyptians, 54.

Isoperimetry, 176.

Israel, meaning of, 93-96.

Italic school of philosophy, 60.

Jeremiah, contemporary with Ancus Martius and Tarquinius Priscus, 62.

Jericho, spiritual meaning of, 207.

Jerome, 7; retraction of error, 16; criticism of Augustine, 17; misjudged in lifetime, 21; on literal translation, 75; his view of Septuagint, 77; not always accurate, 77; his version of Bible when used, 90; on the word Israel, 94; on biblical geography, 204.

Jerusalem, 368; spiritual meaning of, 206, 207.

Jews, imperfection of religion, ii, 789, 790; relation to planet Saturn, ii, 792; discord of sects, ii, 803; their revelation, ii, 805; Seneca's attack on them, ii, 808; expectation of Messiah, ii, 808; dark side of their religion, ii, 810; their testimony to Christ, ii, 812.

John, Bacon's disciple, 24.

John (St., Evangelist), relaxation, ii, 784.

Jordan (river), 358, 359; spiritual meaning of, 206.

Jordanus (Nemorarius), on triangles, 179; on equilibrium, 190-195.

Josephus, chief authority on sacred

Index

history, 78; greatest of historians, 196; capture of Jerusalem, ii, 809.

Joshua, arrest of sun, 202.

Jubilee, derivation of, 99.

Judaea, 364.

Judgment, possessed by animals, ii, 424, 543; animal judgment not distinguished by Aristotle from memory, ii, 427.

Jupiter, dimensions of sphere, 250; religious significance of his conjunctions, 278-280.

Juvenal, 104.

Knowledge, perfection of, unattainable, 24; ii, 803; attained by study of cause, or of effect, 189.

Koran, ii, 810, 814.

Lamentations, book of, 82.

Lamps, ever-burning, ii, 629.

Language, Part III, *passim*.

Latin, insufficiency of, 75, 76; imperfect translations into, 78; foreign words in, 98

Lebanon, 362.

Legislation, principles of, ii, 660-662.

Lens (ocular), ii, 434, 445.

Leo (Pope, the great), decision as to Easter, 303.

Leucippus, 173.

Library, Alexandrian, burning of, ii, 776.

Libya, 334, 335.

Life, brevity of, ii, 739-750; the blessed, ii, 752-767.

Light, necessary for vision, ii, 449, 473; passage of, occupies time, ii, 485-490; regarded by Empedocles as an emanation, ii, 489; a propagation of motion not of particles, ii, 490; apprehended by sensation, ii, 517.

Line, mathematical and physical, 171; force propagated in, 131.

Liturgy, explanation of terms used in, 106-108.

Livia, ii, 737.

Logic, its practical side, 79-81; requires little teaching, ii, 499; its rules followed unconsciously by animals, ii, 544, 545.

Longevity of patriarchs, 214; means of increasing, ii, 617-626.

Longitude, computed sometimes from meridian of Toledo, 318, 319; not yet scientifically determined, 320.

Louis IX sends Franciscans to Tartary, 289, 324; his defeat near Damiata, 339.

Lucan, 324, 343.

Lunar rainbow, 46, 234.

Lunations, 216-220 (see *Moon*).

Lust, ii, 679-682.

Magic, deterred fathers from study of philosophy, 32; introduced by Zoroaster, 54; distinction from mathematics, 261; inconsistent with freewill, 262; involves fraud, 263; discredits Christian miracles, 263; condemned by philosophers, 264-267; imputation of, dreaded by modern theologians, 410; counteracted by experiment, ii, 631, 632.

Magnanimity, ii, 665, 693.

Magnetic force, ii, 616, 630, 631.

Magnitude, a condition of vision, ii, 477; how estimated, ii, 530-532; apparent increase of, due to vapor, ii, 573; how affected by form of refracting surface, ii, 566-570, 573.

Mahomet, accepts miraculous conception of Christ, ii, 810; low moral standard, ii, 811.

Mahommedanism, inferior morals of, 284; speedy destruction of, 287; ii, 811.

Mahommedans, polygamy, ii, 788, 814; partial adoption of Judaism and Christianity, ii, 791; their religion attacked by themselves, ii, 803, 808, 811; their revelation, 805.

Mangu Khan, 385, 415; ii, 788, 806, 807.

Map, Bacon's, 315, 320.

Index

Marcia, Seneca's letter to, ii, 734-738.

Maria, etymology of, 106.

Marianus, on date of Passion, 226.

Marisco, Adam de, 82; mathematical knowledge of, 126.

Marriage, laws respecting, ii, 660.

Mars, dimensions of sphere, 250.

Martianus, on climate, 155; height of clouds, 252; on time in music, 260; on polar regions, 327.

Mathematics, neglected by moderns, 27; the key to the sciences, 116; estimate of, by Boetius, Ptolemy, Alpharabius, and others, 117-120; known to patriarchs, 122; simplicity of, ib.; type of certainty, 123; application to astronomy, 128; explains laws of force, 129; connection of, with theology, 195; appreciation of, by fathers, 196-200; use of, in explanation of Scripture, 201-203, 232-246; in Biblical geography, 203-208; in solving problems of chronology, 208-232; distinction from magic, 261.

Matter, unity of, refuted, 164-169.

Media, 369, 370.

Medicine, known to Adam and Noah, 56.

Medium, transparency of, affected by distance, ii, 481, 482; rarity of, necessary to vision, ii, 484; density and motion of, affect scintillation, ii, 539, 540. See *Species, Refraction*.

Melissus, 169.

Memory, its cerebral position, ii, 422; Aristotle's view criticized, ii, 427-429; recollection of past sensation, ii, 498.

Meni (Manes), origin of his sect, 286.

Mercury, dimensions of sphere, 250; conjunction with Jupiter, 279; complexity of motions, 279; connection of, with the sign Virgo, 283.

Meroe, 330, 332, 343.

Mesopotamia, 351.

Metaphysics, relation to Ethics, ii, 637-640.

Michael Scot, introduced Aristotle's *Physics and Metaphysics,* 63; translation of Avicenna's *De Animalibus,* ii, 427.

Midian, 347.

Milky Way, ii, 517.

Milleius, 233.

Minerva, 54.

Miracles, of Christ, superior to those of Moses and Mahomet, ii, 813; in proof of Eucharistic doctrine, ii, 816, 817.

Mirrors, various kinds of, ii, 550-557; parabolic, 134; reflection from fractured mirror, ii, 561; use of, in warfare, ii, 580-582.

Moab, 346.

Moal (Mongol), 384, 385.

Moon, color of, when eclipsed, ii, 521; why invisible when in conjunction with sun, ii, 522; explanation of phases, ii, 525-529; inherent luminousness of, 150, and ii, 549; dimensions of sphere, 250; diameter of, 254, 255; error in estimating age of, 296; lunar mansions, 399.

Moonstone (Selenitis), 304.

Moral Philosophy, reference to, 66, 72; ii, 635-823; its practical character, ii, 635; relation to theology, ii, 635; relation to metaphysics, ii, 637-640; indicates doctrine of Trinity, ii, 640-643; of Incarnation, ii, 643; of Angels, ii, 646-648; of Immortality, ii, 648-656; civic morality, ii, 660-662; personal morality, ii, 663-786; judgment as to true religion, ii, 787-823; prepares the way for Christian theology, 72-74.

Mortal sins, denounced by ancient philosophers, ii, 675-685.

Moses, difficulty in convincing men of truth, 21; furnished with wisdom of Egyptians, 41, 52; contemporary with Atlas and Prometheus, 55; his miracles in Tampnis, 333; expedition against Ethiopians, 407;

Index

threefold division of moral system, ii, 637; miracles, inferior to those of Christ, ii, 813.

Motion, relation to time, 186; ii, 489; perception of, ii, 520, 533-535; of medium, produces scintillation, ii, 540-542.

Mountains, climate affected by, 155, 156; effect of sun's rays on, 236-238.

Music, theological importance of, 259, 260; moral value of, ii, 786.

Naphtha, ii, 629.

Nero, geographical expedition, 312.

Nestorians, wide diffusion of, 384; imperfect Christianity of, 388.

Nice, Council of, 303-306.

Nile, 337-343.

Noah, instructed Chaldeans, 52, 53; exit from ark, 220-222.

Novara, tables constructed to meridian of, 231.

Numbers, Perfect, 9, 245; errors of, in received version, 243-245.

Obedience, rule of, not inculcated in Mosaic law, ii, 814.

Oblique rays, mostly neutralized by vertical, ii, 456-461.

Octavia, ii, 737.

Octohedron, 181; related by Platonists with sphere of fire, 183.

Odor, propagation of, ii, 491.

Old age, Bacon's work on, ii, 622; State provision for, ii, 661.

Olympus, height of, 252.

Opacity, a condition of vision, ii, 481; of reflection, ii, 548; obstruction to transit of rays not absolute, 133.

Optic nerves, origin and course of, ii, 421, 430-432.

Opus Majus, described as a preliminary work, ii, 615.

Orbs, transparency of, 148; thickness of, 249, 250.

Origen, erroneous belief in ultimate salvation of wicked, 17.

Ormesta Mundi, ii, 633; see *Orosius.*

Orosius, on length of stadium, 252; on southern limits of Spain, 312; Alexander's conquests, ii, 634.

Orpheus, 57.

Osanna, explanation of, 105.

Oscillation, of arms of balance, 194.

Ovid, 278; poem *de Vetula* attributed to, 285, 288.

Pagans, ii, 789, 803, 805, 806.

Palestine, 353-369.

Parabolic, mirrors, 134.

Paradise, site of, 202, 214; rivers of, 352.

Parallel rays, ii, 534.

Paris, Biblical text of, 88; meridian of, 231; latitude of, ii, 593.

Parmenides, 169.

Parthia, 370.

Passion, date of, 224-232.

Pathalis, 328.

Patriarchs, had revelation of scientific truth, 52, 195; book of testaments of, 67; long life necessary for astronomical studies, 64.

Paul, St., conflict with St. Peter, 17; visions of, 23; quotations from heathen poets, 42.

Peace, of mind, ii, 768-786.

Pella, 362, 365.

Pentapolis, 355.

Perception, Analysis of, ii, 493-496, 497-500.

Persuasio, applied to *Opus Majus,* 324, 343; ii, 575.

Philip (of Macedon), example of self-restraint, ii, 705.

Philology, Part III, *passim.*

Philosophy, why neglected by fathers, 31-33; a divine revelation, 48, 52 et seq.; defined by Pythagoras, 59; of small value apart from theology, 66, 74; conscious of its own incompleteness, 71; yet necessary to theology, 72.

Phoenicia, 364.

Index

Phoroneus, beginning of Greek law, 54, 55.

Pia mater (membrane of brain), ii, 421, 431.

Planets, dimensions of, 255-257; of their spheres, 249, 250; influences of, incentive not compulsory, 270, 271, 288; characteristics of, 392-394; conjunctions of, 401.

Plato, respect for truth, 17; better known to fathers than Aristotle, 29, 61; his date and history, 61; could not have conversed with Jeremiah, but may have seen writers of Septuagint, 62; knowledge of Pentateuch, 68; heaven of fiery substance, 202; his *Phaedo*, ii, 684.

Platonists, relation of regular solids to universe, 182, 183.

Pleasure, relation of, to virtue, ii, 755-761.

Pliny, on climate, 155; height of clouds, 251; condemnation of magic, 262; proportions of land and water, 311; on Caspian Sea, 324; on shadows in south latitudes, 324, 325; extent of India, 327; and *passim* in geographical section; on double pupil, ii, 509; instance of longevity, ii, 622; non-sexual conception, ii, 644.

Plurality, of worlds impossible, 186.

Poetry, inspires love of right action, 80.

Points, Hebrew, 84.

Poland, 376, 378.

Polar regions, have more water than equatorial, 314; length of day in, 317.

Polybius, Seneca's dialogue addressed to, ii, 750-752.

Pope, power of, to effect reform, 35; to save Europe from Antichrist, 417.

Popular opinion, errors due to, 10-13.

Porphyrius, anticipated doctrine of Trinity, ii, 641; of Angels, 648.

Poverty, rule of, ii, 814.

Practice opposed to Speculation, ii, 635.

Prerogatives, of experimental science, ii, 587, 615, 627.

Prester John, 384.

Pride, ii, 676, 677.

Principalis Scriptura. See *Scriptum Principale*.

Priscian, 102.

Progress, intellectual, duty of, 66.

Prometheus, contemporary with Moses, 55, 65.

Prosody, mistakes made in, 103, 104.

Providentia (de), Seneca's treatise, ii, 711-716.

Prussians, 377; ii, 789, 796.

Ptolemais, 330.

Ptolemy, *Almagest*, 117, 247, 254-258; ii, 519, 676.

    Astrological works, 196, 279, 401, 404.

    Cosmographia, 315.

    Optica, ii, 419; predecessor of Alhazen, ii, 468; rays of light and color, ii, 495; deep set eyes, ii, 502; shooting stars, ii, 520; effect of distance, ii, 520; mixture of rays in medium, ii, 464; terms for refraction and reflection, ii, 550.

Punctuation, connected with music, 259.

Pupil (of eye), small size of, compatible with vision, ii, 454-456; sometimes double, ii, 509; allegorical meaning of, ii, 576, 577.

Pyramid, round, Bacon's expression for cone, 138.

Pythagoras, 59, 60, 65.

Quadrant, 247.

Qualities, primary, ii, 423.

Quantity, rational and irrational, symbolic meaning of, 240.

Rainbow, errors of Aristotle's translators on lunar, 46, 234; ii, 607; final cause of, 51; geometrical ex-

Index

Index

of environment on character, ii, 628; Aristotle's warning as to lust, ii, 680, 682.

Self-examination, ii, 674.

Seneca, 5, 6, 10, 14, 15; width of sea between India and Spain, 311; inundations of Nile, 340; Alexander's conquests, ii, 634; public spirit, ii, 663; reverence, ii, 666; consistency, ii, 667; reformation of character, ii, 669; sin, ii, 672; self-examination, ii, 673; training of young, ii, 674; exile, ii, 676, 727-730; insignificance of earth, ii, 676; gluttony, ii, 682, 683; fleshly indulgence, ii, 755; charged with inconsistency, ii, 761-766; correspondence with St. Paul, ii, 784.

Sensation, one of the three modes of cognition, ii, 497.

Senses, phenomena apprehended by, ii, 423.

Sensibilia Communia, definition of, ii, 423.

Sensus Communis, cerebral organ of, ii, 421.

Septuagint, 77, 209, 355.

Servius, 102.

Shepherd, seen by Bacon, 417.

Sibyls, 58, 69.

Signs, zodiacal, see *Zodiac*.

Simple, often surpass the learned, 24.

Simplicity of life, ii, 683, 684, 775.

Sin, desert of, 344.

Sin, remission of, ii, 813.

Smell, cerebral organ of, ii, 452; sense of, compared with vision, ii, 476; propagation of, ii, 491.

Socrates, 61; citizen of world, ii, 676; his self-restraint, ii, 702, 709; calmness, ii, 732, 766; behavior under thirty tyrants, ii, 773; relaxation, ii, 784.

Solids, regular, 180-183.

Solinus, *De Mirabilibus Mundi,* 54, 57, 164, 357; on double pupil, ii, 509.

Solomon, miraculous powers, 408.

Solon, enjoyment of wine, ii, 785.

Solstices, variation in date of, 291.

Sound, propagation of, ii, 475, 490.

Southern hemisphere, probably inhabited, 314, 325; superiority of, 326.

Spain, originally continuous with Africa, 312.

Spanish language substituted for Latin, 76.

Species, definition of, 130; is of corporeal nature, ii, 462, 463; mixture of, in medium, ii, 464; transit of, occupies time, ii, 487-489.

Sphere, stellar, force reflected from, 162; figure of greatest content, 176; stellar dimensions of, 249.

Sphericity of world, 173-179; of ocular structures, ii, 436-443.

Spiritual truth underlying physical, 50.

Sport, laws respecting, ii, 661.

Stars, number and magnitude, 257-259, 391; denser than their orbs, ii, 518, 519; shooting, ii, 520; seem larger when near horizon, ii, 532.

Statius, 104.

St. James, ii, 580.

Strabismus, ii, 506.

Sulla, exhibition of lions, ii, 746.

Sun, magnitude of, 150; dimensions of sphere, 250; generative power of, 308.

Sur, desert of, 344.

Syene, 324, 329, 332, 333, 339, 343.

Syllogism, includes instinctive reasoning processes, ii, 499, 544.

Syria, 351-368.

Tabernacle, 233.

Tana, inhabited by Jewish refugees with Jeremiah, 334.

Tangut, their writing, 389.

Taprobane, 325, 329.

Tartars, day's journey of, 375; destruction of Cumanians, ib.; extent of dominion, 378; their origin, 384-

Index

386; their astrology, 416; invasion of Europe, ii, 645; craving for empire, ii, 788; foul habits, ii, 789; recognition of one God, ii, 790, 803; acceptance of Christian rites, ii, 792; retain idolatrous customs, ii, 806; convoke a parliament of religions, ii, 792, 796, 806.

Taurus, full extent of, 369.

Tela araneae, its function described, ii, 446.

Telescope, forecast of, ii, 581.

Temperament, affected by stellar influence, 270.

Temperature of polar and equatorial regions, 153-156.

Terminus (astrological), 282.

Tetrabiblon, of Ptolemy, 265.

Tetrahedron, 181.

Teutonic order, oppresses Prussians, ii, 797.

Text, Biblical, corruption of, 87-93.

Thales, 60, 65; on inundations of Nile, 340.

Thebit, introduced motion of trepidation, 213; on motions of Mercury, 279.

Theodosius on spherics, 178, 248, 310; ii, 437.

Theodotian, translation of Bible, 77.

Theology, the mistress-science, 36; necessary to complete philosophy, 65; how far known to heathen, 66, 70; must avail itself of heathen moralists, 72; connection with mathematics, 195 et seq.

Thinking power of animals, ii, 426.

Thomas of St. David's, 82.

Threshold, Tartar superstition as to, ii, 806.

Tiberias, lake of, 360.

Tides, cause of, 160-162.

Tideus on vision, ii, 468.

Tigris, course of, 352, 353.

Time, unity of, 186; relation to motion, 187; measure of, by water-clocks, 253; needed for passage of radiant force, ii, 486-490.

Toledo, tables of, 318.

Training of young, ii, 674.

Tranquillitas animi, Seneca's discourse on, ii, 768-786.

Transparency of medium, how affected by distance, ii, 481; a condition of vision, ii, 484.

Tribes (ten of Israel), positions of, 321.

Triplicity (astrological), 281.

Tripoli (African), 336.

Tripolis (Syria), 354.

Trinity, geometrical representations of, 240; arithmetical, 245; apprehended by non-Christian thinkers, ii, 640-642.

Tritonia, why Minerva so called, 54.

Troglodytes, 331, 337.

Troy, fall of, how far before founding of Rome, 57.

Turkia, 373, 379.

Twilight, treatise on, 251; why not throughout the night, ii, 519.

Tyrannicide, ii, 662.

Unity of wisdom, 36; of God, man and universe, ii, 805.

Universe, unity of, 185, 186; ii, 800; dimensions of, 249.

Uvea, described, ii, 433, 434, 442; center of, ii, 438, 441.

Vacuum, 172; none between earth and heaven, ii, 485.

Valerius Maximus, ii, 669.

Varro, ii, 729.

Venice, position of, 390.

Venus, dimensions of sphere, 250

Vergil, 102; ii, 670.

Vertical rays, preponderance of, over oblique, ii, 454-461; reflection of, 133; not refracted, ii, 563, 564.

Vertigo, ii, 507.

Virgin, Mahommedan view of, ii, 810.

Virginity, rule of, ii, 814.

Virtue, superiority of heathen to Christian, ii, 664, 738, 739; Aristotle's theory of, ii, 664-667; the

Index

life of man, ii, 667 ; its beauty, ii, 669 ; its possibility, ii, 669.

Vision, how effected, ii, 449-453 ; condition of rectilinear, ii, 449 ; completed not in eye but in brain, ii, 450-453 ; distinct, conditions of, ii, 454-465, 473-492 ; of distant objects, ii, 501-502 ; how affected by age, ii, 503 ; relation of, to quantity of light, ii, 504 ; causes of double, ii, 506-516 ; binocular, ii, 511 ; dependence of, on position of object, ii, 515, 516 ; allegorical interpretation of, ii, 578-580 ; see also *Refraction* and *Reflection*.

Visual angle, limits of, ii, 477-480.

Vita beata, Seneca's dialogue on, ii, 752-767.

Vitreous humor, ii, 435 ; refraction of rays in, ii, 467.

Volga (Ethilia), inundations of, 340.

Vowels, Hebrew, 83 ; Greek, 86.

War, laws respecting, ii, 662.

Water, sphericity of, varies with position, 179, 180.

Water-clocks, 253.

William Rubruquis, see *Rubruquis*.

Wisdom, unity of, 34 ; relation to felicity, ii, 653.

Wise, seven of Greece, with which Hebrews contemporary, 58, 59.

Words, operative force of, 414.

Writing of Asiatic nations, 388, 389.

Xaleuchus, ii, 668.

Xenocrates, disregard of wealth, ii, 675.

Xenophon, reduction of personal wants, ii, 676 ; self-restraint, ii, 703.

Year, Julian, excess in length of, 290.

Zeno, ii, 748, 781.

Zodiac, significance of signs, 280-290, 392, 396.

Zoroaster, inventor of magic, 54.